Praise for *The Healthy CEO*

"Dr. Ohlhauser has created the ultimate guide for the busy executive—not only for superb health but for happiness and quality of life as well. This is a must-read!"

Dr. David Leonardi, President, Leonardi Executive Health Institute

"While there are a great many books on 'health,' this one gives the reader new perspectives. Using the story of two businesspeople and CEO language, Dr. Ohlhauser shows us how each of us, regardless of walk in life, are the ultimate controllers of our destiny. His book deals with several aspects of health—physical, relational and financial—and offers workable advice on how to improve each aspect. This amazing book gives you tools that appeal to the scorekeepers, the competitors, the challenge-seekers and anyone who wishes a healthier and happier life. It is a business book that truly belongs to the mainstream."

Jaynie L. Smith, author, *Creating Competitive Advantage*;
founder, ICS Marketing; President, Smart Advantage, Inc.

"I've met a lot of CEOs and entrepreneurs over my years. Sadly, they too often learn about success outside of their career when it's much too late. I will highly recommend *The Healthy CEO* book and program to every CEO I meet. This book is not only full of practical advice and humor, but it's so timely in today's business climate. The folks who step off the racetrack long enough to read this will be forever thankful they invested in themselves."

Tom Hill, best-selling author, *Living at the Summit*;
co-author, *Chicken Soup for the Entrepreneurial Soul*; President and CEO, Eagle Goal Coach, Inc.

"This book will talk to, encourage and motivate you as you navigate through all aspects of your health. Dr. Ohlhauser's Healthy CEO character becomes the perfect personal mentor on critical issues that will define your future. This is an important read for both the world of business and the world of health!"

Don Kasian, President, Kasian Architecture

D0169986

"I was pleased to find such a strong, coherent and convincing argument for the value of psychotherapy in the life of a CEO. The model presented in the relational wellness section is elegant and insightful, based on solid research and theory, and grounded in relational expertise. It is well described, reinforced with many clear and practical examples, not the least of which is presented in the delightful and true-to-life story of Frank and Katie. As *The Healthy CEO* is shown to be effective in Frank and Katie's imagined lives, its suggestions, invitations and self-assessment questions will undoubtedly make it a very useful addition to the lives of many busy executives."

Dr. John Sneep, Associate Professor of Psychology, King's University College

"Dr. Ohlhauser not only understands leadership, he has provided a blueprint for others in leadership positions to maximize their personal potential. *The Healthy CEO* puts into perspective three oft-neglected areas in the lives of business and organizational executives: physical, relational and financial health. Written in clear language and with appropriate context for executives, this book is a must-read for anyone with a busy career who is trying to ensure balance in their lives."

Dr. Ruth L. Collins-Nakai, Past President, Canadian Medical Association

"Not only is Dr. Ohlhauser's book jam-packed with practical information to better anyone's quality of life, but the Frank and Katie story is wonderful fiction. What a fun way to learn some life-changing lessons!"

Steve Erwin, *New York Times* best-selling author

"As CEO of a national health and fitness business, I thought I had seen every new idea for motivating people to get healthy; then I was introduced to Dr. Ohlhauser's book. If every business leader and influencer in America read this book and passed it along to others, I truly believe our world would be a healthier, happier and more productive place. Thank you, Dr. Ohlhauser, for a fresh approach to an ongoing challenge."

Barbie Hall Gummin, founder, Promote It International

"Dr. Ohlhauser's passion for living a balanced and healthy lifestyle is very clear in this articulate and evidence-based book. A thoughtful, provoking read."

Honorable Iris Evans, Minister of Health, Government of Alberta

"If you want to lead a full, abundant life, one that lets you be a peak performer in all areas of life, read *The Healthy CEO*. Dr. Ohlhauser gives you not only a tool and a guide for living a successful life, but lots of motivation to get you started. No matter your title or position in business or life, this book will help you get all God intends you to have. It's a great story and manual of restoring hope to your healthy life!"

Michael Frank, President, Frank Consulting;
former founding partner, Level (3) Communications

"*The Healthy CEO* is a very unique and important book that every top executive should read. It provides valuable ideas about taking charge of the key areas of our lives, which we often neglect as we charge through life on our way to 'success.' Following this book's prescriptions will empower us to lead a life without regrets."

Larry Absheer, Chief Financial Officer, Missouri Athletic Club

"*The Healthy CEO* is a no-holds-barred wake-up call to CEOs and entrepreneurs who put professional success first, and physical, financial and relational wellness second, if at all. Dr. Ohlhauser's anecdotal style identifies the health issues that plague CEOs and then prescribes understandable action plans to remedy them. Reading *The Healthy CEO* is like having a one-on-one chat with a doctor who still makes house calls and embraces the humanity of a positive bed-side manner. This book is a must-read, not only for CEOs, but for their staff and subordinates as well."

Ned Minor, co-founder and President, Minor & Brown PC;
author, *Deciding to Sell Your Business—The Key to Wealth and Freedom*

"Dr. Ohlhauser's *The Healthy CEO* is just the prescription every CEO needs to get on the road to personal wellness. The book not only provides an exciting vision, it also provides the know-how to assist in the realization of that vision! Congratulations on a terrifically helpful book and an excellent read."

Richard C. Alvarez, President and CEO, Canada Health Infoway

"Your philosophy fits hand-in-glove with the concepts from the World Health Organization—that it takes engagement and responsibility to sustain a healthy lifestyle. Your book is a great translation of how to take that journey to building the systems—personal, familial and social—that support a healthy lifestyle and proactive care for improving health outcomes."

Alison Bourey, Director, ABM Management Company; Past President, Women in Healthcare

"*The Healthy CEO* is a wonderful book designed to show how principles and drive responsible for success at work can be channeled to benefit other areas of your life. It is well-referenced and has thought-provoking quotes to drive home its clear message. Dr. Ohlhauser is to be congratulated on producing such a remarkable compendium of dos and don'ts for the CEO."

Dr. Arvand Khosal, Chief of Cardiac Surgery, Capital Health

"I love this book. It touches on the everyday issues CEOs encounter. The inclusion of Frank and Katie, who seek solutions from the Healthy CEO, made reading the book a personal and non-patronizing experience. Compared to other self-help books on the market, this was a refreshing, informative and enjoyable read—a good reminder and reinforcement."

Diane Brickner, President and CEO, Peace Hills Insurance

"Along with the important areas of physical and relational health, Dr. Ohlhauser's book covers the basics of financial planning, which too often CEOs leave unaddressed until their final years before retirement. It follows a chronological diagnosis of important questions, which are necessary to be the CEO of your financial plan. The plan is both straightforward and covers all the bases. The book provides an important checklist for any CEO."

Angus Watt, Vice President and Managing Director, National Bank Financial

"Dr. Ohlhauser's book is a fresh take on what success really means for a CEO. It's not about power, prestige or money; it's about making your whole life come together to mean something and be truly fulfilling. I recommend his book to anyone who is wondering about the path they are on, and is looking for guidance on how to make positive changes."

Guy Kerr, President and CEO, Workers' Compensation Board - Alberta

"*The Healthy CEO* is a wake-up call to reestablish a winning plan based on wellness, life balance and true focus of available energy. It's inspired me to execute a plan that will deliver success in business and in life! This book prompted me, for the first time, to embark on a workout routine that is delivering huge physical and mental gains. It has helped me rebalance my priorities through sound explanations for wellness that are easily understandable and immediately adaptable. I've seen amazing results."

Bruce Good, General Manager - Canada, IMS Health Canada Limited

"Dr. Ohlhauser's book provides a refreshing perspective on health and wellness using proven research, key insights and relevant examples—and with a no-nonsense but conversational bedside manner. The accompanying workbook helps the reader apply the information in the text and make it instantly personal. *The Healthy CEO* is as good for you as an apple a day."

Russ Phillips, Managing Principal, Transom Partners

"Dr. Ohlhauser clearly understands the rationalizations of many hardworking business leaders and employees who discover, often too late, that they have 'spent their health to get their wealth.' *The Healthy CEO* is an engaging, well-researched and practical guide that will empower readers to realign their physical, relational and financial goals with their work demands. I will definitely recommend it to my clients."

Dr. Susan J. Lea, CEO and Medical Director, Foothills Health Consultants Ltd.

"It never ceases to amaze me that CEOs and senior corporate executives spend the bulk of their waking hours looking after corporate assets while more often than not ignoring their most important asset: their health and overall well-being. Dr. Ohlhauser has written a marvelous book to help those who wish to bring greater physical, emotional and financial balance into their lives. I heartily recommend it."

Ray Levesque, Chair, The Executive Committee (TEC) Canada

"Dr. Ohlhauser will show you how to begin the creation of a life that is thoughtful, balanced and filled with satisfaction, based on your heart's needs—emotionally, physically and mentally."

Dr. Lee Lipsenthal, President, American Board of Holistic Medicine; founder, Finding Balance in a Medical Life

"*The Healthy CEO* is easy to read and highly recommended for CEOs, aspiring CEOs and everyone, in all walks of life, who wants to realize personal wellness. I especially encourage the younger crowd to read it, as it will set the stage for future personal wellness as they move along in their careers—rather than having to make drastic changes in life as Frank and Katie did."

Ivan Radostits, CEO, Radco Group of Sobey's and IGA Stores

"Dr. Ohlhauser has written an important book, one that all CEOs and aspiring CEOs should read and keep in their reference libraries for years to come. CEOs are so focused on monthly, quarterly and annual results that years go by without any attention to one's physical, relational or financial well-being. I can remember one company director saying to me, following a particularly stressful period, 'Please don't you or any of your team get sick.' What he did not say is 'slow down.' Each CEO has to take responsibility for their personal wellness and this book demonstrates how this can be the most rewarding investment one can make. Dr. Ohlhauser's book outlines how this can be successfully achieved."

John McLennan, former President and CEO, Bell Canada

"When people are asked to rate their health, the vast majority of people will say they enjoy very good or excellent health. Do they? Do you? The fact is, most people don't know what they don't know: that wellness is more than the absence of illness. Dr. Ohlhauser's book is an important contribution to those who want to improve their wellness, the quality of their relationships and financial well-being. He puts forward common sense ideas on how to plan the outcomes you desire and record your progress. If you believe that what you don't know can hurt you, then read this book."

Honorable Gary G. Mar, Minister of International and Intergovernmental Relations, Government of Alberta

"A CEO for over 12 years, I have learned the hard way about what not to do. I only wish I could have read *The Healthy CEO* before I started working. From its beginning pages, this book is so insightful about doing the right things for the right reasons that I could not put it down. Whether you are at the top of the organization, at the bottom or anywhere in between, *The Healthy CEO* will empower you to be the CEO of your physical, relational and financial well-being. You'll want to buy extra copies for your friends and colleagues."

Dr. Sam Shaw, President, Northern Alberta Institute of Technology

"*The Healthy CEO* is a thought-provoking wake-up call. It is a how-to book with a plan. It doesn't just tell you to change; it also gives you the tools to do so—to live a vibrant, healthy and inspired life. I highly recommend this book for those who want a better quality of life."

Tessa Greenspan, President and CEO, Sappington International Farmers Market

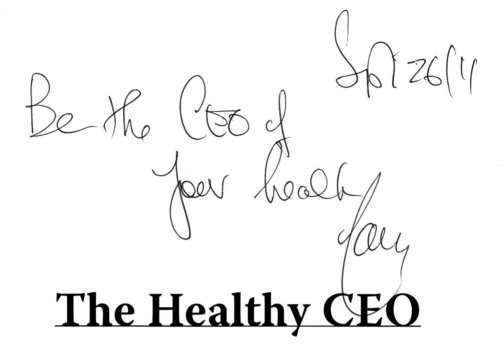

Be the CEO of your health

Sept 26/11

Larry

The Healthy CEO

Taking the lead in your physical,
relational and financial wellness

DR. LARRY OHLHAUSER, M.D.

Library and Archives Canada Cataloguing in Publication

Ohlhauser, Larry, 1945–
    The healthy CEO : taking the lead in your physical, relational and financial wellness / Larry Ohlhauser.

Includes bibliographical references.
ISBN 0-9737342-2-1

    1. Chief executive officers—Health and hygiene. 2. Chief executive officers—Family relationships. 3. Chief executive officers—Finance, Personal. 4. Success. I. Title.

RA776.5.O38 2006   650.102'465842   C2006-906269-2

Published 2007. Printed and bound in Canada.
15 14 13 12 11 10 09 08 07   1 2 3 4 5

JuneWarren Publishing Ltd.
6111-91 Street NW
Edmonton, Alberta
Canada, T6E 6V6

Contents

Preface

I was experiencing shortness of breath. I put it out of my mind and chalked it up to lack of exercise. Walking to and from conference sessions I was giving that day, my breathing got worse. Given my obvious intelligence, professionalism and medical prowess, I responded to the situation in an entirely appropriate manner. I ignored it.

That was a few years back at a business function in Colorado with my wife, Kelay. I decided to skip dinner that evening because I wasn't feeling well. Kelay asked if I was OK. She knew it wasn't like me to duck out of a social event. Pretending it wasn't a big deal, but feeling some alarm, I spent most of that evening checking my pulse.

The next morning, I woke up with mild chest pains and increased breathing difficulty. Kelay knew something was wrong, but I assured her I was fine. (The M.D. after my name stands for medical doctor and massive denial.) It's nothing a little golf can't cure, I told myself. In a few hours, I'd be teeing off at one of America's most picturesque golf courses, and the weather couldn't have been more perfect.

While lunching by the first tee, I was ready to acknowledge that even my best golf game wouldn't fix whatever was wrong. I told Kelay I wasn't well and that I couldn't go golfing. She had never seen me turn down a round before. My admission—tantamount to me saying that my world had just stopped—confirmed her sense that something was seriously wrong. After I told her my symptoms, she insisted I get immediate medical attention. I promised to get myself checked out, but only once we were back home and I could see my own doctor.

I survived the trip and visited my doctor. At my follow-up appointment, once he had completed a 21-point inspection and drawn and scrutinized all the necessary body fluids, he gave me a diagnosis. "You're fat and out of shape," he told me, bluntly. Immediately, I said I wanted a second opinion. Then he said, "OK. You're fat, out of shape and ugly."

He paused. I realized he was preparing to deliver some weighty words. I got serious and prepared myself to listen. He looked me straight in the eye and said, "You are responsible for your health. Get in shape, take care of yourself and reduce your stress. You need to do it now... before it's too late."

In clinical practice, I had given that same advice to countless people. But I'd never really applied it to myself. Not really. A sober challenge from my doctor combined with the emotional experience of terrifying symptoms—and a little tough love from my wife—convinced me to become the CEO of my own wellness. I had to re-evaluate my life and decide what was really important to me. Why couldn't I succeed at what mattered to me most, what gave me a sense of purpose—as expressed through my physical health, my relationships and my finances—to the same degree I had succeeded in my business?

That day, Kelay joined me on what has been a journey of untold rewards for us and our family. We feel deeply grateful to my longtime doctor and friend (you know who you are) who gave us a much-needed wake-up call. We were two successful businesspeople who had everything we could hope for—except a guarantee that we'd survive to enjoy our retirement and a life lived to the fullest.

That day we sat down and decided what really mattered in our lives. Today, we invite you to do the same.

Dr. Larry Ohlhauser
Edmonton, Canada
November 15, 2006

Acknowledgments

I have important people to thank for seeing me through the production of this book. Can you believe we're actually done?

Kelay: You've saved my life, in more ways than one. I will always love you.

My kids and grandkids: You're all so uniquely special to me—Nicole and Dave, Dakoda and Skylar; Robbie and Jen, Derrick and Trace; Kristen, Madisen and Maurghen. I love you all and I celebrate having you in my life.

Tabea Gietz, Faith Farthing, Isabela Varela and the team at FinalEyes Communications: I couldn't have done this book without your enthusiasm, your creative genius, your attention to detail and your unwavering commitment to the project.

Jared Smith and the gang at Incite Solutions: Do you guys ever run out of energy and innovative marketing ideas? Your contributions to my work have been invaluable and truly *inciteful*.

Bill Whitelaw, Michael Gaffney, Jaime McHardy, Audrey Sprinkle and the rest of the gang at JuneWarren Publishing: Thanks for reaching outside your comfort zone and taking a self-help risk. Sarah Whitman, Tara Woloschuk and Rianne Stewart: The book wouldn't be what it is without your talents.

Danny Reaney: Thanks for your research, your knowledge, and for pushing me in my quest for physical fitness.

Bill Bagshaw and my trusty TEC group (#241): Thanks for providing me with a place to practice my passion. You inspire me with your visionary minds and ready solutions to every possible business conundrum. We've been through a lot together. I trust there are more challenges and victories to come.

Dr. Nigel Flook and Dr. Susan Lea: Thanks for your encouragement, support and contribution to the physical wellness content. Every doctor needs his own great doctors.

Angus Watt: You shoot from the hip and always keep me and others accountable, my friend. I am blessed to have you in my TEC group. Thanks for taking the time to share your financial wisdom and insights with the laypeople around you.

Dr. Jonathan Sneep and Dr. Joyce Gillese: Thanks for your expertise, your experience and your patience in helping us through the relational wellness content. There's more to this than meets the eye and you helped us more than we can express.

Tom Hill and Jaynie Smith: Thanks for sharing your insights about the world of writing books. You're tough acts to follow and I appreciate your connections and votes of confidence.

Colin Eicher: My TEC buddy and dear office mate. You've got one of the most generous hearts I've ever encountered. Thanks for opening it up to me and for sticking close by.

Prologue

Katie dropped the phone into the Bavarian cream. She didn't have time for this. Lela, her niece, hadn't bothered showing up for work that morning. Everyone else had been trying to pick up the slack. The Organic Delights catering team was due to set up a corporate luncheon at the Hyatt in two hours, and Katie didn't know how they could possibly make it on time. Now her husband's business associate was calling. In her stirring frenzy, Katie had let the phone slip from her shoulder into the custard. Cursing under her breath, she began digging through the now-ruined mixture. "Why are you bothering me now, George?"

Fifteen minutes earlier, Frank Johnson was hunkered over a 10-foot putt on Grayhawk's No. 18. His board chair, George Fletcher, stood behind him with Kent Merritt, CEO of Chips Corporation—the latest market challengers in systems software design. They were proving to be heavyweights, eating up more and more of the market share. Now they were looking for an innovative firm to ignite and stoke their next marketing push. That afternoon, the three gentlemen had shared some good-natured reverie, had bantered about their favorite PGA pros, and had settled into a low-key discussion about systems software. Friendly exchanges to be sure. But this was a high-stakes, multi-million-dollar job interview. This was a big putt. Frank was cool on the surface. Confidence was key. To the putt and to securing the contract. Wound up tight on the inside, Frank was desperate not to let his nervousness show. The marketing business was all about image. Whatever he felt inside, he couldn't risk anything short of a competent display. Today, he wasn't just selling a product. He was selling the firm.

The ball kissed the edge of the cup and seemed to linger there for an eternity before it dropped and rattled inside. Victory. Frank looked up at the scene in front of him. The contrast of the cool green against the blaze of the red rock in the Arizona sun was breathtaking. Beauty. Serenity.

Pain. Fire. But the fire was not in the red rock. It was in Frank's chest and surging through his arms. With ferocity the pain gripped him, stole his breath and made him swoon. "Frank?" George's voice sounded far away. Frank fell to the green. Above him the sky was brilliant blue. The sun was a fire, burning through him, fierce. Then it was dark.

"Oh my God, George! Where are you?" Katie held the custard-coated phone close to her ear. A heart attack? How could Frank have had a heart attack? For a moment she didn't know what to do. Her first thought was that the luncheon was doomed to failure. She winced at her selfishness. "Okay, George, I'll be right there." She dropped the phone into her apron pocket and grabbed her assistant Jude's arm. "Listen. You have to make this go. My husband's had a heart attack." Flustered, she didn't know where to begin giving instructions. "I'll call you from the car and try to talk you through this. I'm sorry."

Katie was out the door. She was weighed down with guilt for leaving her team in crisis. And guilt because, while her husband might be dying, her first worry was having enough strawberry tart for Elizabeth Warren and the 76 national managers of Utopia Spa.

Introduction

It's no longer a question of staying healthy. It's a question of finding a sickness you like.

Jackie Mason, comedian

Frank and Katie Johnson thought they were doing everything right. They were productive, successful, even powerful people—leaders in the professional world. But they had been putting themselves at risk without really even realizing it. Crisis came, but were they prepared to deal with it? Had they lost sight of what was most important? What *was* most important, for that matter? Was it too late to turn things around?

You are a leader in business—a success. *But are you successfully leading your life?*

The Healthy CEO is designed specifically for CEOs who want to guarantee greater returns on their most important investment—themselves. Business leaders often lose sight of what's most important and what they truly want. In the climb to corporate success—balancing budgets, improving the bottom line, minimizing investment risk and working toward fiscal growth—CEOs often neglect their personal health and well-being. Their lives are unbalanced, their health is often at a deficit, they face many real health risks, and they neglect their personal and relational growth. Having previously made honest attempts to improve their wellness in several areas, many of these CEOs have found the enterprise of lifestyle improvement cumbersome, disillusioning and often all but impossible. While trying to manage corporation and career, they've also been managing marriages, families, personal finances and seemingly limitless demands on their time, with varying degrees of success.

"So many people want a 'piece' of me. Giving people uninterrupted time and attention is kind of a full-time job—and the 'real' job still needs attention every day."

Paul, director of a university department

"I have a 10-year-old. I struggle with giving her time and attention. I also worry that I'm not being a proper role model."

Mark, CEO of an international IT firm

"I have different ideas than my husband does when it comes to raising my kids. We also have difficulty finding quality time for ourselves. I really dislike talking about work (which is sometimes necessary) when we are at home—or even on a vacation."

Eileen, owner of a marketing firm

Frank Johnson had been CEO of a successful marketing firm for 11 years before he collapsed on the green—11 years of seeing changes in technology, budget cutbacks in stagnant departments, staff turnover (including the loss of his right-hand woman, Cecilia, who retired to spend time with her grandkids), a rogue colleague jump ship and start his own marketing agency *and* steady growth in company revenue. He got credit for a large measure of the company's growth, but Frank felt pressure all the time to deliver more. The best way, he thought, to deal with all the demands he felt both from within and without was to try to stay on task and not let himself become too emotionally engaged. He was a machine: efficient, consistent and productive. It was a coping mechanism, for sure. Frank felt steady and competent, forging ahead and delivering consistent results. But the price he paid was feeling more and more disconnected from his... well, his heart. He'd lost his passion for the business and maybe even for life. It wasn't fun anymore. And he didn't know what to do about it. It seemed easier to just avoid these issues and keep pushing along. But he could feel himself shutting down.

Frank's wife, Katie, on the other hand, thrived on stress. Pressure was a rush—a kind of high that made her feel alive. When there were no ripples on the surface of her life, she would soon stir some up, preferring to go hard and fast even if it might mean going down the wrong road. She had started her catering business almost two years ago after nearly 15 years of managing a downtown restaurant. Though she had handled her responsibilities with finesse and had been able to connect with some fascinating people, the job had lost its thrill. Now, her business was a thrill a minute. When potential clients called, she would immediately say yes to their requests and then do whatever was necessary to deliver. That meant long, busy days at a frenetic pace that spent her reserves. She loved it. Still, there was a nagging thought picking at her from the back of her brain that she was letting herself be defined solely by her work and was ripping herself off. Truthfully, she was terrified to pause long enough to discover that perhaps she was no more than her work after all. Going hard all the time was her way of hiding.

Many CEOs find ways to hide or shrink back, and end up spending their lives without savoring them. CEOs "manage" their time. They divide tasks into "manageable" pieces. Many times, they feel like they're just "managing" to keep their head above water. When asked if they need help, they might say, "I'll manage." But merely managing life leaves us wanting, tired and unfulfilled. Wouldn't we much rather be leading our lives? Steering a course to a destination we have chosen carefully, a place we truly want to go? *The Healthy CEO* is here to help you take the lead in your physical, relational and financial health by empowering you. Even if you're not a CEO, you can apply these principles effectively to become CEO of your wellness. *You* are the source of this power: your purpose, your passion and your proficiency. By discovering and pursuing your life's purpose and maximizing your physical, relational and financial fitness, you can lead a truly exhilarating, dynamic and fulfilling life.

The fact that you have picked up this book indicates that you have at least an interest in improving your overall wellness. That's one very important step toward greater physical, relational and financial health. You want to do more than just manage your life—and you can.

By applying to your lifestyle the same principles and drive you've applied to your corporate success, you can achieve tremendous results in all areas of your life—even additional financial and professional dividends. True success is success that can be fully and freely enjoyed. After all, what good is corporate conquest or financial security at the expense of your body, sanity, relationships or longevity? Be well. Be well-off. You *can* do both. *The Healthy CEO* can help you lead the life you've always wanted to live.

Our general health: Wellness in crisis

Our culture pushes the mantra, "You can have it all!" Yet, for many, "having it all" costs them dearly through debilitating stress, failing health, unbalanced lifestyles, suffering relationships, anxiety over finances and overall disappointment with quality of life. Frank and Katie were getting through each day, but their health, marriage and financial focus were suffering.

PHYSICAL WELLNESS

Both an increased understanding of human physiology and advances in medical science have introduced new ways to promote health and increase average life span. However, there are still no easy solutions for the treatment, let alone the eradication, of a vast number of diseases and medical conditions. Preventative strategies are key to taking charge of one's health and investing in long-term quality of life. Still, many North Americans don't seem to pay attention.

Obesity—what the Surgeon General in 2003 called a "health crisis"—costs Americans dollars and, more importantly, lives. Consider the following statistics:

> "In the year 2000, the total annual cost of obesity in the United States was $117 billion."

> "Nearly two out of every three Americans are overweight or obese."

> "One out of every eight deaths in America is caused by illness directly related to overweight and obesity."[1]

The prevalence of largely preventable illnesses such as Type II diabetes is on the rise. According to information published by the American Diabetes Association, "1.5 million new cases of diabetes were diagnosed in people aged 20 years or older" in 2005. In 2002, diabetes contributed to at least 224,092 deaths;[2] that number is conservative since many cases go undiagnosed.

TV watching has become our culture's favorite leisure activity, with people watching an average of over four hours per day.[3] The American Heart Association reported, "In 2004, 30.1 percent of Americans age 18 or older engaged in any regular leisure-time physical activity."[4] Our sedentary lifestyle is killing us. The increase in risk of coronary heart disease associated with physical inactivity is comparable to the increased risk associated with high blood cholesterol, high blood pressure or cigarette smoking.[5]

America is stressed out. "Twenty percent of Americans are worried that stress will affect their health, yet 36 percent say they deal with stress by eating or drinking alcohol."[6] Is one problem "solved" by creating another? It's possible that no one knows about stress more than CEOs. Job-related stresses faced by CEOs can increase their risk of disease, burnout and depression, and can negatively impact their time spent *away* from work.

> "I wish I was 20 pounds lighter and had more energy. Work and relationship stresses cause me to lose a lot of sleep, and then I find I get sick more easily."
>
> **Mitch,** real estate executive

Real stress creates a real impact—on health and peace of mind.

RELATIONAL WELLNESS

> "Since my divorce, I feel endless pressure to do it all. I have to be a leader, manager, caregiver, housekeeper, provider, friend.... I never seem to be able to let my guard down and just relax. There's always more to do and to do better. Sometimes I can't help but feel like I'm almost, but not quite, failing at everything. My family is the most important thing in the world to me, but would they believe that?"
>
> **Carrie,** partner in an advertising agency

Friends, couples and families are struggling to stay connected given many of today's challenges: two-working-parent homes, an alarming divorce rate, aging parents who need care, career demands and a host of other day-to-day difficulties. Fast-paced home-to-work-and-back days create emotional isolation for many, even for those honestly seeking meaningful relationships. Where significant relationships do exist, work-related stresses can be caustic to closeness and emotionally nourishing pursuits. One respondent to a government study revealed the following:

> For me, the biggest challenge of trying to achieve a balance is the fatigue I feel constantly and the job stress I take home with me. This impacts on my relationship with my spouse and the energy I have for my children. There is always a feeling of guilt.[7]

Emotional and relational problems are stressful in and of themselves, but they also have a negative impact on job satisfaction and work performance. Relational challenges travel with us from one setting to another and have a direct impact on us physiologically. Stress takes its toll on our bodies—in ways we'll explore more closely later. Unchecked, the relational-work stress cycle continues—and a downward spiral begins.

So, what's the bottom line?

FINANCIAL WELLNESS

Sadly, while many continue to devote their best energy to earning a living, they never seem to realize their financial goals. Consider these statistics:

- The average credit card debt among Americans with at least one card is $9,205.
- The average household debt, not counting mortgage debt, is about $14,500.
- Families annually spending more than they earn is estimated at 40 percent.
- The number of households filing for bankruptcy in 2003 is 1.6 million (or one out of every 73).[8]

> ## "My friends would be shocked at my financial situation. My credit cards are maxed because I always assume more client checks are bound to arrive next week. At month's end, I 'rob Peter to pay Paul' and I spend more than most people earn in a year on interest."
>
> **Rhonda,** owner of a corporate communications firm

Debt plagues people in every income bracket. No matter how much you make, poor financial decisions can create havoc. The critical issue is not how much income is enough, but how to best manage the income you have.

An unbalanced checkbook, schedule, list of priorities, lifestyle or perspective can lead to a decline in overall wellness. Is genuine, comprehensive and pervasive health and wellness possible? Can one experience success in all areas of life? Does anyone ever "have it all"? Leading a life that's healthy, satisfying and rewarding *is* possible. There is hope.

But first, let's look at some of the specific challenges facing many CEOs.

Health of CEOs

Achieving wellness and balance can be difficult for the CEO—perhaps even more so than for most people. Whether you're running a multi-million-dollar, multinational company or your own small business, there are unique challenges to being the boss.

THE BIGGER THE SHOULDERS, THE BIGGER THE PAIN IN THE NECK

The buck stops, literally, with you. You are responsible for hiring, firing and managing staff. You make critical decisions daily that catalyze growth or setback, or could even determine the viability of your company. Though several others are accountable to you, they also rely on your success to realize their own. When your staff scores a touchdown, you get to celebrate, but when they fumble, *you* take the biggest hit. You're accountable to others as well—a board, a parent-company CEO, shareholders, customers, and even the tax man. In those rare nirvanic moments when everyone above and below you is happy, you still face relentless pressure to keep the edge on the competition, stay technologically current, build your own skill base and portfolio, and know your market intuitively. Hopefully, you don't also have to watch your back.

> "I have to multitask at five-minute intervals and fine-tune the whole game every 15 seconds."
>
> **Darren,** design agency owner

The buck stops here. So do most deadline crunches, staff conflicts, market fluctuations and countless administrative details. It's no wonder CEOs are stressed out and at increased risk of heart problems, high blood pressure, some types of cancer and other serious illness, including depression. Philip J. Burguieres, once the youngest CEO to ever lead a Fortune 500 company, battled a crippling depression that climaxed in a three-month stay at a mental hospital. He's recovered since and now speaks to other distressed CEOs about his experience. He contends that "at some point in their careers, fully 25 percent of top-level executives go through a severe depression. You would be shocked at the number of CEOs, now running big companies, who are suicidally depressed."[9]

PRACTICE MAKES PERFECT. PERFECTION MEANS PRESSURE.

High achievers by nature, many CEOs push themselves not only to do their best, but to *be* the best—and by virtue of their title, they are. Ironically, the inner drive to get everything right, make everything just so and fiercely guard against making mistakes can work against a perfectionist. The stress of self-imposed expectations can lead to

- physical symptoms such as headaches, chest pain, depression, chronic fatigue and high blood pressure;

- high levels of anxiety;

- strained relationships with family, friends and other loved ones;

- decreased productivity, as trivial tasks take undue time and attention;

- stagnation due to fear of failure; and

- a lack or absence of personal satisfaction—nothing is ever quite good enough.[10]

CEOs used to being rewarded professionally for their high standards succumb easily to drivenness. Their perspective can become skewed, and expectations they impose on themselves and others can become impossible, even though the perfectionist views them as "perfectly reasonable." Katie, for example, couldn't relinquish many tasks in her catering business to others. She had good people working for her, but to delegate, for her, meant to lose control. She reasoned that it was more efficient to do as much as she could herself rather than train her people to do the same—especially if there was a risk they might make mistakes.

IT'S LONELY AT THE TOP

Many leaders are afraid to admit any weakness that might jeopardize their position. These dynamos have excelled because of strength, perseverance and an absolute refusal to be hindered by roadblocks. When very real—even dangerous—health problems surface, many CEOs put on a mask of self-sufficiency, loath to acknowledge any weakness. They don't want anyone to think they can't handle the job. The pressure to perform increases while their ability to perform often decreases. The stress escalates, as do the health risks.

Many CEOs have classic "type A" personalities with insatiable appetites for success and achievement, which create an adrenaline rush unlike any other. But success, once achieved, is an ending. The goal has been reached. The mountain has been climbed. Now energy must be channeled into *staying* on top. *Preserving* one's position, as opposed to *advancing* it, is a balancing act that breeds insecurity. The focus shifts from the excitement of risk-taking to conservative, even mundane duties that are much less exhilarating. Frank knew this all too well. Every deal he secured felt like receiving just another poker chip—never winning a whole pot.

"I feel an unimaginable amount of pressure in my job. People envy me and my accomplishments, but I don't think they realize the cost. Now that I do, it's too late. I've invested too much getting here to give any of it up. And I can't admit this to anyone around me."

Steve, vice president of a brokerage firm and senior investment advisor to affluent business owners

By definition, CEOs are part of a select group. Kindred spirits who understand this way of life are few and far between. Even fewer are those who will take off their game face long enough to admit sometimes-intense vulnerability.

"I'LL PENCIL YOU IN."

CEOs are usually in a time crunch. Many would say, "Time for myself? What's *that*?" Sixty-plus-hour work weeks limit personal time and challenge the relational ability of many CEOs. Dana Friedman, Ph.D and head of Corporate Solutions, a New York–based consulting firm, reports that "the impact of work issues on home life is three times greater than the impact of home life on work." Of note, "those who achieve... balance between home life and work life... become the most motivated workers."[11] A healthy personal life is what creates the most momentum at work. Yet that balance is so difficult to realize. Time is the rarest commodity; time for relationships has to be scheduled. Leisure time is more like "recovery time" when it can be found. There's nothing left over.

> ## "I am running my own life, but I'm over 60 now. It's only been that way for a few years. There are so many things that I am trying to balance."
>
> **Grant,** president of an architecture firm

CEOs rarely spend the time that does remain in their schedules seeking advice or assistance from others. Visits to the doctor are put off, counseling and personal growth are crisis measures only, and financial advisors are dismissed as redundant for CEOs who deal with numbers regularly—whether or not they've taken the time to plan, set goals or even take stock of their personal finances.

Does this seem like an unfair synopsis of the CEO experience, or does it paint an all-too-familiar picture? It is apparent that we all—CEOs or not—can take steps to improve our overall wellness, in one or several areas of our lives. While change is often daunting, improvements in only one aspect of your life will positively affect the other aspects. Nevertheless, the question remains: how does one begin?

What comes first?

Without a strong sense of who you are and what you personally want, the decisions you make in life will be random, aimless, potentially insignificant or lacking in integrity. Every decision you make, every course you take and every conversation you have is personally motivated. For example, you may have chosen your vocation for any number of personal reasons, with equally personal motivations: your parents promised you a beautiful new car if you completed business graduate school (motivation: new wheels), you dated someone who had well-defined aspirations for you (motivation: approval or acceptance), you set out to make as much money as possible (motivation: wealth or status), you felt responsible to carry on the family business (motivation: pleasing others), you simply couldn't imagine doing anything else (motivation: life purpose), you thought it was the best way to make a difference with your life (motivation: philanthropy), and so on. How often do you examine your goals and decisions to ensure that you are accomplishing what is most important to you, at the core of your being? Are you putting those central purposes first?

> ## "The most important life lesson I've learned is that what you say and do defines who you are. And that lasts forever."
>
> **Don,** president of a private and business aviation company

With the varying demands placed on you and the many roles to fill within life's job description, it's easy to lose sight of "first things." In his essay "First and Second Things," C. S. Lewis wrote: "You can't get second things by putting them first; you can get second things only by putting first things first."[12] What if the futility we experience so much of the time comes from pursuing what are really just "second things" before we've gotten a good grasp of what needs to come first? Stephen R. Covey, author of *First Things First*, puts it this way: "We often get so busy 'sawing' (producing results) that we forget to 'sharpen our saw' (maintain or increase our capacity to produce results in the future)."[13]

"First things" are those things born out of our life purpose, our raison d'être. In *The Monk Who Sold His Ferrari*, Robin Sharma maintains that "the purpose of life is a life of purpose. Those who are truly enlightened know what they want out of life, emotionally, materially, physically and spiritually."[14] Achievement cannot be defined strictly by material or professional gain. Finding and devoting our lives to our life purpose—the thing that gives life meaning—will create lasting and inexpressible satisfaction. This is life's greatest achievement. Frank, for one, had certainly achieved success by professional standards, but he found his job to be lackluster. He'd lost his passion for it. If you asked him why he was doing what he was doing, he certainly wouldn't cite passion or a sense of purpose as his reason. He *was* clear, however, that something was missing—that he wanted his experience of 24/7 to be different somehow.

So how do we identify our life purpose? Your life purpose will be unique to you. You probably know what it is instinctively, but you may have dulled your awareness of it by focusing on "second things"—the pursuits, responsibilities and roles that can consume people without them even realizing.

You may have lost sight of your life purpose, but it's still there. How do you discover (or rediscover) it? Questions like these can help you:

- What inspires me? What moves me?

- What am I most passionate about? What brings me joy?

- What am I good at?

- What do I have to offer that the world needs?

- What needs around me most capture my attention?

- When I let myself dream—even of the impossible—what do I dream about? What am I doing in those dreams?

- When I felt carefree as a child, what was I doing? What did I dream about then?

- What do others say about me? What skills, talents and gifts do they affirm in me?

When you explore questions like these, certain personal themes begin to emerge: you love to see others discover their hidden potential, you are a born leader with natural charisma, you are sensitive to aesthetic beauty and have an artistic flair, you are an innovator who naturally sees new and better ways of doing things.... You can find tremendous ways to exercise your gifts in and beyond a vocational capacity. This is exercising your life purpose.

> ## "I want to see and 'be in' the beauty of each day—to listen to that still small voice."
>
> **Vivian,** spa owner

You might be able to distill your life purpose into a clear mission statement: "I want to help build a universal-access medical facility in a third-world country," "I want to run an inner-city art program," "I want to make enough money to personally fund a low-income housing development," "I want to make my business a model of ecological consciousness for the global community," and so on. Or more broadly, "I want to serve others selflessly," "I want to make a lasting positive impact in my community," "I want to be fully present in every moment" or "I want to raise a socially conscious family." Implementing strategies to realize these personal missions can become your life purpose.

When Katie first started her company, she was focused on offering healthy food that tasted great while creating increased consciousness of environmental issues in the food industry. Her organic approach was something she believed in. Now, her convictions and inspiration had been edged out by eking out some credibility with customers, keeping balanced books and staying out of the red while building her brand. Her entrepreneurial spirit, the part of her that was once so full of big dreams, was now fast asleep. Was it too late to revisit and reawaken her early inspiration?

Are you living your life purpose? Is your life full of passion? If not, it's vital to fan the embers and kindle that flame. The process will vary depending on where you are now. It may not be realistic for you to leave your job to become an artist, but it might be worth carving out more time to surround yourself with the raw beauty of nature or scheduling blocks of time to paint or sculpt. The satisfaction found in living purposefully and passionately will enhance everything you do in every area of your life—including your professional life—bringing energy and vitality to your physical, relational and financial wellness. In turn, as you make adjustments in your lifestyle, relationships and finances that harmonize with your life purpose, you'll experience even greater satisfaction. Letting "first things" trump our decisions and our motivation—putting first things first—enables us to pursue "second things" from a place of confidence, clarity and purpose. In the absence of clear, well-defined, first-things-driven goals, we fail to *lead* lives. We struggle to *manage* them instead. One is deliberate. The other is deflating. If we haven't taken the time to truly evaluate what's important, how can we help but be caught up in the maelstrom of the urgent or lulled into complacency with what seems good enough?

> "I want to live life hard and enjoy it. I want to let go of those things I can't control and feel good about it. I want to help the people who want to be helped and distance myself from those who just want to be negative."
>
> **Dave,** real-estate-agency owner

Have you asked yourself, What's most important to me? Why is it important to me? Where should I refuse to compromise? Is my lifestyle steering me toward or away from my purpose and passion? Do I know what I really want, not only for my career, my relationships or my finances, but for my *life*? What is my foundational purpose, my rudder? What are my primary goals? At the end of my life, what will have been my greatest achievements?

You can take the lead in your wellness as intelligently and effectively as in your business or career—and your return on investment will be exponential. When you have a clear sense of who you are, what you want, and why you want it, you can begin to lead your life in intentional, empowered ways, moving step by step toward what is truly important. You can do well at being well.

How are you doing?

The following diagram illustrates how our personal core—our individual sense of purpose—has a direct impact on our physical, relational and financial wellness:

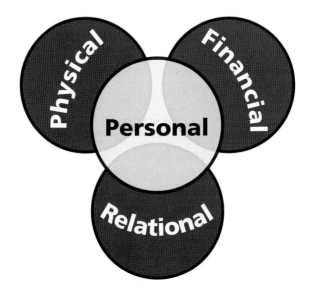

If this core is "ill" in any respect—if we are doing the wrong things, or even the right things for the wrong reasons—our physical health, relationships and finances will reflect that disconnect in subtle or acute ways. We may get headaches or have chronic high blood pressure. We may lack rich intimacy in our most important relationships and tolerate dull mediocrity instead. If we've neglected our health in any area, we may feel like our money is spending us. We may even be at risk for serious health problems, relational disaster or financial collapse.

Conversely, once we examine and attend to our sense of purpose and align our thinking and behavior accordingly, we can begin to effectively and healthfully lead our lives.

As illustrated by the diagram, our lives cannot be compartmentalized into isolated components. Every aspect intrinsically impacts every other one. Financial stress will lead to relational strain and physical manifestations of that stress. A relationship crisis may rob you of sleep and your productivity at work. If you neglect your physical health, your work performance flags and psychological side effects reduce your relational capacity. All fundamental aspects of our lives overlap and interact. This can be good news or bad news depending on the dynamics happening in your life right now: bad news if you ignore your physical, relational or financial health, great news if you launch significant changes in any of these areas. Don't just manage your life. Lead it... and lead it well.

It's your move.

"Reflux esophagitis!?" For a moment, Katie completely forgot that Frank shared a room with another patient. Frank put his hand to his forehead, as though he was shielding his eyes from the sun. "You're telling me that I lost a huge client and maybe the reputation of my business because you had gas!?" The curtain next to them fluttered.

"Indigestion." Frank couldn't resist.

Katie's eyes shot holes through Frank. Her tone chilled to ice. "This is not the least bit amusing, Frank. This is my business. This is my life. And you're just... just going along with your own set of priorities while I'm struggling...," her voice broke, "working my ass off on something that's so important to me while you... while you scarf down a bean burrito with your white-collared butt-kissers." The curtain fluttered more noticeably. "This is my life, Frank, and you just don't care."

Fight or flight. Frank wasn't good at either. "K, I didn't plan this. You think I want to be lying here? I may have lost a big client today. This deal with Chips Corporation would cinch more revenue for our company than what we made in the last two years combined." He clenched his jaw. "Do you even care that it could have been a heart attack? They've been running tests and they're telling me I need to get my blood pressure and cholesterol in check. I'm supposed to get my weight under control and watch what I eat... cut down my drinking some. They're saying that this was just a dress rehearsal for serious problems if I don't straighten some things out."

Katie had walked over to the window. The sun bathed her face in warmth. Frank thought she looked beautiful, but tired. Her face was expressionless. "K?"

"A dress rehearsal, Frank?" She turned her face slightly toward him and then back to the window, as if she couldn't look at him. "We already have *serious problems." There was a deliberate cough, now, from behind the curtain. Katie went on anyway. "I hate that I'm so used to being wound up so tight that when I catch myself relaxing— even for just a moment—I feel like something must be wrong. I hate that the thing I thought I would love most—having everybody answer to me and think I'm something else—feels like a vice. I hate that when you come home from the office, you'd rather hang out with the golf channel than with me." She stopped and then reconsidered. "I hate that I'm angry at my husband for landing in the hospital. I hate that I don't have a clue any more what* he *hates... or what he loves, for that matter. Serious problems, indeed, Frank." She gathered her jacket and briefcase from the chair. "I have to salvage what's left of my luncheon. I'll see you later." She walked deliberately out the door. Frank sighed and was silent. The curtain hung still.*

1 Principles of change

"A goal without a plan is just a wish."

Antoine de Saint-Exupéry, French writer

Frank looked around the room. It was divided exactly in two. On one half, the walls were painted cherry red; on the other, sky blue. Hardwood floor framed two large area rugs—one red shag and one blue berber. The red side reminded him of a child's room. A couple of overstuffed chairs, one red and one purple, flanked a lime green leatherette cube that doubled as a table. A set of markers, a pad of paper, a red bottle of bubble-blowing mix, what looked like a clown puppet, and a bowl of coffee beans were arranged on top. Coffee beans? Not a child's room after all. Mother would surely disapprove. Frank didn't know what to think. What bizarre therapy was he getting himself into? He didn't want to know what the puppet was for.

On the other side of the room—the blue side—was a chaise lounge upholstered in light blue suede and draped with a cable-knit navy throw. Like bookends, wicker side tables hugged the chaise. On one table was a mason jar filled with layers of white sand, small round pebbles and seashells; on the other, a cluster of candles of varying heights in different seaside hues. It looked like a great place to take a nap. On opposite ends of the room hung full-length mirrors framed in red and blue, respectively. Squarely straddling both sides, near the windowed wall joining both realms, sat a large ebony desk. Behind it, outlined by sunlight streaming into the room, stood The Healthy CEO.

Frank couldn't guess how old he might be. He was ruggedly handsome without being especially notable. Salt-and-pepper grey marked his temples and curled up and over his ears. He wore simple wire-rimmed glasses, a beige sweater (so as not to clash with his two-toned room?) and black slacks. He looked at Frank and smiled. Smiled and hummed. Hummed and smiled. They had exchanged greetings, but that was all. Is he waiting for me to say something? Is he trying to read my mind? Is he waiting for his assistant to pop through the door?

He seemed to bounce slightly on the balls of his feet. Maybe he'd been munching on those coffee beans.

Who was this Healthy CEO character anyway? Frank eyed the room some more. Creative? Eccentric? Crazy? He'd never seen a room decorated this way. Maybe the lifestyle coach had a split personality.

Frank remembered Fletcher's words... his biting tone.... It had been a not-so-veiled threat: "Look, Frank, you need to get your act together. The Chips Corporation project is hanging by a thread. Jerry lost a lot of confidence in you—in us—because of the crap you pulled the other day. He'll be looking at other players real soon if we can't convince him solidly that we can handle this. You're a mess, Johnson, and I can't have a mess heading up this division." A mess. He was a mess. Now, he was here, staring at this man who wouldn't say anything. But Fletcher had said this Healthy CEO guy was a genius. "He helped me get on track, Frank, and I think you should go see him. I think you better go see him soon." So, here he sat, just a few inches farther on the red side than the blue, waiting for Fletcher's "guru" to say something. Frank finally smiled back.

Perhaps sensing Frank's discomfort, the guru spoke. "So, Mr. Johnson, why are you here?"

Because I talked in class and got sent to the principal's office. Because my portfolio isn't balanced and everyone wants to be Donald Trump. Because I can't make my wife giggle like she used to anymore. Because... "A colleague, George Fletcher, recommended I see you. He said you'd be able to help me get back on top of things at work. And I've got some health issues I need to address, and he spoke very highly of you... as someone who knew how to balance things out and who could coach me."

"I see." He still smiled. "May I call you Frank?" Frank nodded. "Do you want to be here, Frank?" Frank nodded again. "That's very important, you know. If at any point in our journey, you decide that you don't want this... well, it's no longer effective." The coach came out from behind the desk and perched on one of its front corners. "Now first, I'd like you to make yourself comfortable. How are you feeling today? If you're feeling indifferent or 'low'—sluggish—then choose a spot over here." He gestured to the red side. "You might find the environment stimulating and energizing. However, if you're feeling stress, jitters, restlessness, that sort of thing, I recommend a spot over here." He gestured to the blue side. "What do you choose?"

Yeesh. Choices. So many choices. Maybe he needed a boost. Frank knew for sure he wasn't ready for the chaise. He got up and settled into one of the overstuffed red chairs. The Healthy CEO joined him in a chair of his own.

Still smiling, more softly now, The Healthy CEO began to speak. Frank felt like he was supposed to catch this point for sure. "You've mentioned 'balance' and wanting to 'get on top of things.' You've already shared that your physical health isn't what it should be, and apparently that's impacting things at work. Is that right?"

Frank found his voice. "Yes."

The Healthy CEO continued, "May I ask about your relationships?"

"Pardon?" *Frank said.*

"Your relationships. Are you married?"

"Yes."

"Do you have children?"

"No," *Frank answered.* "Not yet." *Married. No kids. I live in an apartment-style condo and drive a Honda. My shoe size is 11.*

"I don't mean to make you uncomfortable, Frank. I ask because most often when things are 'unhealthy' in one area of our lives, that usually translates in some way to all the others. Balance comes through evaluating all areas of our lives and addressing any problems we find—much the same way you would in your work." *The Healthy CEO continued to smile, gently. He looked at Frank as if expecting a response.*

Come on, Frank. Get in the game. You're a corporate success. You're acting like a scared little kid. "I can see that. It makes sense…. It's what's happening with me, for sure."

"Okay," *The Healthy CEO said.* "Let's start by talking about how we assess where we are and how we get to where we want to be. Let's talk about change, Frank…."

Change. It's not always easy. Frank wanted his life to change, to be sure. Dissatisfied with the status quo, he was looking for something to fire him back up. But he was resistant to change, too. The thought of it made him tired, and he feared it would be one more thing placing demands on him when he wasn't sure he had anything left to offer. Change means leaving the place we know and going somewhere that's new, strange. There is safety and comfort in what we know, even if it's not the best place for us to be. Change can be frightening because there is no guarantee that the new territory—or the new you—will really be worth the effort, or that you can even make it happen in the first place. To some degree, all change is a leap of faith.

When we have positive past experience with change, new territory is less daunting. Change can be very good: changing a diaper, changing a light bulb or changing your oil. We're pretty convinced before we make those changes that positive gains lie on the other side. Tremendous benefits lie on the other side of the deliberate and positive changes you can make in your lifestyle. The way you approach change can make it much less daunting and much more appealing—very much like an adventure!

The very process of change, not only the outcome, can be extremely rewarding. First, let's look at how we actually create change. Here are the essential ingredients for real and lasting change, in business and in every other area of life:

- Knowledge

- Attitude

- Preparation

- Action

- Evaluation

Let's examine each of these in more detail.

Knowledge

Knowledge is the first key to change because we change only what we recognize needs improving. This knowledge may come *actively* or *passively*. Here are some examples:

- In your business, you discover that a number of your employees are dissatisfied at work a) by deliberately facilitating open communication and feedback, or b) when the employees initiate strike action.

🗅 In your physical health, you discover that your blood pressure is out of control because a) you went for a routine physical, or b) you collapsed and landed in the hospital.

🗅 In your most significant personal relationship, you discover that your partner is feeling neglected because a) you noticed that he or she has been withdrawn and you simply asked why, or b) he or she just tore a strip off you.

🗅 In your finances, you realize that the bank has made an error because a) you found it when you reviewed your statement online, or b) you suddenly don't have enough money this month to cover your mortgage payment.

We discover how well our lives are working through deliberate observation or through untimely, often very emotional wake-up calls. Both Frank and Katie got a wake-up call when he landed in the hospital. Frank was forced to finally stop and look at his life, trapped as he was in a hospital bed and backed into a corner by his board chair. Katie's life was abruptly disturbed, too, and she resented it. The interruption meant having to stop the fervor that kept her from looking at her deeper discontent. Now that both of them were obliged to recognize the gap between how they were living and what they really wanted, what would they do? Would they grab hold of the opportunity and impetus for change, or would they retreat to "good enough"? Would change, for either or both of them, become *necessary*? Frank was obligated by circumstance to alter his lifestyle, but could he put his heart into it?

Once we recognize that change is necessary, gathering accurate and relevant information helps us decide how best to produce results. Do I understand what the real problem is? Is there more than one problem? What's the best solution? Do I know what I have to do? What will be the benefits of making this change?

We've all heard, "It's not what you know, it's who you know." The truth is, it's both. Information and insight are gained in three primary ways:

🗅 personal experience

🗅 the experience and knowledge of others

🗅 reading or research

We learn through research, analysis, introspection, observation and intuition, and by consulting people who have more experience and knowledge than we do. If my employees are disgruntled, I might ask them why, research the competition to see what incentives they offer their employees, examine my communication methods, look for a good book on office relationships or ask other CEOs for insight. Any or all of these exercises may prove helpful. Only one or two may be necessary.

Knowledge gives insight into where change is needed, informs how best to progress through that change and provides the necessary incentive to commit to change. Knowledge truly is power. The following chapters will help you to identify where you are, access the information you need and identify motivators to get you from start to finish.

Attitude

Literally, attitude is an outlook, a mindset or a way of thinking. It also speaks of our position. Our attitude is our standpoint, viewpoint or stance. So where *do* we stand? It is critical to identify both *what* we stand for and *why*.

ASSUMING RESPONSIBILITY

Some things we have the power to change and others we have no control over. Some things are our responsibility and others are not. When we identify a problem, we must honestly determine if it is ours to solve or if it is someone else's responsibility. At work, this is usually easy enough to sort out. If my client has a problem with my work, I had better fix it—or prepare to lose the client. If my colleague is losing sales, it's not my job to bail him out. In other areas of life, it can get trickier. For example,

- Nearly every morning I blow up at my children because we can't get out of the house on time. Are the children slacking off when they should be getting ready, or is my surly mood just the consequence of my own choice to go to bed late and then sleep in?

- I'm constantly arguing with my spouse. Is that the inevitable result of growing up in a home where conflict was handled poorly, or have I neglected to look at my own patterns of relating?

- I'm perpetually stressed about my finances. Is it because of rising gas prices and fluctuating markets, or because I overspend on luxuries?

Much of life happens to us—including inevitable challenges and difficulties—but our quality of life is based on what we *make* happen. We may have bad genes, bad role models, bad luck, bad traffic, bad neighbors—even limiting illness, debilitating personal crisis, serious financial setbacks or the bitter sting of suffered injustice. We may be shouldering the weight of someone else's bad choices. However, whether we ask for them, deserve them, or not, our circumstances are what they are. Whatever confronts us, we can choose our response. We are the only ones with the power to alter our circumstances, lead our lives and take ourselves where we really want to go. If we don't assume responsibility—100 percent responsibility—we won't get anywhere, and we'll have no one to blame but ourselves.

FINDING MOTIVATION
SETTLING THE "WHYS" OF CHANGE
Before Frank could begin to see any transformation in his life, he needed to tip the scales in favor of purposeful change versus self-protective, but self-defeating, fear. He needed a "good enough" reason, a catalyst, to step out into new territory.

Fundamental to any change that counts is framing it within a larger, life-sized "why." This kind of "why" has to do with quality of life, personal satisfaction and the principles of life purpose we talked about earlier. It's important to get to the deeper, "first things" reasons for making changes. For example, you may want to lose weight. Why is that change *reasonable*? Here are some reasons a person might want to lose weight:

- "I've realized that I'm putting my health at risk."
- "I want to have more energy."
- "I want to look younger."
- "I want to be more attractive."
- "I want to hike the Grand Canyon."

If your reasons for losing weight are short-term, the results are likely to be short-lived. If you strictly want to change the way you look, your results may be less and less fulfilling with age. If your goal is to improve your long-term health, you are more likely to achieve long-term results. Have you asked yourself, "*Why* do I want to be healthy?" What lifesized "why" might good health address? How does this goal contribute to my life purpose?

Stephen Covey, author of *The 7 Habits of Highly Effective People* and *First Things First*, asserts that there are four basic human needs: "to live, to love, to learn, [and] to leave a legacy" (addressing the physical, social, mental and spiritual aspects of human existence).[1] If you look at how you take care of your body, your physical being, in the context of how you want to live your life, you can begin to see that better physical health can also mean more energy to devote to loved ones, a sharper and more creative mind and the capacity to participate in a broader range of activities and opportunities. Losing the weight becomes suddenly much more meaningful than changing the way you look.

The life-sized "whys" can also be expressed as those things that give life meaning. The larger "whys" should be answered in ways that fulfill your life purpose. You may have very good reasons for wanting to make the changes you do, but translating them into life-sized, "first things," purposeful "whys" will help you assess which changes are best and which are simply good. As you proceed through this book, you'll find tools to help you prioritize, focus and synergize the changes you want to make in different areas (physical, relational and financial), and you'll walk through the process of answering your own "whys." You'll be motivated to make changes that are real, life-long and life-giving.

A sense of purpose fuels good decision making, helps focus your goals and provides impetus for positive change. In his acclaimed book *The Success Principles*, Jack Canfield (co-creator of the *Chicken Soup* series) says, "To be 'on purpose' means you're doing what you love to do, doing what you're good at and accomplishing what's important to you."[2] Once you've clarified your life purpose and harnessed your passion, you can apply the knowledge you've gleaned more effectively. If you know why you want to change, it's much easier to keep goals in sight, stay motivated and have fun along the way.

POSITIVE AND NEGATIVE MOTIVATORS

Knowledge itself is a prime motivator—whether the information received is positive or negative. When I discover a $2,000 bank error, I'm motivated to be more on top of my finances. When I learn that regular exercise actually helps me sleep better and think more creatively, thereby increasing my productivity, I'm motivated to make it happen. When I learn that my daughter is more agreeable when I let her make a greater number of her own age-appropriate decisions, I'm more likely to let her pick out her own clothes. These are all positive motivators.

Conversely, good information gives us some powerful negative motivators: If I don't solve this crisis at work, the investors will lose confidence in the company. If I don't eat better and exercise, I'm at a higher risk for a heart attack. If I don't become a better communicator in my marriage, this problem may quickly become a crisis. If I don't find a way to put more money into my retirement plan every month, I'll have to work until I'm 65 or older.

After an hour and a half with The Healthy CEO, talking about Frank's health, hopes and disappointment with where his "success" had taken him, Frank, though still tentative, began to feel something stir inside. It had been a while since he had let himself feel a desire for more, let alone *pursue* more. Though it made him nervous, Frank liked the stirring he was feeling. It reminded him of earlier days when he cared passionately about every business meeting, about giving 100 percent to every task, about what made his wife tick. Lately, all he was clear on was what ticked her off. Something was shifting, and Frank decided to go with it, to be intentional about turning his life, especially his health, around. He had so many reasons to do so.

Want to make changes? Start by changing your attitude. Take leadership in your life: take responsibility and make change about total and lifelong wellness—about your *whole* life.

Preparation

Only a fool would try to climb Mount Everest without first preparing carefully and adequately. Good preparation becomes the difference between life and death. It is also the difference between success and failure. How many times have you gone into an important meeting—one where contracts, your job status, your reputation or serious dollars were on the line—without preparing adequately? You probably did your homework diligently and carefully first. The more there is at stake, the more important preparation becomes.

To facilitate change, you acquire the knowledge you need and check your attitude. Then you map out how you're going to make it happen. You come up with an effective game plan. You think strategically and set goals.

SETTING GOALS: THINKING IN THE LONG AND SHORT TERM

Increase revenue by five percent this year, bring my cholesterol levels down to normal within the year, achieve greater intimacy in my relationship with my spouse this year, put an extra $10,000 in my retirement savings this year—these are all great goals to have. They are all realistic, beneficial, life-giving goals. However, they can all seem like Everests if you don't have a good plan to achieve them. The larger long-term goal has to be broken down into smaller goals that you implement progressively, one step at a time. You've used goal-setting tools in the business context, to be sure. In making personal lifestyle changes, the following approach to goal setting can help you "go **FAR**":

GO **F**ocus your goals

Add value to your goals

Relish your goals

🔲 **F**ocus your goals. We focus a microscope or a lens on a camera to look at a select area or at smaller details within a larger backdrop. We should bring our goals into sharp focus in the same way.

- *Make them specific.* Set clear parameters with explicit expectations, timeframes (including deadlines) and ways of measuring improvement quantitatively. Itemize goals into even more specific action steps. For example, the goal to lose weight becomes "I will bring my body mass index down to 24 by 12 months from now." Broken down further, the goal might include the action steps: "Work out three hours weekly, including three 30-minute cardio sessions and three 30-minute weight training sessions," "Eat at a fast-food restaurant only once a month" and so on. Plan for progress and chart your strategy.

- *Create a mental picture.* Bring your goals into focus by visualizing the process and the end results. Using the example goal of losing weight, ask, "What will I be able to do, once I've lost the weight, that I can't do now? What will that look like? How will I look different physically? How will others see me?" Picture yourself in these settings. Imagine yourself in the middle of the process, seeing results. These snapshots will be powerful motivators.

Add *value to your goals.* In business, all tasks—large and small—have one primary aim: to improve the bottom line, or add *value* to your business. The same should be true of your goals. How will realizing them add value to your life? What "fluctuations" might you encounter?

- *Do a cost-benefit analysis.* What is reaching this goal worth to you? What will it cost if you don't follow through? For Frank, the cost of not improving his health might even be his job. There really is a lot at stake. "If I get my body mass index down, I'll have more energy, feel more attractive, have a great sense of accomplishment, be stronger..." "If I *don't* lower my body mass index, my blood pressure will continue to rise, I won't have the energy to do the things in life I really want to do, I'm at greater risk for heart attack..."

- *Identify potential barriers.* Setbacks will be inevitable. If you expect them and are mentally prepared to face them, you're less likely to be overwhelmed when they occur. Stay determined to keep going even if you fail. Success is not an absence of failure; it is the refusal to let any failure finish you.

Relish *your goals.* Why would anyone keep doing something they hate or find discouraging? No matter how accomplished or talented you are, you're only human. Unless an endeavor is pleasurable or provides perceptible returns, you're not likely to keep at it.

- *Tailor your goals to fit you.* At the outset, examine your lifestyle and personalize your goals accordingly. Accommodate your interests, schedule and temperament. Take a creative approach. If you're a morning person, schedule your exercise sessions in the morning. If you love to cook, invest in a cookbook that features low-calorie, healthy but flavorful dishes. If you have a brainstorming session scheduled with a colleague, ask if you can walk and talk, and document the discussion with a voice recorder.

- *Make them realistic.* If you've never exercised regularly for a prolonged period of time, it doesn't make sense to set a goal of being a competitive bodybuilder in a few months' time. That might *become* one of your goals eventually, but as a place to start, you'd be setting yourself up for failure. Set goals that are challenging enough while still being within reach. Don't make yourself miserable in an attempt to realize better health. If you love chocolate desserts and you regularly indulge, don't cut out chocolate altogether. Limit yourself to a couple times a month instead.

- *Build in fun.* Getting healthy is good for you. You'll feel great. Let the journey of realizing your health be pleasurable too. If you love the outdoors, plan a monthly weekend hiking trip with a handful of close friends. Start a healthy-eating dinner club. Sign up to play your favorite sport in a community league. And as you set your goals, don't forget to build in rewards.

Your professional goals have helped you establish your career. Your business goals have helped you establish your business. Your strategic personal go-**FAR** goals will help you take the lead in every area of your life.

Action

GET MOVING

While research and planning are necessary to achieve any goal, if you never get started, or if you never implement your strategies, they are useless. The course of action should be clear if you've made good goals. You'll be able to actualize your plan by taking individual, calculated steps toward your chosen destination. Remember that progress is made by taking a series of small but deliberate action steps. Each step is vital to reaching your goal. Resist the temptation to procrastinate, quit or take shortcuts; keep going no matter what.

ENLIST SUPPORT

As a CEO, you see growth in your business due largely to the contributions and input of people who care about the success of your company. If your team at work isn't personally invested in your company, it's much more difficult for you to reach any of your goals. Part of your performance as a leader also hinges on how accountable you are to your investors, clients, staff and board. That accountability heightens your performance.

The same is true as you work to achieve personal goals. If you enlist the support of people who believe in you and your goals, it'll be easier to stay on track. Tell at least one other person what you're doing (this makes it more real) and ask him or her to hold you accountable. If you try to go it alone, your chances of quitting go way up. If you create even a small support network, you'll feel much more empowered.

REFRAME SETBACKS AND REENGAGE

Babies learning to walk inevitably stumble. Many new business ventures fail. But perseverance pays off. We all learn to stand (and walk) on our own two feet if we are able to frame each setback as a learning opportunity. Each stumble becomes another way *not* to accomplish our goal. If we can recognize this, we automatically improve our odds at success. We regroup and try again. Companies and people on top of their games have had their share of failures; they just didn't let any roadblocks stop them. They learned to walk, and then to run.

Evaluation

TAKE STOCK REGULARLY

When you go on a long journey through unfamiliar territory, you check from time to time to make sure you are on course and still have everything you need. You check a compass, look for landmarks or confirm your bearing. You check your oil and keep one eye on the fuel gauge. In business, you watch the market, consult clients, monitor profits relative to expenditures and track sales.

Evaluating your progress at regular intervals keeps you on the right track. If you notice you're getting slightly off course, you can correct your orientation. If you've under- or overestimated the distance to your destination, you can shore up your resources or gear down as necessary. You may even have to revisit the goals you've set and make some adjustments. As you set goals for lifestyle changes and work through specific action steps, you will encounter surprises. Focus with *flexibility* allows you to adapt, refuel and keep going.

For each of your goals, schedule regular evaluation appointments. Regular appraisals afford you the opportunity to mark and measure progress and to celebrate successes. For some goals, such as weight loss or debt reduction, the quantitative measurements of dropped pounds or accounts paid track improvement tangibly. Seeing positive movement by marking key milestones is encouraging.

For other goals, qualitative indicators will give you a better idea of the ground you've covered. In your relationship with your spouse, the effectiveness of your deliberate action steps toward better communication might be observed in your increased intimacy and connection. With some goals, it might make more sense to determine your progress on the basis of whether or not you have followed through on your proposed action steps.

REASSESS AS NECESSARY

As you evaluate, ask yourself, "Have I actually set achievable goals, or even the right goals to achieve what I *really* want? Do I need to go back through the steps—*Knowledge, Attitude, Preparation, Action*—to see where I may have gone awry? Do I need expert advice or assessment to help identify something I might be missing?" Don't be afraid to revisit your goals and make adjustments. Tweaking the process is much better than just giving up because it's "not working."

BUILD IN REWARDS

To maintain your initial motivation and drive, build in a system of re-wards for each time you reach certain milestones. For example,

- for every 15 pounds you lose (in your longer-term goal to lose 60 pounds), treat yourself to a new outfit and a night out to show yourself off;

- for every relationship milestone—workshop, seminar, finishing a relationship coaching book—that you reach with your partner, treat yourselves to a fun date; or

- for every debt you pay off, reward yourself with a modest splurge on a luxury item.

Don't forget to place ultimate rewards within sight for when you've reached your longer-term goal—perhaps a trip or some other prize.

The cycle of change

Change starts with *Knowledge* and proceeds through *Evaluation*, then the cycle begins again, with sights on new goals that are not necessarily all about problem solving. Change—a way to solve a problem—becomes growth—a dynamic, exciting, continual evolution toward greater satisfac-tion in all areas of life. Continued improvement and sustained growth pre-vails as the cycle is repeated. Using this approach in a disciplined way, you will significantly increase your level of success.

Respected economist W. Edwards Deming, Ph.D, developed "total quality management" methods to be applied in manufacturing after World War II. Within this model, he outlined "continuous quality improvement" as a cyclical approach to improvement—in other words, continual change for the better. This approach has since been adapted by businesses and public-sector organizations to improve products and services.

The same principles apply to sustained improvements in any area, including personal changes for individuals. The following diagram, based in part on Deming's ideas, demonstrates the three A's within the cycle of sustained improvement in overall wellness: Assess, Act and Analyze. The five fundamentals of change—*Knowledge, Attitude, Preparation, Action* and *Evaluation*—fit nicely within the cycle. We'll apply these concepts to physical, relational and financial wellness.

The Success Cycle

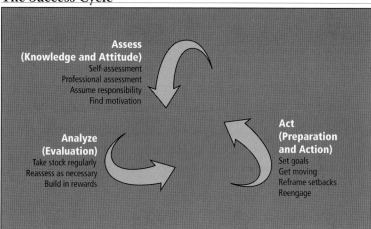

Real change is possible. You have the power to make it happen. But you must take the lead.

Katie looked at Frank in disbelief. "You went to a shrink today?"

"A life coach. He calls himself The Healthy CEO," Frank said. "He's going to help me make some changes."

"What kind of changes?" Katie asked suspiciously, noshing a carrot muffin she'd brought home from work.

"Well," Frank began, "I need to get healthier. George said if I don't get that straightened out for sure, I may not have a job." He was more tentative now. "But K, I also think it wouldn't hurt to try to make some changes between us."

She shot him a dirty look. "Are you serious?"

"Well, yeah. And it wouldn't hurt for you and I to talk about what we're doing with our work, you know. We can look at how things are with your business and ways we can make my schedule and yours and all the money stuff fit together better."

Katie's mouth was still full of muffin, but she spoke anyway. "You want to fix things now*? Do you know that I lost that client, Frank? The one from the lunch the other day? They're never going to hire me again, and who knows how many people they're going to tell about my dismal failure!"*

"You know," Frank ventured, trying to be helpful, "if you could find someone who could run things so you don't always have to be around..."

"In case I get an emergency call to the hospital? There is *no one, Frank! It's all me. It's going to take a lot of time and money to try to get someone in there who knows what they're doing and can run my staff. I haven't got that kind of time right now. I'm just getting from one gig to another, Frank. It's all on me."*

She could use some time on the blue side of the room, Frank thought. "I'm sorry, K. I really am. That's why I'm thinking we should work on this together. I really do want things to change. I want us to be better, too." He went to her and put his hand on her arm. She flinched at first and then relaxed some. "This is something we could do together. I don't see how that could hurt *anything."*

Katie pulled away and disappeared into the kitchen. She threw her half-eaten muffin in the garbage. It was her supper, but she couldn't finish it. Her stomach felt sour. She was agitated, tense. This scheme of Frank's felt like just one more thing on her already-full plate. She leaned on the counter and closed her eyes, shutting out the room— shutting out everything. She let herself disappear into the dark of it. "I don't know, Frank. I don't know."

2 *Your physical wellness:* Body wisdom

Our own physical body possesses a wisdom which we who inhabit the body lack.

Henry Miller, author

Swish. Swish. Swish. Swish. Note to self, Katie thought, don't wear these pants when on a covert mission. She already felt absolutely conspicuous in this... this smile-mongering building, this "Healthy CEO Corporation." Everybody was so friendly and helpful. People had been greeting her warmly, introducing themselves, offering her warm beverages. It was disgusting. They probably had pep rallies every morning, she thought. She could see it: this Healthy CEO character holding a glitter-encrusted megaphone at the front of a large room, flanked by stupidly obedient, platinum-coiffed Barbie dolls donned in pink from head to toe. They were rallying the troops, chanting to the office lapdogs: "Smile! Love! Heal! Grow! We love a healthy CEO!"

Swish. Swish. Swish. Swish. She could hear the pompoms swishing through the air. No... that was her pants. The hallway seemed interminable, but she finally reached the door at the end. The smiling, maybe-even-naturally-brunette office assistant had told her she could just go in. She paused with her hand on the door knob. What was she thinking? What was she doing here? This was terrifying. She didn't know what she was walking into—or out of. She knew she didn't like her life the way it was, but at least it was hers. She knew it well enough to feel safe there. Sure, there were dark corners, but at least she knew where they all were. She thought she did, anyway. But this... this wasn't safe. It wasn't her turf.

After sucking in air, she opened the door and stepped inside the room. Red. Blue. A quizzical-looking character in an easy chair. Not the megaphone-wielding charlatan she had imagined. And Frank. Frank. He was familiar. A small measure of safety in this new, dangerous world. He looked at her and smiled. She surrendered to his smile. Frank rose, went over to a blue chaise and lifted a cable-knit throw from its arm. Silently, he came to her and—gently wrapping her in the blanket—drew her to another chair. It was blue. Soothing. Safe. He smiled at her again and she felt the warmth of his smile blanket her body.

             ⌐   ⌐   ⌐   ⌐

Your body is your energy source. It supports your every activity, whether physical, mental, relational or spiritual. It comes complete with highly specialized tools—arms, legs, heart, brain, kidneys—that help you perform your daily tasks. When your body is doing well, all of your options are open. When it's not, especially when poor health becomes physically incapacitating, you lose capacity in every other area. Your whole life can shut down. The more efficiently your body is running, the more efficient your life becomes—at work, at play and at rest. Your success in your business, relationships and quality of life is inextricably linked to your physical health. If you aren't convinced that physical health makes a difference to your professional success, for instance, consider the following findings documented in *Fit to Lead: The Proven 8-Week Solution for Shaping Up Your Body*, a fitness book directed at leaders:

> A survey of executives from the top three thousand U.S. companies (identified from Fortune 500, the Inc. 100, the Venture Fast Track 100, and Dun's List of Large and Small Companies) revealed that two-thirds of the executives exercised at least three times weekly, with more than 90 percent of that group using aerobic exercise as the cornerstone of their workouts. Also, more than 90 percent reported being careful about their diet, 81 percent had a complete physical exam within the previous two years, and only 10 percent of the executives smoked (compared with the national average of more than 25 percent).[1]

Conversely, health problems cost major companies major dollars and hours of lost productivity. According to a study on human capital in the *Journal of Occupational and Environmental Medicine*, illness and disability reduced total work hours in 1996 by approximately 8.6 percent, effectively reducing the U.S. labor force by roughly 6.6 percent. Nearly 8.7 million Americans (18 to 64 years of age) were completely unable to work, and the hours worked per employed person were reduced by 2 percent. The loss to the U.S. economy represented about $468 billion.[2]

While good physical health can help you succeed in your career, it can also improve your state of mind. A healthy body contributes to your psychological well-being, confidence and outlook on life. There are so many good reasons to look after your physical health.

In Frank and Katie Johnson's case, Frank's health crisis had pointed to a latent relational crisis. Now that Frank was vested in improving his health, Katie had decided, somewhat reluctantly, to at least hear what The Healthy CEO had to say. She felt she owed Frank that much. Her cynical side said that participating even nominally in the process would appease Frank and keep conflict at bay. But the part of her that was just as dissatisfied as Frank with what their lives had become was secretly looking for possibilities. She was daring to hope that there was something better and that it wasn't beyond reach after all.

What about you?

Are you physically well? Are you sure? Where are you paying the price of poor health habits or lack of knowledge? Before you can make improvements to your physical health, you must first accurately and honestly assess where you are now. In the previous chapter, we looked at the ingredients necessary for change and for sustained growth within the Success Cycle:

- Assess
  - Knowledge
  - Attitude
- Act
  - Preparation
  - Action
- Analyze
  - Evaluation

Now, let's put what you've learned to work by first assessing your physical wellness.

Knowledge of physical wellness

If we apply the steps within the Success Cycle to improving our physical health, we must establish a solid, accurate knowledge base before we can assess how our own health compares. What constitutes good physical health? How can you identify the areas where you are healthy and those where you are ailing? Once you know the criteria for physical wellness, you can assess yourself accordingly.

You were born preprogrammed with genes that create inevitable imprints. Your genetic makeup is beyond your control. However, many of your choices can maximize positive genetic imprints and minimize—even supersede—the negative ones. Poor health choices can exacerbate your genetic disadvantages. The first part of the self-assessment process involves identifying any red flags that should be noted to your primary health practitioner or that, at first glance, clearly need your attention. This initial stage of self-assessment is the "check-in." Next, you need the assistance of health care providers who can apply science and expertise to help you with your self-appraisal. Once you have gathered all of the necessary information, you can do a meaningful overall self-assessment of your physical wellness and identify and prioritize areas that require change.

Just what will you be assessing? These are the factors of physical wellness over which you have influence:

- body composition
- level of exercise
- quality of nutrition
- dental care
- sleep patterns
- stress level
- capacity for leisure
- mental state
- substance use

To build your knowledge base, let's look at each of these factors in a little more detail.

BODY COMPOSITION

BODY MASS INDEX AND WAIST CIRCUMFERENCE

Body mass index (BMI) is a measuring tool widely accepted and used within the medical community to determine an individual's height-to-weight ratio. This is a more meaningful measurement than simply looking at one's weight, since weight alone is inadequate in evaluating body composition.

In addition to the BMI, waist-to-hip ratio or waist circumference is becoming a standard body composition assessment tool. Abdominal obesity (when abdominal girth exceeds the maximum measurement around the hips) or a waist circumference of greater than 40 inches (102 cm) in men or greater than 35 inches (89 cm) in women,[3] independent of one's weight, is associated with a significant risk of hypertension, cardiovascular disease, stroke, gallbladder disease, insulin resistance (and ultimately type II diabetes), joint problems, obstructive sleep apnea—even certain kinds of cancer.

In some cases, an extremely fit, well-muscled individual will have a BMI that falls within the category of "overweight." Exceptions, however, should be readily apparent. Standing six feet and two inches tall (74 inches in total) and weighing 223 pounds, Frank had a BMI of 28, which, to his alarm, was approaching obesity. His waist circumference was 41 inches, another indication that his weight was in an unhealthy range.

Frank's not alone. Consider these alarming statistics:

- Percentage of Americans who were obese in 1971: 14.5

- Percentage in 2002: 30.9

- Number of Americans with diabetes in 1980: 5.8 million

- Number in 2002: 13.3 million

- Number of deaths each year associated with being overweight: 400,000[4]

With epidemic and ever-increasing levels of obesity, our culture is paradoxical. We manage fast-paced lifestyles, running on high-fat fast food while being perpetually surrounded by marketing and media messages that preach about the importance of fitness and celebrate the lives of the rich and skinny. Why this conflict? Why aren't we getting the fitness message? Or are we just not listening?

In a society where "thin is in," it's easy to forget that there are also increased health risks associated with being underweight: osteoporosis, anemia, irregular menstruation or even infertility in women, and immune system deficiencies. Rapid or undesired weight loss can indicate some medical conditions, including eating disorders, chronic stress and other health problems. Katie wasn't prepared to learn that she was actually *underweight*, but when she weighed herself, she discovered that her BMI number worked out to 17.

MAKING MUSCLES

Lean muscle mass helps the body burn calories, it helps make all of our movement more efficient, and it helps prevent injury. For example, a well-toned "core," or mid-section, will help prevent back strain or injury, a common modern-day complaint. Strong muscles support joints and protect the body. Many people focus strictly on weight loss without considering how important it is to build and maintain their muscle mass. This becomes increasingly important since muscle mass is consistently lost as the body ages if it is not deliberately maintained. Without strength-building exercise, we lose 5 percent of our muscle mass every 10 years after the age of 35.[5]

HOW DENSE ARE YOU?

After age 35, bone density is gradually lost, making bones more porous, weaker and vulnerable to stress and fracture. Osteoporosis, a condition in which loss of bone density gets to the point where bones can break very easily, affects more than 28 million Americans.[6] Average onset of the disease happens after age 65 in 25 percent of the total population of women. However, it is not only a women's condition, as some believe. With our increasing life span, the disease is being seen in more and more men: after age 75, it is diagnosed in 25 percent of the male population.[7] Prevention of osteoporosis is entirely possible, however. Steps can be taken to protect and rebuild bone density.

LEVEL OF EXERCISE

Our bodies were designed to move. Not many generations ago, people expended a tremendous amount of physical energy on basic everyday tasks associated with earning a wage and maintaining a home. Today, with all the advancements and conveniences of our modern age, most of us have to put exercise back into our lives over and above the time we spend working. This is especially true for office-bound executives.

There are four important ways to exercise: cardiovascular training, strength training, flexibility training and balance exercises. Each of these provides your body with important benefits.

CARDIOVASCULAR TRAINING

Simply put, cardiovascular or stamina training is exercise that gets your heart pumping. Besides helping you lose weight or maintain a healthy weight, it strengthens your heart, keeps your arteries healthy, elevates your metabolism, stabilizes your blood sugar, increases energy, helps you sleep better, optimizes respiration, and can alleviate depression, stress and anxiety. To maintain optimal health, get a 30-minute workout on most (preferably all) days of the week at a heart rate that's 60 to 80 percent or more of your age-adjusted maximum.[8] To calculate your age-adjusted maximum heart rate, subtract your age from the number 220. If you're trying to lose weight, you'll probably need to work out at least four days per week, ideally for longer durations. One half hour of exercise, such as a brisk daily walk, has important health benefits including reducing the risk of strokes, heart attacks, hypertension, Type II diabetes and some types of cancer. Any amount of regular exercise will decrease your risk, compared to being sedentary. It is vitally important that an inactive person with cardiovascular risk factors consult a physician knowledgeable in cardiovascular risk assessment before engaging in exercise more vigorous than walking.

Elevating your heart rate boosts your body's functioning in every area. This is good news if you're worried that time spent on exercise will cut into your productivity at work. Michael Mangus, president and CEO of a company that employs over 350 people and generates over 80 million dollars in annual revenue, says, "My thoughts tend toward work while exercising. I have some of my most creative thoughts when working out."[9] The endorphins released while exercising can stimulate brain function, make you more creative, boost your energy and help you to focus more when you're back on the job. There may even be links between physical exercise and reducing the onset of dementia in later life. Ongoing research is gathering evidence that physical activity may delay cognitive decline and Alzheimer's disease.[10]

Exercise such as vigorous walking, cycling, swimming or using an elliptical trainer elevates your heart rate with minimal impact on your joints. Overzealous or high-impact exercise can be as hard on your body as not getting enough exercise. Your joints pay for the abuse later in life with problems like chronic pain or osteoarthritis.

STRENGTH TRAINING

Strength training helps you develop lean muscle mass, which in turn helps you burn more calories. As your muscles become stronger, all of your activities can be performed more efficiently, decreasing your risk of joint strain or other injury. Strength training also helps build bone density and prevent osteoporosis. It doesn't take a lot of load to produce results; the key is to create enough resistance to take your muscles to the point of fatigue at between 8 and 12 repetitions. After age 35, strength training also helps prevent the otherwise inevitable loss of lean muscle tissue.

FLEXIBILITY TRAINING

Yoga or tai chi—or any other deliberate series of stretching exercises where you move your body more slowly, are more aware of your breathing and tune into the way your body is moving—helps keep joints flexible and maximizes your range of motion in all muscle groups. It also protects your joints from undue strain. Americans are catching on to yoga's wonderful health benefits: as of 2006, more than 16.5 million Americans practiced yoga, an increase of 30 percent since 2002.[11]

BALANCE EXERCISES

Many preventable injuries caused by falling happen due to a loss of balance. The strength and tone of your core muscles—those of the back and abdomen—determine your posture and ability to recover successfully if you lose your balance. Exercises to strengthen your core—your center of gravity—can not only improve balance, but they can balance the muscle tone of your front and back. These opposing muscles act in relationship to one another. For example, if stomach muscles are stronger than back muscles, the shoulders may slump, increasing the likelihood of back pain. Balance exercises help with equilibrium and ensure that specialized muscle groups are working in concert, not in competition.

When they looked at their level of exercise, Frank and Katie both had to admit that they got little exercise at all. Katie hadn't given it much thought, since she hadn't had any problems with gaining too much weight. And Frank? He preferred not to give it any thought at all. They knew that exercise provided health benefits other than weight maintenance, but they were startled to discover just how much exercise contributes to one's health.

QUALITY OF NUTRITION

You've heard the expressions "You are what you eat" and "Food is fuel." As trite as these statements have become, they are absolutely correct. What you put into your body has a direct impact on your performance and endurance. You wouldn't put diesel fuel in your gasoline-powered vehicle. Use the wrong fuel and you gum up the engine. The same is true for your body.

A BALANCED DIET

There's a lot of controversy and conflicting information about what constitutes a balanced diet, which types of foods and what quantities are appropriate, which foods to avoid and which to eat regularly. The Harvard School of Public Health created the Healthy Eating Pyramid based on "the best available scientific evidence about the links between diet and health"[12] (see adaptation of the pyramid, figure 1). This pyramid is described in greater detail in Dr. Walter C. Willett's *Eat, Drink, and be Healthy: The Harvard Medical School Guide to Healthy Eating.*

The base of the Healthy Eating Pyramid is daily exercise and weight control because these two related elements are foundational to staying healthy. They also affect how many servings of each of the food groups you need and how efficiently you will be able to metabolize what you do eat. The building blocks of the Healthy Eating Pyramid include the following:

- *Whole grain foods (at most meals)* – Grains provide carbohydrates, which are an essential food source. However, whole grains in particular offer unique benefits over refined grain products. Whole grain products are a great source of nutrients and dietary fiber, which keeps digested food bulky and soft so it can pass through the colon more easily. Fiber also helps regulate metabolism and digestion and stabilize blood sugar levels. Try to get between 25 and 35 grams of fiber daily.[13] Whole grain foods are digested relatively slowly, keeping you feeling fuller longer and preventing your blood insulin level from spiking and then falling too quickly.

- *Plant oils* – Healthy unsaturated fats such as olive, canola, soy, corn, sunflower, peanut and other vegetable oils help improve blood cholesterol levels and can be used in place of unhealthy fats.

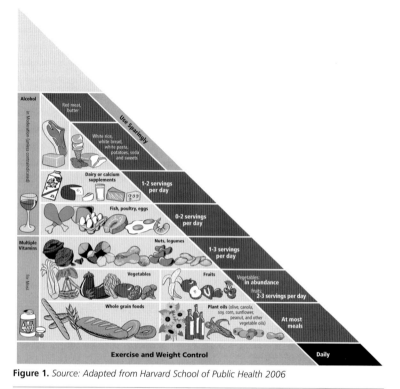

Figure 1. *Source: Adapted from Harvard School of Public Health 2006*

▢ *Vegetables (in abundance) and fruits (2 to 3 times daily)* – A diet rich in fruits and vegetables can combat cardiovascular disease and protect against the onset of a variety of cancers and other diseases. Cruciferous vegetables—vegetables like broccoli, Brussels sprouts, cabbage and cauliflower—help prevent cancer. Flavonoids are powerful antioxidants and anti-inflammatory substances found in plant foods such as grapes, berries, onions and tomatoes. (They're also in black and green tea and red wine.) In addition, fruits and vegetables are an excellent source of fiber, vitamins and minerals. Sampling a wide variety will ensure you get the full spectrum of available nutrients.

▢ *Fish, poultry and eggs (up to 2 times daily)* – These are all important sources of protein. Multiple studies suggest that eating fish can reduce the risk of heart disease. In particular, wild salmon and whitefish are high in omega-3 fatty acids, which are highly beneficial to the cardiovascular system.

🗂 *Nuts and legumes (1 to 3 times daily)* – Nuts and legumes are excellent sources of protein, fiber, vitamins and minerals. Many kinds of nuts are a great source of essential fatty acids that contribute to heart health.

🗂 *Dairy or calcium source (1 to 2 times daily)* – Dairy products provide calcium and vitamin D, which help build and maintain bones. However, they often also contain a lot of fat, so choose low- or non-fat dairy alternatives wherever possible. If you are lactose intolerant or don't like dairy products, calcium supplements offer an easy way to get your daily calcium.

🗂 *Red meat and butter (consume sparingly)* – These sit at the top of the Healthy Eating Pyramid because they contain a lot of saturated fat. While red meat is a good source of iron, if you are anemic, consider alternatives (such as legumes) or supplements.

🗂 *White rice, white bread, potatoes, white pasta, soda and sweets (consume sparingly)* – Digestion of these foods results in a rapid increase in blood sugar (insulin) that can lead to weight gain, diabetes, heart disease and other chronic disorders. As mentioned above, whole grain carbohydrates cause a slower, steadier increase in blood sugar, producing available energy without overwhelming the body.

🗂 *Supplements* – A daily multivitamin, multi-mineral supplement offers some nutritional backup. It can fill in some inevitable nutrient gaps for even the most careful eaters, but should never be relied on to make up for unhealthy eating choices. Consult your primary health practitioner if you're not sure which supplement is right for you. Some people also require additional calcium or iron to supplement their diets. It is important to consult your physician about any supplements you are considering taking. Some vitamins and minerals are toxic if taken in excess, and some interact with certain medications.

For a number of years now, the American Heart Association (AHA) has recommended that patients with coronary heart disease take a daily dose of aspirin. Some people at risk for developing coronary heart disease may also benefit from daily aspirin therapy.[14] The benefits and risks of taking aspirin regularly are case-specific, and you should discuss your own situation with your primary health practitioner.

  Alcohol (in moderation) – Scores of studies suggest that having an alcoholic drink a day lowers the risk of heart disease. Alcohol exerts a protective effect against coronary heart disease, when consumed in moderation: for men, one to two drinks per day; for women, just one.[15]

When the subject of nutrition came up in their discussion with The Healthy CEO, Katie felt sheepish. She was very well educated when it came to what foods were healthy and why; in fact, it was that knowledge that had inspired, at least in part, her motivation to start her catering company. She would offer delicious food, even indulgent delicacies, but provide an ample variety of healthy options. It was a classic case of someone not practicing what they preached. Surrounded by food nearly all day and going hard all day, Katie simply didn't take time to eat, let alone eat well.

For Frank, food was everywhere—at meetings, on business trips, at the corner burger joint—and it offered an easy escape from whatever was pressing at the moment. To eat was to find comfort and a diversion. To complicate things, Frank had a tendency to drink alcohol to soothe himself, too. He didn't necessarily enjoy admitting his tendency to use food and drink for emotional reasons, but when he came out with it and was able to assess his behavior realistically, it was a relief, too.

WATER

For all the body's organ systems to function properly, you need to consume plenty of water. A lack of hydration puts you at risk for many ailments and annoyances, from kidney stones to bad breath. Most people don't drink nearly the recommended six to eight glasses of water per day. If you're especially active or if you consume a lot of caffeine, you'll need more.

FOOD "FOES"

In addition to using the Healthy Eating Pyramid as a guideline for what kinds of foods to choose, these are the foods—and the term "food" is used loosely here—that you should avoid:

  Most saturated and all trans fats – Mostly found in meats, full-fat dairy products, fast foods and baked goods, these fats are the cardiovascular system's nemesis. They increase bad cholesterol, promote narrowing of the arteries and may contribute to the formation of some cancers.

- *Simple carbohydrates (starches) and sugars* – These are the white foods located at the top of the pyramid: white sugar, white flour, white bread and so on, and any other sugars (brown sugar, syrup or honey). These foods quickly raise blood sugar levels, which makes arteries more vulnerable to inflammation and plaque buildup. They can also contribute to obesity and, ultimately, to diabetes.

- *Preservatives and processed foods* – These foods are the furthest removed from their natural state. Many hand-to-mouth snacks fit in this category—potato chips for example. To extend the shelf life of these foods or to make them more visually appealing, chemicals have been added—chemicals that are foreign to the human body.

- *Too much salt* – A little salt is important to the body's normal function. However, too much salt can cause high blood pressure.

QUESTION YOUR EATING HABITS

We've looked at what to eat and what not to eat. When it comes to our eating habits, there are other important questions to ask:

- *"Why should I eat?"* If you're eating to console yourself as a reward, because you're bored, or because you don't know when to quit, you're putting your body at risk for a wide spectrum of health problems, excessive weight gain being but one. But don't ignore your hunger either. You need a regular, measured fuel source to be able to function optimally. If you skip meals, your body interprets it as a signal to slow your metabolism and store fat.

- *"When should I eat?"* Several small meals a day are better than a few large ones. Always eat breakfast and don't eat within the three-hour window before you go to bed. Snacking is fine, as long as you're snacking when you're hungry and you're making good food choices. Try to have protein at several points throughout the day, starting at breakfast. Protein helps you feel full longer because it takes longer to digest.

- *"How should I eat?"* Make food choices deliberately. Try to set aside adequate time to have proper meals. Mom said chew your food, and she was right. Stop eating when you're full. Don't eat in the name of keeping food from going to waste. Start with smaller portions and have more if you're still hungry. Don't let extra food go to *waist*.

DENTAL CARE

Your teeth and gums provide important clues to your general physical health. Periodontal (gum) disease is linked to cardiovascular problems, as the same bacteria that cause periodontal disease can also trigger an immune response that leads to inflammation and hardening of the arteries. A good dental care regime contributes considerably to your oral health as well as to the health of your whole body. The American Dental Association (ADA) recommends the following:

- brushing your teeth twice a day with an ADA-accepted fluoride toothpaste

- cleaning between your teeth daily with floss or an inter-dental cleaner to remove plaque and food particles from between the teeth and under the gum line

- visiting your dentist regularly for professional cleanings and oral exams

- replacing your toothbrush every three or four months, or sooner if the bristles become frayed[16]

The Johnsons were proud to say that their oral hygiene was excellent overall, but they made a note to schedule check-ups with their dentist.

SLEEP PATTERNS

Chances are you're not getting enough sleep. If you're under pressure or facing a deadline, sleep is likely the first thing you let fall by the wayside. Yet sleep, or a lack of it, affects our performance in all areas of life. Reduced quality or quantity of sleep contributes to a significant lapse in productivity, alertness and cognitive ability, and increases the risk of injury due to falls, for example. It can also cause friction in relationships because of increased irritability and, in the case of some sleep disorders, secondhand sleep disturbance. Untreated sleep disorders are associated with serious medical conditions, such as high blood pressure, heart disease, stroke, obesity, and psychiatric and mood disorders.

HOW MUCH SLEEP DO YOU NEED?

Proper body function is dependent upon getting enough sleep. Restorative processes, such as protein synthesis, release of certain hormones, decrease in brain wave and organ activity, and decreases in blood pressure and heart rate occur during sleep; in fact, some occur only during sleep. How much sleep individuals need may vary, but the average adult requires between seven and eight hours of quality sleep in every 24-hour period. According to a 2005 poll conducted by the National Sleep Foundation, Americans were sleeping an average of 6.8 hours per night on weekdays and 7.4 hours on weekends. Many reported fatigue, exhaustion and other problematic symptoms.[17]

Katie didn't seem to need more than seven hours on any given night, but she rarely got that much. Most of the time, it was easy for her to get up in the morning, but harder to slow down and then shut down in the evening. Frank, on the other hand, never seemed to be able to get enough sleep. He would doze off when he watched TV, he would fight sleep during the post-lunch doldrums at work, and he rarely felt very energetic.

COMMON SLEEP DISORDERS

Insomnia – One-fourth to one-third of the general population reports difficulty falling or staying asleep. Many others complain of waking too early or of having trouble getting back to sleep. Insomnia is associated with increased hypertension, and the development of major psychiatric disorders.[18] While sleeping pills may be helpful in the short term, many are harmful over an extended period of time because of their addictive qualities. Use natural strategies to combat insomnia wherever possible, such as reducing caffeine intake, establishing a regular sleep schedule and keeping your bedroom a little cooler. You may need to address psychological factors, such as stress, as well.

Snoring – Snoring happens due to an obstruction of the free flow of air through the passages in the back of the mouth. On its own, it's not necessarily a health problem, although it may point to a more serious disorder such as sleep apnea.

Sleep apnea – This condition is defined as any period during sleep when breathing stops for more than 10 seconds at a time. It can occur due to the physical closing of the airway or due to neurological problems. As sleep apnea progresses, the risk of high blood pressure, stroke and dangerous cardiovascular events increases.

The link between sleep apnea and high blood pressure is so strong that individuals who are having difficulty controlling their blood pressure should be checked for sleep apnea.

Because persistent sleep disturbance can have such serious consequences, it's very important to discuss any problems with a physician.

STRESS LEVEL

Stress is a response—of the body, mind and immune system—to a stressor. Hans Seleye, an endocrinologist who did important theoretical work in the area of stress, coined the terms "eustress" and "distress" for good and bad stress.[19] The body responds to both in similar ways. The body's "fight or flight" response, for example, kicks the body into high alert, ready to meet the stress trigger head on or get out of harm's way. Physiologically, this response elevates the level of a hormone called cortisol. At the right level, cortisol equips you to do what you need to do. However, if it reaches a level that is too high, or if this level is sustained for a prolonged period of time, your adrenal glands can become exhausted.

Some stress—like the adrenalin rush of making a PowerPoint presentation to potential clients—can be highly gratifying. Often, if we are able to identify the warning signs of the stress response and take appropriate action, we can turn the stress into a trigger for making positive change. Consequently, the stress response diminishes as the cause of the stress is managed. "Eustress" can therefore be a stimulus that moves us in positive directions.

The stress that kills isn't this motivating stress or the day-to-day pressure we experience in our routine activities. Toxic stress comes in the events that occur unexpectedly, the events over which we have no control, are unable to "fix," or that persist for an extended period. Letting a list of unfinished tasks grow or avoiding dealing with problems can also create a stress overload. "Distress" leaves us feeling out of control and unable to make positive changes, and the stress response continues with unrelenting harm to our mind and body. If you feel out of control, overwhelmed and "stressed out"—or what Katie described as feeling "wound up so tight"— take heed. Chronic stress can seriously damage your heart, impair the body's immune system and jeopardize your mental health.

CAPACITY FOR LEISURE

Closely tied to your stress level is how often you take downtime and the quality of that time. If you're going full tilt all day and all week long, without both leisure and activities that replenish you, you're going to be at a net personal deficit. Every day involves some mental problem solving, physical work and personal engagement. To be efficient and effective in meeting these demands—and to derive pleasure from them—you need to replenish your reserves by intentionally and regularly creating an environment where these demands and stimuli are set aside temporarily. Leisure, this space for renewal and replenishing, can occur in five realms. Pay attention to all five in your own life.

REST

This is the cessation of physical activity. Sleep is an obvious way to rest, but there are others. Sitting in your backyard with a magazine or an escapist novel, working on a jigsaw puzzle at your coffee table, soaking in a warm bath, watching a football game or favorite movie, being pampered at the spa or enjoying a relaxing massage—these are all ways you can slow down physically and let your body refuel in ways that are highly enjoyable.

SERENITY

Serenity is inner rest—mental and emotional quiet. A common misconception is that serenity is dependent upon the circumstances being agreeable and peaceful enough to warrant that mental state. But what if your circumstances can't always be pleasant? Is serenity impossible? Not at all. We can create serenity in our lives by reordering our circumstances where possible, to be sure. But serenity is also something we practice. It is a discipline whereby we deliberately shut out unwanted sensory stimuli and the demands of our lives. To achieve serenity, people practice meditation, prayer, aromatherapy or visualization, or they may get away to environments they find soothing: a quiet meadow, an ocean pier, a mountain vista or a special corner of their home or yard.

SOLITUDE

Do you enjoy your own company? Solitude is the ability to be alone and to embrace it. This is an opportunity to find quiet, to reflect and to recenter. Solitude is often a prerequisite for rest, serenity and creativity. For some, time alone can be very productive—as a place to focus all the energy accumulated while in the busyness of schedules and the stimulation of human interaction. For others, time alone renews and equips them to increase their productivity in outside responsibilities and relationships.

CREATIVITY

This wonderful human attribute allows us to express our inner life in the outside world. It fulfills our desire to contribute something of value, to impart beauty to others, in our lives and upon the world. This contribution might come in the form of gardening or sculpture, cooking or woodworking, caring for animals or volunteering in the community.

FUN

Having fun should be simple enough, but many of us have scheduled fun right out of our lives. Joy and pleasure add to making life meaningful and fulfilling. Fun is also very good for you; it's a great antidote to stress. Laughter, specifically, can be very good for your heart. It causes the endothelium, the lining of blood vessels, to dilate, increasing blood flow.[20] A study conducted by researchers at the University of Maryland Medical Center in Baltimore found that people with heart disease were 40 percent less likely to laugh in a variety of situations compared with people of the same age without heart disease.[21] Fun can motivate us to be physically active, spend time with other people, or even study or engage in various disciplines, not because we have to, but because these activities, such as golf, team sports, participating in a book club or taking music lessons, are highly enjoyable and replenishing for us.

Some activities might combine several aspects of leisure—rest, serenity, solitude, creativity and fun—or fit into only one category, but all five categories should be represented in our lives somehow. In an average week, how much unscheduled time do you have? When was the last time you enjoyed a favorite hobby? At one time, Katie was growing her own herbs and found tending them relaxing. Frank had loved buying and remodeling old clunkers. But that seemed like ages ago. When they began to discuss their interests outside of work, their eyes lit up and they even laughed about some of the fun things they had done together—like building a gazebo at a former home and dancing on the driveway without music during a torrential downpour. It was dialogue that connected them and made them want to create some similar experiences now. It was enough for them to want to find a way to change their schedules.

Do you feel driven by your timetable, or are you confidently setting your own pace? Where might you personally contribute something of yourself that may make a difference? What do you do just for pleasure? Many people are beset by *making a living* and leave no room for *a life*. Leisure is as important to your physical health—and your effectiveness in all areas of life—as the more tangible, readily apparent aspects of wellness.

MENTAL STATE

The biochemistry of the brain is in delicate balance, managing the intricacies of every system of the human body. When the chemical makeup of the brain becomes unbalanced, the impact is felt in many ways. If we lack dopamine, for example, we won't feel as good psychologically. If we are addicted to certain substances, our brains are tricked into telling us that we need those chemicals to function.

A chemical-related illness significant among CEOs is depression. This highly misunderstood illness is different from the usual sadness that accompanies hardship. Sadness is a legitimate response to certain circumstances. Although illness, significant stress or tragedy can *trigger* depression, this disorder is more than just feeling "the blues." Clinical depression is a debilitating illness with sadness as just one of several symptoms. It cannot be overcome willingly, simply by putting "mind over matter." Generally, people with depression have low levels of the "feel good" substance serotonin—one of several brain chemicals that are critical to normal feelings and thought processes. Depression is associated with an imbalance in serotonin and other neurotransmitter levels. This imbalance can be treated with medication and the help of natural methods such as exercise or meditation.

Depression can have an extensive, even devastating influence. People who have heart disease and depression have a much higher rate of death from heart disease than those who have heart disease and no depression.[22] Depression can also contribute to the loss of bone density,[23] a compromised immune system and high-risk behaviors that have overall ill effects on health. People struggling with depression are less likely to take measures to improve their diet, exercise habits or general lifestyle. Their relationships often suffer, too. Untreated, depression frequently leads to suicide.

Depression is a clinical diagnosis that should be made by a physician or psychologist. After discussing some of the symptoms—lethargy, prolonged sadness and loss of interest in favorite activities, to name a few—Frank decided it was worth taking up the subject with his primary health practitioner.

SUBSTANCE USE

Used in good measure and for the right reasons, drugs can help. Abused, they can do a lot of harm—to our bodies and to our relationships. Then there are the substances we should avoid ingesting altogether or that we should use within strict guidelines. Let's look at some of these.

CAFFEINE

The major source of caffeine in developed countries is coffee, but other sources include soft drinks (especially colas), teas, chocolate and cocoa. Medical research across several studies now suggests that a moderate amount of caffeine can actually be good for you. Two to four cups, or up to 24 oz. (200 to 300 mg. of caffeine), of coffee a day, for example, can reduce the risk of Parkinson's disease by 40 percent and the risk of Alzheimer's disease by about 20 percent.[24] Moderation is key. Too much caffeine can cause irritability, anxiety, sleep problems, irregular heartbeat, upset stomach, difficulty with diabetes, and migraines. Katie used coffee as a "boost" when she needed it, sometimes drinking as much as six cups a day. Frank, only half-jokingly, said it was no wonder she was so irritable and uptight.

NICOTINE

The main source of nicotine is cigarette smoke, but cigars, pipe tobacco and chewing tobacco are other dangerous sources of the drug. Conclusive studies prove the devastating effects of smoking and secondhand smoke on our bodies. In the United States, "about 90% of lung cancer deaths in men and almost 80% of lung cancer deaths in women are due to smoking."[25] Cancer is the disease most associated with smoking; however, smoking is also the primary cause of most cases of crippling lung disease in the form of emphysema and chronic bronchitis. It wreaks havoc on the body's other systems, too, contributing to high blood pressure, hardening of the arteries, osteoporosis and many other conditions. No amount of smoking is safe.

Smoking also reduces the skin's elasticity, making it more prone to sag and wrinkle. Add the expense and addictiveness of nicotine, and there are plenty of reasons to quit. Kicking the butt is difficult but possible with a good plan, the help of a knowledgeable health professional and sometimes prescription medication, and much of the damage done by smoking can be reversed. That's good news.

ALCOHOL

In moderation, alcohol can actually be beneficial. The flavonoids in red wine act as antioxidants, helping to reduce the aging of arteries and the immune system. Exceeding the recommended limits of alcohol consumption increases the risk of hypertension, diabetes and common, potentially life-threatening malignancies such as breast, colon and prostate cancer. Excessive amounts of alcohol can be toxic to your liver and put you at increased risk for other health problems, including anxiety and depression. Frank made a note to limit his alcohol consumption.

Addiction to alcohol can have profoundly negative effects on your relationships, your body and your mental health. Many people addicted to alcohol or who are negatively affected by their alcohol use fail to see this reality or refuse to acknowledge the evidence.

ILLICIT DRUGS

These include prescription or non-prescription drugs, such as pain-killers or sleeping pills, used inappropriately, as well as banned sub-stances. In 2002, the National Survey on Drug Use and Health found that "9.4 percent (22 million) of the U.S. adult population had substance abuse or dependence issues. Of these, 3.2 million individuals had co-occurring drug and alcohol use problems, 3.9 million had illicit substance use abuse or dependence only, and 14.9 million had alcohol abuse or dependence is-sues only."[26] Drug abuse can contribute to cirrhosis, cardiovascular disor-ders, certain types of cancers, various types of infections, digestive problems and pneumonia, as well as depression, psychosis and suicide.

As highly educated executive professionals, many CEOs think they and their businesses are insulated from substance abuse. Frank and Katie rolled their eyes at the suggestion that they should consider drug use in a physical health self-assessment. They were educated professionals, after all. But this perceived immunity couldn't be further from reality. Respected and established businesses have seen the effects of substance abuse on their personnel and finances. Mortimer Feinberg, chairman of BFS Psychological Associates Inc., a New York consulting firm, estimates that between 15 and 20 percent of U.S. CEOs have a drinking or drug problem, slightly *higher* than the national average.[27] Companies lose money and ex-pose themselves to liability when drug and alcohol abuse problems go un-detected or unchecked. Because of their relative isolation and rank, CEOs who abuse substances can experience serious personal and professional consequences before they acknowledge their problem or others intervene.

Once you complete the Chapter 2 *Workbook* exercises, your "check-in"—the first step in your self-assessment—will be complete. Good health knowledge comes from information (like the information in this chapter), through your own research (there is a list of great physical wellness re-sources at the end of this book) and from consulting experts. Before you can examine and fully assess your current physical wellness, you must en-list the help of your primary health practitioner—the doctor you see for ongoing medical care. He or she will give you a baseline assessment and be able to recommend further consultation, as necessary, with other health care providers such as specialists, nutritionists, dentists, optometrists, audiologists and physicians who specialize in preventative medicine and health risk assessment.

For the purposes of this program, you absolutely must consult your primary health practitioner. He or she knows your medical history best and can give you personalized health information.

Consulting your primary health practitioner

PREPARING FOR YOUR DOCTOR'S VISIT

To make the most of your appointment, prepare questions or a list of concerns in advance. Note any issues that have been raised in your mind, carefully considering the physical wellness factors described in this chapter. Take a completed copy of the various information sheets explaining your medical and family history, current medications and so on, and the other personal health data you compiled in the *Workbook*. Most doctors appreciate this preparedness by their patients.

WHAT TO EXPECT FROM YOUR CHECK-UP

A FOCUSED MEDICAL HISTORY

Your medical history gives your primary health practitioner the context for any current concerns you might have and for anything the exam reveals. The more concise and accurate your history, the more easily your doctor can assess and diagnose your symptoms. The components of your medical history that your doctor will look at usually include the following:

- *Personal medical history* – any significant surgeries or illnesses you may have experienced, tests, screenings or treatments you have undergone (including self-directed treatments or remedies), immunizations you've had and when you had them, and allergies or sensitivities to any medications or other substances

- *Family medical history* – medical conditions, diseases or genetic predispositions that exist in your family tree

- *Social history* – a summary of your work, family and leisure activities and dynamics, factors specific to your routine—such as night shifts or frequent travel, habits related to diet and exercise, alcohol consumption, smoking or drug use and so on

🗐 *Current medical information*

- current medications (both prescription and non-prescription), herbal supplements, and vitamin and mineral supplements

- your "check-in": the self-assessment exercises you completed in the *Workbook* thus far

- current illnesses, symptoms, questions or concerns you may have, as well as your personal preferences for treatment—non-drug therapies or avoiding blood products, for example.

A COMPLETE PHYSICAL EXAMINATION

A comprehensive physical exam will include an assessment of all organ systems, blood pressure and basic "stats" such as abdominal girth, height and weight. Men over 40 should have annual prostate exams. Both men and women over 50 should have annual rectal exams. Generally, women over 40 should have annual mammograms. Regular Pap smears should be started at age 21 or three years after becoming sexually active, whichever comes first.[28] Fitness testing can and should be performed on anyone intending to begin training to improve fitness or lose weight.

A DIAGNOSTIC ASSESSMENT

Once your doctor has performed the physical exam, he or she will discuss preliminary results and may recommend further testing, such as the following:

🗐 *Laboratory testing (including blood testing)* – This will be an automatic part of a comprehensive exam, since blood testing will show cholesterol levels and other critical information necessary to make an accurate assessment of overall physical health.

🗐 *Scans and other diagnostic imaging techniques* – These can often detect disease in early stages or explain curious findings from the physical exam.

🗐 *Screenings or risk assessment tests* – These may be performed for diseases or conditions as indicated by the physical exam. For example, if you are over 50 and have a family history of cardiovascular disease, your doctor may test you specifically for any signs of early or silent heart disease. If you are a woman on hormone replacement therapy, regular bone-density scans are prudent.

🗐 *Assessment by a specialist.*

Your doctor should explain what each recommended test is for, how it works and the kinds of results you can expect. Ask whatever questions you need until you feel comfortable and in control of your own health choices.

UNDERSTANDING THE RESULTS

Make an appointment to visit your doctor after all tests have been completed to discuss test results and what they mean. Once the physical exam and any additional testing have been completed, your doctor will go over the results with you and give you a diagnosis and plan for treatment, as required, which may include introduction of medications or changes to your current medication, treatments such as surgery, further testing, lifestyle changes and additional resources to consult.

Ask for clarification where you need it. The acceptable limits for cholesterol, for example, are variable depending on each patient's medical history, so ask your doctor what your target numbers should be. Ask for specific feedback and practical suggestions for areas where you want to improve. If you need time to process the information, make another appointment to discuss your case when you can feel more confident.

EVALUATING THE RESULTS

Get a copy of the results of your check-up and record them in the *Workbook*. In the column beside these results, record the target levels or numbers you discussed with your doctor in each category. Once you have test results in front of you, compare them with the levels your doctor suggested were optimum for you.

In the next chapter, you will learn to prioritize the areas you've isolated and identify motivators to make changes. You'll use your *knowledge* to check and refine your *attitude*, *prepare* for change through goal setting, take precise and deliberate *action* steps toward wholeness, and mark and *evaluate* your progress.

You're on your way!

The next morning at home, Katie began to feel the implications of what Frank was suggesting. Yesterday, in The Healthy CEO's office, it had all just seemed like benign talk about physical wellness theory. She

could agree to it in theory. But Frank was actually talking about making wholesale changes. That meant her life was going to have to change, too. She hated being forced into anything, even if it would be good for her.

"You *calm down!*" Katie screamed. "I don't want to hear you shoveling any more of that health crap at me, you understand? Maybe I like *being stressed and neurotic. Maybe I* like *that I only get five hours of sleep a night. Maybe I* enjoy *being crabby! Did you ever think of that?!*"

Frank knew that she knew better, and he wasn't going to let her get away with it. They'd both gotten the results of their physical exams, and each of them had been surprised. Their doctor had suggested that Katie's stress level might be a problem. He was concerned that she wasn't getting enough to eat on a regular basis. And, of course, they were asked to address their weights. Katie's BMI number had turned out to be pretty low. Frank's was too high. In fact, if you averaged the two of them out, together they were about right. Frank had asked the doctor if they could just do that—average them out. Chuckling to himself, the doctor had just shaken his head. Frank had received more bad news: His cholesterol levels and his blood pressure were too high. He'd also scored pretty high on a lot of the symptoms for depression. Wasn't life *just a little depressing? Did he dare to expect more?*

"You're an idiot. A fat idiot, and I'm tired of you acting like you think I don't know what I'm doing—like my business is a cute little hobby while you do the real work."

Frank thought it might be good to let her talk.

"Well, let me tell you something, corporate big shot. You play it safe in that office of yours—your ivory tower—that somebody else handed to you, while I am down here in the trenches—the real world— where there is no backup plan. I'm it. You have no idea what that's like, do you?"

Now Frank thought it might be good if she shut up. She didn't.

"Don't patronize me and tell me I need to relax, or eat, or... whatever. Don't pretend you care about what goes on in my life. You don't have a clue, and that suits you just fine!"

Now Frank was steamed. "Hold on a minute, Katie. If I don't have a clue, it's because you don't tell me. You've got this chip on your shoulder that I didn't put there. You hear me: I am not the enemy. I do care. I want you to be happy. And yeah, I want you to be happy for your sake, but I want you to be happy for me, too. I'd like to live with someone who isn't miserable all the time and who doesn't think being kind and a few degrees above sub-zero is a sign of weakness."

Katie wouldn't back down. "You don't think I'm warm?" Frank was walking out the door. "I'm very warm, you hear me! I'm an incredibly warm person!" He was gone, and she was yelling at the door. She looked at her hands. They were shaking. She hated this. The arguing, the positioning she knew they were always doing. Could she be honest with herself? With Frank? Could she admit that she was terrified? She was scared she was going to have a nervous breakdown, scared she was going to get sick, scared her business would fall apart if she let herself fall apart. She had watched the numbers on the scale steadily drop for the last year or so. She had grown accustomed to feeling like life was a race, and she hated it.

But admitting she needed help felt like falling apart. She had always been tough as nails. A survivor. But she knew she was tired of surviving. She wanted to live. Could she really get there? Could she face reality and actually do something about it? Would that really make a difference? She buried her face in her hands and cried. She hadn't let herself cry for months. Now, the emotion came in a flood. It didn't overwhelm her or even sweep her away. There was release. After the torrent, she was still there.

3 *Your physical wellness:*
Putting knowledge into action

"Quit worrying about your health. It'll go away."

Robert Orben, magician and comedy writer

Katie surveyed the room. The candlelight was soothing... beautiful. The condo hadn't seemed so inviting, so serene since... well, she couldn't remember. Nor could she remember the last time she had cooked an entire meal at home. Salmon in dill sauce was baking in the oven, her spinach salad amandine was already plated on the table, the wine was on ice, and the wild and brown rice pilaf was steaming on the stove. She had to admit, the aroma was intoxicating. Frank's favorite CD was playing, and she was wearing his favorite dress—the slinky green one that made her eyes gleam. Everything was ready. Now, she just needed her husband to show up. He had said he'd be home by six o'clock.

If he was late, she'd kill him.

She heard his key turn in the door—at 6:04 p.m.—and she froze where she stood. Geez, she thought, I feel as skittish as I did at my first freshman dance. Frank entered the room, and once he had gotten over his surprise, he looked at her inquisitively. This made her even more self-conscious. What would he think? What would he say? Part of her dared to feel hopeful. Part of her felt ridiculous.

She saw him grow shy, too, which made her feel a little better. "Wow," he said. "What's all this?" He put his briefcase down and took a couple steps toward her. He stopped and sighed. "You look amazing."

Yeah, Katie was feeling better now. She gestured to the candles, "Care for a guilt-induced, yet slightly romantic candlelit dinner? I'm even serving healthy food."

"I'd love it," Frank replied.

Katie ventured, "I was awful this morning." She didn't know where to fix her eyes. "It's not you. I do know you care. I'm totally frustrated with life right now, but it's not your fault—well, not entirely, anyway." She couldn't do this totally straight.

Frank wanted to let her off the hook and get on with the evening. "K, it's OK."

"No. Shut up," she insisted. "You may never get a confession like this from me again, so relish this rare moment."

"Is it OK if I relish the moment while sitting down? Can I pour you a glass of wine?"

"Good idea." Yes, this was better, she thought. It'd be better if they were both busy and not having to make eye contact. She pulled the fish out of the oven. "I'm not happy with the way things are, Frank. I don't like being miserable and I'm angry—at myself even more than at you, I think. I'm tired of going 100 miles an hour and giving 110 percent, but I'm afraid that if I slow down or ease up even just a little, everything will fall apart. With all this talk about changing things to make them better and getting our lives on track, and seeing how serious you are about it.... Well, it all sounds great, but..." She lost some confidence.

"... but what?" Frank coaxed gently.

"I'm scared to try these things only to have them fail. If we try and fail, then that's it. We've tried and there's nothing left. There's no more hope. Right now, even though I know it's crazy, I have hope enough to keep going because... because... there might be some magic somehow... if we end up needing it. Do you know what I'm trying to say?"

"I think so. But there's no magic, K."

He sounded oddly paternal, but she didn't mind. She sat down. She was beat. The jig was up. "I know you're right, Frank. I know there's no magic. But I still wish there were." She looked him right in the eye then. He was really listening to her.

"K, there may not be any magic, but there are things we can do. I don't believe in magic, but I believe in you and in me—in us—enough to do whatever it takes. I believe things can be better. I believe we can be better." He handed her a glass of wine. "Maybe I'm a bit crazy, but I think there's always hope as long as we don't quit. And K, I'm not going to."

She held his gaze. They were still for a moment. She was still and it was OK. The world continued on. It was going on all around her, most of it without her, and she was OK. This was her world right now, slow and still. It was good.

Katie reached for Frank's plate. "So, you're game to try some things, huh? How about this salad? It's no KFC, but..."

Frank laughed, "Bring it on." He picked up his fork. "This is nice. I like just being with you. We hardly do that anymore, do we?" She shook her head in agreement. "You really do look amazing, you know." He looked at her with bedroom eyes. "Maybe we could..."

"Not on your life, Frank. I worked hard on this meal and you're damn well gonna take your time eating it." But she tossed her head and cooed, "Although, you know, I didn't make anything for dessert...."

She filled her fork and then her mouth with food. She rolled it around her tongue and savored it. It was good. Frank raised his glass and made a toast: "To magic."

You've heard it said, "If you know better, you do better." But can knowledge alone facilitate change? Daily, we are bombarded by health messages telling us to eat right, move more, stop smoking, avoid prolonged sun exposure and use a condom, to name a few. But we are still overweight, struggling with preventable illness, smoking a pack a day, developing skin cancer and facing unwanted pregnancy or sexually transmitted disease. Knowledge alone can't magically transform us. It is not enough. We can know all the right things, yet continue to do all the wrong things. Why is this so? It was hard for the Johnsons to hear exactly where their health problems lay and, in the case of some factors, how far they were off track.

Remember that *Knowledge* is only the first step in making real and lasting change. Change also involves *Attitude, Preparation, Action* and *Evaluation.*

Your attitude toward physical wellness

ASSUMING RESPONSIBILITY

If something means something to us, we usually want to take care of it. When we buy a new car, we wash it frequently, keep it serviced, avoid eating in it and often park well away from other cars. We do everything we can to keep the motor running smoothly, to keep the finish pristine and to preserve that heady new-car smell. In time, the novelty wears off and we're a little less careful. If we *are* meticulous with an older vehicle, it's perhaps because we need to keep ourselves on the road until we're in a position to buy something new.

We often treat our bodies like old cars. They get us from point A to B, make our daily tasks possible and facilitate our lifestyle, but they also house our souls and minds, and even sustain life! While the human body has an amazing ability to renew, replenish and heal itself, it is also vulnerable and responsive to the sometimes-poor choices we make. The "model" we were born with is the one we'll drive for life. There's no trading in or buying new—although some of us have had the odd part refinished! Your body is the only one you'll ever have, and it has to last you for the long haul. How well you maintain it will determine how long you'll be able to drive and how much you'll enjoy the ride. As we saw in the last chapter, many factors of physical wellness are entirely within your control. You are responsible for your quality of life.

The fact is, you can choose to live up to your full physical wellness potential—or not.

FINDING MOTIVATION

Settling the "whys" of change

For you to become personally invested in true change, you need to find personal reasons for making that change. Obviously, improving your physical wellness is wise on several levels. Who doesn't want to experience more energy, feel stronger or live longer? You've probably given mental assent to all of these reasons for improving your health. But what will be the personal and powerful motivators that truly inspire you to change? Perhaps you want to be able to retire early. You might dream of starting your own business or philanthropic organization, or expanding the venture you're already in. Maybe you want to be able to give a significant amount of money or time to a cause that's dear to you. You may have identified a desire to create deep, meaningful relationships. Maybe you want to write a book, climb a mountain or circumnavigate the globe. Being at the top of your physical game will help you better realize each of these life goals, as well as thrive in them.

If one of your life goals is to create deep, meaningful relationships, think about the ways improved health will contribute to intimacy. If you work to reduce your stress, you'll be more emotionally available to others. If you need to improve your sleep habits, how might doing so improve your mood and level of tolerance with others? If you want to exercise more, could you create a plan that involves relationship building at the same time, like going for an evening walk regularly with your spouse or helping coach your child's sports team? Part of Katie's motivation to improve her health included a desire to connect better with Frank. This was something they could work on together. If one of your life goals is to retire early, visualize the impact healthy choices *now* will have on your life 10 or 20 years in the future. Imagine the activities you might otherwise have to pass by. Let these images and opportunities motivate you.

Depending on where you want to improve, you will be influenced by *positive* or *negative motivators*, or a combination of both. Positive motivators are the *benefits* of change—the advantages of being in good physical health that encourage you to reach your goals. Negative motivators are the *costs* of not changing—the health risks associated with not pursuing your goals. Regular exercise and healthy eating may lower your cholesterol (decreasing a negative motivator), but they will also boost your energy and sense of well-being. They may also help you lose weight and improve your appearance. Use what works for you. If you need to reduce stress, the prospect of a pleasurable massage or trip to the spa may positively motivate you to produce real change. Teaming up with a friend or a coworker to pursue your fitness goals—by playing racquetball or going to the gym, for example—can turn a potentially dreary task into a lot of fun.

Positive motivation is very subjective. It is derived from what makes *you* feel good, what brings *you* pleasure or what moves *you* closer to your life goals.

Your consultation with your doctor may have been a wake-up call, like it was for Frank. If your blood pressure or cholesterol level is dangerously high, the threat of a heart attack may be a powerful negative motivator: it's something you obviously want to avoid. Sometimes it takes a diagnosis such as cancer or irritable bowel syndrome to finally incite us to make changes. These warnings or wake-up calls can hit hard. We often give *intellectual* assent to all the data that tells us we should be living differently, but it may take a significant *emotional* event to shake us into action. My cardiogram showing that I experienced an actual heart attack might be alarming, but the realization that I could have died will have the most impact.

We don't have to wait for a crisis to initiate health changes. It's never too soon. It's also never too late to reverse poor health or experience new health benefits. Your doctor may have cautioned you about staying your current course. Heed these warnings; look at them as checks and balances. You wouldn't ignore a negative bottom line in your business. You'd take the information and do everything in your power to turn things around. Do the same for your health. Look honestly at your physiological bottom line. If you need to turn things around, let the "bad" numbers or the imminent threat of physical crisis spur you to invest in your health with more focus, drive and determination. Face the facts honestly. Writing them down as a way of targeting them can be extremely empowering.

Preparing to improve physical wellness

SETTING GOALS: THINKING IN THE LONG AND SHORT TERM

If you've started your own business, you know there are important preparatory steps to take before you actually launch. You may do product testing, market research or consumer surveys. You estimate start-up and operating costs, and you consider your investment capital or some of the options for acquiring it. You identify the human resources you need. You scope out what the competition is doing. You price out equipment and investigate leasing as compared to purchasing work space. Each of these matters is broken down further into step-by-step processes. For example, in the hiring process, you will go through a series of smaller steps: deciding what you want to do yourself and what you want to delegate (create job descriptions), identifying your skill set and the skills you need to rely on from others, researching the best ways to find the right people (networking with other professionals, placing an ad in the newspaper or online, or hiring professional recruiters) and so on.

Each of the smaller steps becomes vital to the goal of establishing a workforce, which in turn contributes to the larger goal of starting your business. In the same way, to improve your physical wellness, you need to break this larger goal into smaller, more specialized tasks.

If you're reading this book, it's safe to assume that one of your long-term goals is to improve your physical health. You now have some more specific goals to work toward after having completed your personal "check-in" and your check-up with your doctor. Depending on what the results revealed, you may feel daunted as you look at that list. "Fixing" what's wrong or making some of the improvements might seem over-whelming or out of reach. Unless you break those goals down into man-ageable chunks, they will be beyond you. You will become discouraged and likely give up.

In the previous chapter, we outlined how go-**FAR** goals work. Now, you can create your own goals to improve your physical health. If, for ex-ample, one of your health goals is to eat better, you need to define what eating better actually means and what it will look like for you.

Focus your physical wellness goals

Make them specific

Focused goals break your larger goals into smaller action steps that are explicit, specific and measurable. These smaller goals can help you track your progress at several points. Regular success intervals will keep you motivated to move through the steps. For Frank and Katie's shared goal of wanting to eat better, these are some of the action steps they set out to help keep their goal focused:

- I will create a menu with regular meals for the next seven days. I'll include more fresh fruits and vegetables, have fish at least twice this week and eat regular meals. I'll make a lunch to take to work on at least four out of five days.

- I'll make a list of healthy snacks to have around, such as nuts, fruit and vegetables, and make selections only from that list for the next week. I'll keep a healthy snack in my briefcase at all times, just in case.

- I will make sure to eat breakfast every day.

- Every morning this week, I'll take the supplements my doctor has recommended: folate, calcium with vitamin D, and aspirin.

- I'll go to the market today to purchase the ingredients, snacks and supplements I'll need for the week.

⬜ I'll drink more water. To help with this, I'll take a water bottle to work with me, keep it at my desk and make sure it's empty by the time there's a coffee or lunch break. At the break, I'll refill it.

⬜ I'll read one chapter of Bob Greene's *Get With the Program* on Wednesday, when I know I'll have the time.

Each of the goals above not only defines the tasks to be performed, but includes the detailed strategy involved. The goals include specific details: "fish," "folate" and "in my briefcase," for example. There are quantitative measures included, such as "at least twice," "four out of five" and plans to "make a list." These goals have a fixed timeframe as well: a seven-day period, in this case. Itemized action steps make the goals explicit, specific and measurable.

Many changes can be made almost instantly and don't have to be drawn out. Tackle these first. Do you need to purchase some supplements? Fill a prescription for medication? Have some dental work done? Get these tasks done now so you can turn your attention to the goals that will need your focus and commitment over the longer term. The added benefit of tackling the shortest-term goals first is that you can check these goals off as you accomplish them *now*. You'll achieve much in a short time and see quick results that remind you of the progress you've already made.

Set benchmarks for success. Do you want to be exercising more days per week at 90 days into your program than at 60? For more minutes at each session? With heavier weights than when you started? Is one of your goals to have lost a set number of pounds by the time you reach the two- or six-month mark? You might want to get your doctor's feedback in setting meaningful and safe goals in things like lowering cholesterol or blood pressure. What does he or she recommend as a reasonable period of time to lower these numbers, and by what increments? For Frank, steady but gradual weight loss was the aim. He was targeting a BMI of 24 (down from 28)—which was a loss of about 30 pounds—within the next six months.

CREATE A MENTAL PICTURE

Once you've identified your goals and focused them to measurable specifics, visualize the results. If one of your goals is to eat better, paint a positive picture of the outcome. Visualize your arteries being "cleaned out," with blood flowing through them efficiently. Imagine that life stream carrying vital nutrients to every system, organ, tissue and cell of your body, energizing and restoring you. Picture your skin glowing, your healthy body in a new outfit or yourself as an elderly but vigorous man or woman. Take a glimpse into what might happen if you don't improve your eating habits, too. Take that same journey through your arteries. What plaque buildup do you see? Does your heart struggle to pump blood? How does your lifestyle look different? Are you heavier? Slowing down? At what age might you anticipate suffering a fatal heart attack? Are you truly struck by that image?

Hopefully, you can see a stark difference. Keep those images in your mind to help stimulate progress. Press on to see the positive results you've visualized until they become reality.

Add value to your physical wellness goals

Do a cost-benefit analysis

What will it cost you *not* to change? How will you benefit by seeing your goals through? And, perhaps the most difficult questions to answer: What are you *really* willing to do to get the results you want? What are you willing to give up to achieve what you most want? Plan ahead to make adjustments, or even sacrifices, that you can live with. Remember: the bigger the investment up front, the greater the returns and the sooner you'll realize your goal. To improve your nutrition, you might be willing to take the following steps:

- When I get home today, I'll throw out all the junk food I have in my pantry.

- I won't eat fast food this week.

- At my dinner meeting on Thursday, I'll order the salad with low-fat dressing on the side instead of the loaded baked potato (God help me!).

It may seem drastic—costly—to completely purge the pantry of junk food. However, if you know you're likely to be tempted beyond your power to resist these unhealthy snacks, it might be an entirely realistic goal and a sacrifice that's worth making. The benefits outstrip the cost. If you're used to eating fast food several times a week, opting out will be a big, but consequential, step. Are you able to see what you stand to gain by skipping the fries? Altering your behavior—even just being more intentional about your food choices—will require a deliberate shift in thinking. What is good health *really* worth to you?

IDENTIFY POTENTIAL BARRIERS

Once you've created your go-**FAR** goals, don't let unexpected road-blocks thwart them. When you launch a new initiative in your business, it's not without carefully considering and planning for inevitable challenges and setbacks, for the "what ifs" and the unpredictable. The same must be true in your pursuit of physical wellness. An essential part of preparation is anticipation.

Expect adversity. If you are not experiencing some difficulties in life, you're not really living. Don't be surprised when you encounter them. Plan for them. Identify the potential obstacles to the changes you want to make and take steps to address them now. Where are you vulnerable to temptation? Take a moment to anticipate and identify some barriers to your success in this process. For each barrier, brainstorm ways you might go around it or eliminate it altogether. Maybe one of your goals is to be in bed and reading every night by ten o'clock. If you know that once you turn the TV on in the evening, you can't shut it off until after midnight, decide now not to even turn it on. If you've quit exercise programs in the past, build in ways that will make it hard for you to quit: invest in a Pilates class and partner with someone else who will nag you to be there, for example. If you've been invited to a cocktail party where you know there'll be a lot of sweets and high-fat appetizers, eat before you get there. Katie knew she'd have a hard time keeping her stress levels down if she didn't learn to delegate. She began to spend some time each day teaching her assistant, Jude, some tasks that she normally performed herself. It was hard to let go, but she knew trying to do everything herself would be a huge roadblock to improving her health.

RELISH YOUR PHYSICAL WELLNESS GOALS

TAILOR YOUR GOALS TO FIT YOU

For your goals to be meaningful, they should be tailored to your needs and personality. You could have the same larger goal—"I want to eat better"—as someone else, but have slightly different smaller goals. Depending on where you're at, eating better might mean less salt, more fiber, less eating on the run—or even eating more if you're underweight. You may want to learn some new cooking methods or recipes, or research quick-but-healthy restaurants or shopping options—whichever best fits your lifestyle. Your goals might also be set within a tighter or broader time span. When setting your goals, you need to be honest with yourself and introduce challenges while keeping the adjustments realistic. For example, the timeframe of a week is wise if you know you want to make significant lifestyle changes but aren't sure what impact the changes will actually have. In a week, you can learn a lot about what works, what doesn't and how to adjust the next set of goals accordingly. The next goal-setting session might cover a lengthier period given your new experiential insight. Experience will teach you how to further tailor your goals.

MAKE THEM REALISTIC

Don't set overzealous goals. If you have a sweet tooth and normally give yourself a sugar "fix" every night, cutting out sweets but allowing yourself dessert on Friday and Saturday is reasonable, especially if you are making other lifestyle changes at the same time. The coffee shop on the first floor of Frank's building served the best brownies—fudgy and rich. He'd been downing one a day with afternoon coffee. Now they were reserved for his TGIF (and Friday only) treat. Some concessions sustain the motivation you need to achieve your health goals. Goals should be challenging, but not out of reach. They must be inspirational without being impossible.

BUILD IN FUN

Look for ways to bring in the "fun factor." Again, if you want to improve your nutrition, take a cooking class with a friend, grow fresh vegetables if you have a green thumb or make a friend at the farmers' market. Although she and Frank now lived in a high-rise condo, Katie set up a small table by a sunny window and resurrected her herb garden. The full-flavored plants would complement some of the new vegetable-laden dishes she was trying, and she would enjoy finding her green thumb once again.

Physical wellness in action

GET MOVING

It seems straightforward enough: set goals and follow through. Yet so many people with the very best intentions don't end up where they want to go simply because... well, they just don't go. Goal setting is an empowering step in realizing change; however, it's easy to stop there, believing that the process of setting goals, even great ones, is enough to produce change by itself. Preparation is key, but it's only one step along the way.

Bob Greene, in his highly regarded book *Get With the Program: Getting Real About Your Weight, Health and Emotional Well-Being*, says,

"Procrastination is often really fear masked by laziness."[1] We might be afraid of failure, or of change itself. Let the smaller goals you've set help dissipate some of the fear incited by the larger, often overwhelming goals in front of you. Remember that progress is simply taking small deliberate steps, one at a time, in a positive direction. It's more important that you take the next small step than that you are able to take them all. Starting is often the most difficult part of this process, but you can do it.

Think about what you need to do to start working toward your goals and begin to take those smaller steps. Do you need to buy a particular book? Go out and buy it. Do you need to arrange for childcare so you can go to the gym? Track down a good sitter and schedule the appointments. Frank took advantage of the gym close to his office and bought a membership. Do you need to follow up on a concern your doctor expressed? Do you need to cancel or reschedule some things to give your critical health goals the attention they deserve? Make the adjustments today. Do you need to get support for overcoming an addiction? Call a treatment center or support group immediately. Don't put off anything that is in your power to do right now. Do it.

Where it makes sense to do so, pace yourself to avoid burnout. If you do too much too soon, you could overtax your system. If you do too little too slowly, you won't see results and discouragement may set in. Rely on your physician's advice to make some of these decisions.

ENLIST SUPPORT

Improve your odds of succeeding by building in a support system. Think of who will also benefit from a better you. Your spouse? Your children? Your business partner? Let them in on your plans and explain why they should care. For example, a more fit and better-rested you will be more productive at work and more sympathetic at home. Everyone you rub shoulders with stands to benefit from a healthier you. Talk to one or two people who have a personal stake in your goals. An obvious choice might be your spouse, a close friend or a colleague. Involve them in whatever way you can.

ACCOUNTABILITY PARTNERS

Have at least one person check with you regularly to see how you're doing. Suggest that he or she ask you specific questions at regular intervals, such as "What did you eat yesterday?" "What time did you get to bed last night?" "Did you give up that volunteer position that you said was putting you over the edge?" Choose someone who will offer encouragement and celebrate your victories, but also be tough on you if you need a swift kick to the hindquarters.

CO-PARTICIPANTS

Frank knew his chances of staying on any fitness program were slim to none if he tried to do it himself. He invited Robert, a colleague, to join him at the gym. It gave them the opportunity to brainstorm marketing ideas together while they were on the treadmill, as well as socialize. Talk to your spouse and friends about *The Healthy CEO* program and invite them to join you. Link together in those areas where you share a desire to improve. Recognize it as an opportunity to improve both your physical and relational wellness. This becomes a way to spend your time and energy even more efficiently.

COMPETITORS

If you are competitive by nature, take things a step further and engage with someone in some healthy competition. See who can reach certain benchmarks sooner or who is more consistent. Katie loved to compete, and she would often good-naturedly taunt Frank by bragging about how effective her new eating strategies were: "I've had all my servings of veggies today, Frank. How about you?" Build in fun "penalties" for slip-ups— washing the competitor's car perhaps—and rewards for "wins," like gift certificates to a movie.

STAKEHOLDERS

Tell your boss and coworkers about your goals, insofar as your initiative reflects your desire to be a leader in all areas of your life. Sell yourself and your successes to those you network with professionally—within reason, of course. More and more, cross-disciplinary success outside of the professional arena is becoming a powerful draw for investors and clients. If people are confident in the human capital you possess as an individual, they'll be more likely to invest their resources with you. Success in one area begets success in another.

REFRAME SETBACKS AND REENGAGE

Maybe an unexpected bout with the flu foils your new exercise schedule. Perhaps your teen reveals a drug habit in the midst of your campaign to reduce stress. What if you joined Alcoholics Anonymous sincerely, but fell off the wagon last night?

See adversity as opportunity. Physical and mental fitness coach and author of *Body for Life*, Bill Phillips, says:

> We are all capable of so much more than we might believe we are, but our ultimate potential is often smothered by what society teaches us—that pressure is a bad thing, that it hurts rather than helps our efforts to improve and become successful.... The truth of the matter is that it's through pressure or "stress" that we evolve—that we grow.[2]

So when impediments slow you down, when crisis comes, or when you fail outright, you get plenty of rest so you can get back on your feet (and the treadmill) sooner, you embrace your teen—and his addiction— as your moment to really learn how to meet challenges head on with focus and grace, and you quit drinking for good—again.

Wherever possible, look at setbacks and hindrances as motivators. Turn pressure into power. If something comes to you too easily, you won't really appreciate it. Learn to value struggle as a character-shaping force and lean into whatever is challenging you. In the same way that resistance training builds your muscles and makes you stronger, your resolve will be strengthened each time you deliberately push against resistance. Every challenge you push through will build your perseverance "muscle."

Refuse to let setbacks derail you. Every step in the process of change is important to your success. However, the most powerful and telling one is the step you take right after you fall. Get back up, brush yourself off, and let that step define you as a success and a true leader in your physical wellness.

> ## "Pain is temporary. It may last a minute, or an hour, or a day, or a year, but eventually it will subside and something else will take its place. If I quit, however, it lasts forever."

Lance Armstrong, cancer survivor, cyclist and winner of 7 Tour de France titles.

Evaluating your progress

Once you've set your goals, determined benchmarks and actually begun to take action, you'll need to honestly and intentionally observe what's happening.

TAKE STOCK REGULARLY

Evaluate your progress on a regular basis, scheduling checkpoints into your appointment book or PDA. If one of your goals is to lose weight, are you weighing yourself weekly and tracking your progress? If your doctor has helped you create a plan to lower your cholesterol through increased activity and better nutrition, do you pause regularly to see if you're actually following it? Are you following through with regular cholesterol monitoring to see if you're getting results? As Frank watched pounds drop off, he was also pleased to discover that his bad cholesterol levels were coming down and his good cholesterol was going up. Same effort, more than one positive result. Are you actually guarding the leisure time you've set aside? Are you monitoring the amount of rest you're getting by keeping a sleep log? Depending on the goal you set, different markers, benchmarks or measurements will help clarify your direction and the amount of momentum you really have. Intermittent, intentional evaluations are critical.

REASSESS AS NECESSARY

In setting goals for change, you are unable to anticipate every little bend in the road. That's okay. Katie was frustrated by the up-front investment of time to train Jude. It seemed like more work, not less. She had to remind herself that it was this initial investment of time that would save her a lot of work in the long run. But she knew she needed to build in even more strategies to help her relax. Mondays were slow for the business, so she began to go to weekly massage appointments and leave Jude in charge for that time. It wasn't easy, but she was committed. Remember that your goals should be focused, but flexible. Which action steps have you found to be unrealistic? How can you revise them so they work? If you've discovered you hate your treadmill, sign up for an exercise class or find a racquetball partner instead. Which of your action steps were perfectly reasonable, but you fudged on? Can you strengthen your resolve and try again? What's left to be done? Are there areas where you're not sure you're really making headway? Go for another check-up if necessary to get your latest medical numbers or feedback from your primary health practitioner.

BUILD IN REWARDS

Find fun ways to achieve your goals, then create payoffs for results. Design a system of rewards. "If I can stick to this eating plan for the next two weeks, I'll treat myself to premium seats at the next home hockey game." The reward of hockey tickets is a great motivator and a built-in high at the end of the process. If you're trying to lose weight, buy yourself a new outfit once you've hit an important milestone. The promise of a tangible reward for real results will be a fun motivator to keep going. When you evaluate, be disciplined—even hard on yourself—where you need to be. But by all means, celebrate your victories!

Here again, is the Success Cycle introduced in Chapter 1:

The Success Cycle

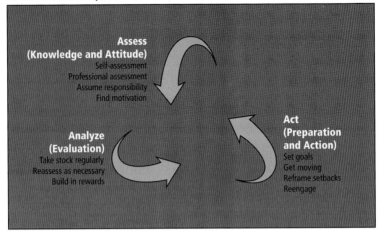

Using the *Knowledge* we acquired in Chapter 2, we were able to walk through the steps of *Attitude, Preparation, Action* and *Evaluation,* and apply them to improving our physical wellness. Repetition of these steps in the cycle will help you maintain and continuously improve your health. One success builds upon another, and every change realized creates momentum for new ones. With this in mind, every time you complete the cycle, start again at the beginning with a fresh "check-in." Hopefully, you are starting from a new vantage point, having gained real ground. As you set new goals, adjust your strategy. Maybe you targeted your diet and activity level in the last cycle. This time, you might want to improve your sleep habits and stress levels in particular while sustaining the momentum you achieved in your diet and exercise programs.

Let progress encourage you. Let setbacks inform you and steel your resolve. Let experience give you confidence. Let the progress you've already made motivate you to keep going. Let your improving health revitalize the way you live.

The next couple of chapters will help you apply the principles you've learned about making positive and lasting changes to your relational wellness.

Frank and Katie were left alone in The Healthy CEO's office. He had been called out front to sign something that a courier had whisked in urgently. Probably to do with some malpractice suit, Katie thought snidely, partly to humor herself. She and Frank had been there an hour already, talking about how they were progressing with their physical wellness goals. She was eating more, getting her weight up to a healthier level. She knew her "predicament" was probably the envy of most women, but there was a catch: she had to gain the weight by eating healthy foods, not pack-on-some-quick-pounds Ben and Jerry's. She was also trying to control her stress by practicing relaxation techniques, and cutting down on caffeine. She had signed up for yoga. She liked that part all right. She was doing okay. But she wasn't as committed as Frank; something inside wouldn't let go of her. There was a tightness, an urgency, a restlessness that wouldn't let her be.

Katie pushed back all of her cuticles and then pushed them back some more. She couldn't stop fidgeting. Oh, God. What was wrong with her? Why couldn't she just relax? Launching herself from her chair on the cool, soothing blue side of the room, Katie dove for the jar of coffee beans on the red side. She grabbed a handful and scarfed them, like a kid stealing penny candy.

"Katie, you shouldn't," Frank scolded mildly.

"Back off, Frank. I had one cup of coffee this morning and that's it. It's not like I'm shooting heroin or anything. Give me a break." She retreated to the blue chair, chomping on the beans, fidgeting some more.

Frank had been on a new exercise program—following it religiously like the good Yale boy he was—and a self-directed healthy eating plan. After eight weeks, Katie could see a difference. He had lost some weight and he seemed to have more energy. But she had been scared by the rest of the doctor's report on Frank. He was depressed. Not the "home team lost the World Series" kind of depressed, or the blues because business wasn't good. Business was great. No, Frank was clinically depressed, Dr. Staples had said.

Katie shuddered at the things she had been thinking—sometimes verbalizing—about Frank in recent months: He's lazy. He's dull. He's in some pathetic mid-life crisis. Turns out it was at least partly chemical, and Frank was now on a low dose of antidepressants to help him get back on his feet. The doctor was going to reevaluate once some time had passed and he could see what some lifestyle changes would mean to Frank's overall chemistry. He was now on his second kind of medication. The first had made him want to sleep all the time—not great for a guy who had wanted to sleep just most of the time previously. These meds seemed better. He was doing well. He was making changes. Good job, Frank. Way to go, Yale boy.

What's wrong with me? Katie was playing with her fingernails now and humming. Frank tried to soothe her. "K, honey..." She didn't hear it as soothing.

She heard her mother's annoyance and impatience almost 30 years ago: "Katie, honey, please sit still and be quiet." Another family dinner. Six o'clock sharp. Four square. Father still in his tie. Mother quietly, almost desperately, begging her three hapless offspring not to set off their father, his moods the perpetual cloud brooding over their home.

The Healthy CEO reentered the room and they continued. He wanted to discuss relational health now: how their emotions and interactions impacted their wellness. For Katie, talking about her physical health was one thing, but peeling back the layers of her psyche was a less-than-inviting prospect. She had been assured that she would leave the office that day with her dignity and autonomy intact. Squirming on the inside, torn between her crazy-making yet familiar dysfunction and a relentless hope for something better, Katie braced herself but leaned in. Sit still, Katie, and be quiet....

"To thine own self be true, and it must follow, as the night the day, thou canst not then be false to any man."

William Shakespeare, sixteenth-century playwright

Katie sipped gingerly at her soy chai latte. Her mother, who sat across the table from her, had ordered a Lipton tea, but settled for Earl Grey when the service clerk drew a blank on her request. There was nothing fancy or adventurous about her mother, including her beverages. Only once or twice a year did they meet like this, even though her mother lived in the same city. After her dad's liver had given out and he had passed on, Katie's mother had moved into a condominium. Rita could handle herself quite nicely, thanks, and took living alone in stride. She never initiated their mother-daughter meetings, although she whimpered when Katie didn't initiate them herself. The "coffees" were always the same, with the same conversation and Rita doing most of the talking: "How's Frankie doing?" "You look like a stick." "Stewart just expanded his practice again. Isn't that something?"

"So, when are you going to make me a grandmother?" Katie knew, of course, that this was coming. When I bloody well feel like it, she thought.

"Frank and I are both very busy with work right now." Same wistful sigh from her mother. Why couldn't Stewart produce some offspring for her?

Katie ventured, "But we are talking about it more. We're actually trying to make some positive changes in our lives right now."

"Changes?" Her mother spit the word out like it was a fur ball. She wasn't a great agent of change. She was a "trooper." She held in there and stuck to it. She never rocked the boat. She had watched her husband shoot holes in the boat for years, and she'd just silently bailed water.

"Yes, Mom. We're trying to get healthier, and...," Katie held onto her cup with both hands, "...we're looking at ways to make our relationship better." She knew she meant them, but the words just seemed so foreign to her—as did any talk of relationships or emotions or closeness. She had learned to shut those things off to survive, to make life happen, to be a trooper. Now, she sat across the table from her teacher.

Rita leaned back in her chair and folded her arms. "Whatsa matter? Has Frankie got a girl?"

"No!" Katie retorted, insulted. "Of course not!"

"Then what's the problem?" Rita was incredulous.

"Mom, please don't be offended when I say this, but...," Katie felt some courage rising, "I don't want Frank and me to end up like you and Dad. You were strangers living in the same house and I never felt... safe there. And neither of you cared to do anything about it."

Rita played with the chain at her neck and shook her head. "Oh, Katherine. Isn't that just like you. So selfish. Never satisfied. Never happy."

"No. You're wrong about me, Mom. It isn't selfish to want to have an actual relationship with my husband. And you can't call yourself 'happy' or what you had 'happy.' I love you, Mom, I do. But I want more for myself. And you know what? I want more for Frank's sake too. That's not selfish."

That was all the reality Rita could handle. She went into her rehearsed run-down of the last bridge gathering, the maintenance guy who acted "funny," Mrs. Wiggins, who kept a cat even though she wasn't supposed to. Katie let her talk. She had been brave enough today to say things to her mother that she had never said before, and she felt as though her soul had grown a little for it.

When the last dregs had been consumed, Katie took their cups to the counter, walked with her mother to the door and hugged and kissed her goodbye. Katie stood on the sidewalk for a few moments. She watched the strangers walking by and met some of their glances, her eyes warm. Before she walked away from the coffee shop, she opened and held the door for a college-aged girl. "How are you?" Katie ventured. "Fine," the girl replied. "And you?" "Fine," Katie said and walked away, smiling. "Just fine, thanks."

In the mid-1980s, Tina Turner plaintively belted out, "What's love got to do with it? What's love, but a secondhand emotion? Who needs a heart when a heart can be broken?"[1] Over 20 years later, that sentiment still rings true for many. Emotions are messy, and it's hard to navigate matters of the heart in relationships.

What part could the heart possibly play in the workplace? In the corporate world, the buildings are made of steel and so are the nerves of CEOs. In business, it's the kiss of death to be all heart. "Don't let your emotions get in the way," "Think things through," "Look for the logic in everything." Sounds reasonable, doesn't it? It makes sense. But what if these common beliefs are really myths, and making sense is only part of the CEO's success equation?

The fact is, we are composite creatures with hearts and minds, *with emotions*. It's difficult, if not impossible, to take in experiences, make decisions, walk through the day's appointments or conduct business without our emotional selves coming to bear in very real and powerful ways. And that's a good thing—even in our work. How many transactions have you been involved in where you went ahead because, yes, the numbers were right, but it also just "felt" right? You went with your gut. You likely also have examples of when you ignored your instincts and made decisions you now regret.

As CEO or navigator of your own business, you rely on the assistance of colleagues and support staff. There is wisdom in leading teams with plenty of heart. In *The Power of Full Engagement*, performance consultants Jim Loehr and Tony Schwartz point to observations the Gallup Organization made in interviews with a large sample of managers and their employees:

> No single factor more clearly predicts the productivity of an employee than his relationship with his direct supervisor. More specifically... the key drivers of productivity for employees include whether they feel cared for by a supervisor or someone at work; whether they [have] received recognition or praise during the past seven days; and whether someone at work regularly encourages their development.[2]

Respected leadership educator Robert K. Cooper says that employees are responsive to a leader who cares about not only their professional development, but also their *personal* development. "After an extensive three-year study of the critical variables for leadership success, the Center for Creative Leadership... concluded that the only statistically significant factor differentiating the very best leaders from the mediocre ones is *caring* about people."[3] CEOs with a particularly authoritarian style of leadership and a results-driven, no-nonsense focus on performance may, in fact, be undermining efficiency and productivity. Unwarranted fear of appearing too "touchy-feely" may cause CEOs to alienate staff and fellow management, and give prospective clients the cold shoulder. *Administrative Science Quarterly* noted that the more positive the overall moods of people in the top management team, the more cooperatively they worked together—and the better the company's business results.[4]

Even your mood matters. Empathetic people, who can accurately assess the emotional climate of their office and of their customers, are better at anticipating and meeting client needs. Emotions and astute customer service go hand in hand. Obviously, happy customers build your reputation and your profits. And it *feels* good to create rapport and emotional connection, even in business.

We'll look at more ways relational proficiency can boost business, but what about how it contributes to your physical health? Is there a connection between feelings and physiology? You bet. And it's a very strong connection. Here are just some of the phenomena highlighted by medical and psychological research:

- Social isolation, or feeling like you have nobody with whom you can share your vulnerabilities, doubles the chance of sickness or death.[5]

- Multiple episodes of intense stress within the same year can translate to a significantly higher death rate in socially isolated middle-aged men, as compared to men who cultivate many close relationships.[6]

- Negative emotions can suppress immune function and natural anti-inflammatory processes both in patients with CAD (coronary artery disease) and in healthy individuals.[7]

- Negative emotions can increase the levels of stress hormones in the bloodstream throughout the day or during times of stress.[8]

- Positive emotions can promote immune functioning.[9]

The marriage relationship, specifically, has profound effects on your physical health. An American Heart Association study of 15,000 men and women found that "those who have a spouse, go to church, join social clubs, and have a lot of friends and relatives have significantly lower blood pressure and other heart disease risk factors than unmarried loners."[10] According to a Centers for Disease Control and Prevention report, "married people were half as likely to be smokers than non-marrieds, were less likely to drink alcohol, were more physically active than non-marrieds, and were also less likely to suffer from headaches, back pain and psychological stress disorders."[11] One study tracked the immune response of married couples to their stressful shared relational events:

> Marital couples who for three months kept daily checklists of hassles and upsetting events such as marital fights showed a strong pattern: three or four days after an especially intense batch of upsets, they came down with a cold or upper-respiratory infection.[12]

For women, the correlation between emotional or mental health and physical health appears to be even stronger. Women in stressful marriages, for example, seem to suffer greater physiological consequences than their male counterparts. Women in unhappy marriages are at the highest risk for poor health, compared with happily married women, who generally exercise more, are thinner, age better and are less likely to develop heart disease.[13] New research suggests that grief over a lost relationship can elicit changes in a woman's brain function significant enough to be detected by an MRI.[14] Breaking up is hard to do, and loneliness is hard on your body. Apparently, Tina Turner was wrong: love's got a lot to do with it.

In Chapter 2, we looked at specific ways you can assess your physical health. The indexes helped categorize factors over which you have control or influence, and most were pretty tangible. While there are bona fide ways to measure relational health, the indexes tend either to be qualitative—not as readily defined or measurable—or defined in terms of effects. For example, the efficacy of your communication style is evidenced by how well you feel understood by others and whether or not they feel understood by you. Sometimes we know that something is acutely wrong with our relationships or our inner world, but we can't put our finger on why.

Abraham Maslow, the mind behind the widely used hierarchy of needs, is renowned for his theories in humanistic psychology (and, incidentally, the way he applied those theories to business). He said that much of how we define psychological or emotional health is in terms of what's *not* wrong: "What we call 'normal' in psychology is really a psychopathology of the average, so undramatic and so widely spread that we don't even notice it ordinarily."[15] In other words, relational health is defined as an absence of disease. But like physical health, there is a range of vitality and fulfillment in relational health, even without the presence of relational "illness." Frank and Katie got along. Neither was threatening to leave the other. Yet both felt a general dissatisfaction with their relationship. There is always more to glean from experience, more to build into relationships and more benefits to enjoy as a result.

We have a host of relationships—all distinct and with their own paths and mazes to navigate—with any or all of the following: spouses, children, parents, siblings, extended relatives, friends, exes, mentors, colleagues, staff, superiors, clients, complete strangers and so on. As we discuss relational capacity and look at one kind of relationship—a committed romantic relationship between two partners—we can apply the fundamental principles we uncover to other relationships.

The relational-wellness factors listed in the next section cover categories that broadly but comprehensively define your relational capacity and the status of your relationship with your spouse or partner. We'll look at relational capacity in this chapter and your most significant personal relationship in the next. Extensive research into emotional intelligence by Daniel Goleman contributes much to this discussion, however, with some modifications other valid schools of thought have been included.

Knowledge of relational wellness

In the next chapter, we'll identify the factors for relational wellness in your most significant personal relationship. Here are the factors for relational wellness in terms of individual relational capacity (the ability to relate with oneself and with others):

- self-awareness
- self-regulation
- motivation
- empathy
- communication skills
- conflict management[16]

These traits are the result of both nature and nurture. Each of us has inborn relational capacities; however, they can also be learned, practiced and polished. Our relational wellness consists of how personally healthy we are with or without being involved in significant relationships. Being relationally well as individuals allows us to engage in meaningful, successful relationships. Later, as you consider your relationship with your partner, you'll assess how well you apply some of these relational competencies. This will lay a foundation of relational *Knowledge* before you move through *Attitude, Preparation, Action* and *Evaluation* in the context of relational health. Let's look at each of these capacities in greater detail.

SELF-AWARENESS

Self-awareness is knowing your personal values, abilities, tendencies and emotional range. Socrates said, "The unexamined life is not worth living." Self-aware people are introspective and thoughtful, and they routinely engage in self-reflection. By knowing themselves intimately, they can recognize how their inner world is functioning from one moment and one experience to the next.

PERSONAL VALUES
Values are the guiding principles by which we live our lives. Our values are derived from our life purpose, as defined in the introduction of this book. Values are those things we regard as self-defining or that we use to measure personal satisfaction. They are our "non-negotiables," the things that are deeply important to us and that we build our lives around.

You might value security, growth, integrity or freedom. (See Chapter 4 in the *Workbook* for a list of personal values.) The particular values you hold are less important than your ability to define which are of highest priority to you. When you identify the values that are essential to you, you can begin to look at how you construct your life using that framework. For example, if the values of "friendship" and "marriage" are of high priority to you, look to see if the ways you spend your money, time and attention reflect what you claim you believe in most. Often, just taking some time to look at our commitments in light of our values reminds us of the ways we have succumbed to external pressures—perhaps the expectations of others, societal ideals or media messages—instead of aligning our goals and activities with our values. Being aware of your personal values helps you actualize your purpose with greater clarity.

EMOTIONAL AWARENESS
Many of us believe we are at the mercy of our feelings, so we discount the merit of paying attention to our emotions in present context and identifying our general emotional tendencies. In the ebb and flow of day-to-day

events, how often do we *think* about how we feel rather than just feeling what we feel and letting our emotional experiences fly past us?

Our emotions influence us, whether or not we are aware of them. However, we can draw on emotions to our advantage or correct our emotional course once we begin to practice greater emotional awareness. Goleman advocates "emotional intelligence"—operating in concert with or even overriding IQ—as a way to measure aptitude for success in life: "Emotional aptitude is a *meta-ability*, determining how well we can use whatever other skills we have, including raw intellect."[17]

Those with keen emotional awareness are skilled at reading people—themselves and others—and the situations around them, and can therefore respond appropriately. Emotional awareness means not only knowing what you feel, but how what you feel impacts your thinking, your behavior and those around you. Once your emotional awareness is honed, you can even begin to select emotions to match the circumstances. There are times when toughness is required and others when tenderness is more important. Both are critical components of an emotional repertoire. Katie was afraid to be tender because it might leave her vulnerable to injury. Frank had the capacity to be tough—to stand up to Katie when she was being unduly harsh—but he opted out much of the time in favor of the path of least resistance.

Emotional health means having a range to draw from, along with an accurate sense of which responses to either manage as they arise or call upon for the occasion. Goleman says, "Self-awareness is not an attention that gets carried away by emotions, overreacting and amplifying what is perceived. Rather, it is a neutral mode that maintains self-reflectiveness even amidst turbulent emotions."[18] We can choose to initiate, maintain or cease our thoughts, feelings and actions. People with this competency become emotional *agents* as opposed to emotional *reactors*.

Closely related to emotional awareness is the sense of being fully "present" in every circumstance. Being present means actively observing, in your thoughts and feelings, how you respond to situations and how others respond to you. It sounds more active than it really is, although it is a discipline you can initiate or improve. Have you ever had a conversation with someone who nods and grunts to indicate that he or she hears you, but looks over your shoulder intermittently while you're talking? Being present is a state of undistracted awareness—the difference between going through life only partly "there" or with your whole being fully "dialed in." If you are aware of what you are feeling, how you are responding and, in some cases, how your body is reacting (to stress triggers, for example), you can better direct your energy to things like problem solving, and demonstrating care or unhindered enjoyment.

ACCURATE SELF-ASSESSMENT

Within self-awareness, the capacity for authentic self-assessment—being able to readily identify one's strengths and weaknesses—helps maximize personal potential. In the NHL, a good coach knows how to put together effective lines of players—how to leverage strengths and minimize weaknesses—to score goals and win games. In the same way, the ability to assess your strengths and weaknesses, whether professional or personal, helps you to achieve results.

Our self-perception can be blurry for a number of reasons. For one thing, it's natural to protect ourselves from thoughts about what we may lack in ability or character. We want to present well and we back that with our own buy-in. Secondly, we can't possibly be objective; we are myopic. We don't have the benefit of being able to step outside of ourselves. As a result, our self-analysis is always internal and limited. Finally, for many people, feedback is terrifying. Instead of seeing feedback as a resource, some see it as an indictment of their character or personality, or as a threat.

Perhaps more than anyone, CEOs have difficulty getting good feedback. Colleagues, clients and subordinates, those in a CEO's immediate circle, are often reluctant to offer honest feedback. Goleman says, "Leaders have more trouble than anybody else when it comes to receiving candid feedback, particularly about how they are doing *as leaders*."[19] The higher a leader climbs on the corporate ladder, the more difficult it is to elicit any kind of critique, but the more valuable this information becomes.

Smart leaders ask for regular feedback from a variety of sources to help get a 360-degree perspective on their performance, both in their professional and personal lives. After all, our best personal skills are used in all venues. Insight from our spouse about some of our blind spots—those things we hold to be true about ourselves, but that aren't—will cue us to better address demands at work. People skills are indispensable whether we are on the clock, working overtime or enjoying downtime. When did you last ask for feedback? How many people have lost their jobs, important contracts or even relationships because when they finally got the real story, it was too late to write a better ending? Ask for feedback regularly and heed what is said. If you're worried you won't receive honest answers, look for ways to allow people to be frank with you anonymously.

Feedback is useless if it isn't applied. What did you hear that you believe is unfounded? How can you change the way you conduct yourself to communicate better or clear up that misperception? What did you hear that, while difficult to receive, is admittedly true? Take deliberate steps to grow in those areas, and then ask for feedback again to see how you're doing. Leaders who can evolve and adapt to better themselves gain more respect and loyalty from staff, therefore increasing productivity in the long run.

SELF-CONFIDENCE

As leaders, CEOs may take confidence for granted. Achievement speaks for itself, right? Not necessarily. What we label "confidence" may only be manipulation, bravado or intimidation, stances that are actually counterfeits of confidence. With self-awareness—of our values, emotions and abilities—we can function out of authentic confidence, which doesn't stoop to posturing, slick self-marketing or maneuvering. Important components of confidence include the following:

> *Assertiveness* – Confidence is assertion with integrity and forthrightness that attracts and offers genuine respect. Many people lack confidence to deal with problems constructively because they are afraid they might offend. There are times when it is appropriate to do or say things that might hurt someone's feelings—which is altogether different from doing them harm. Obviously, if your bookkeeper consistently makes mistakes in your financial records, even after having been alerted to the errors repeatedly, terminating his or her employment is justified. It's also conscientious and responsible in light of what's at stake, in both the cost to your business and staff morale. To not act for fear of upsetting the bookkeeper would be foolish and cowardly when swift and sure action is what's called for. Both aggression, sometimes mistaken for assertiveness, and passivity can be very destructive to relationships.

> *Awareness of boundaries* – Personal boundaries include our personal space and psychological limits, as well as the limits of our responsibility. In other words, I am solely responsible for my feelings, my choices and my happiness. I cannot be responsible for anyone else's, and no one else can be responsible for mine. Boundaries define where my emotional space ends and where

yours begins. These limits are determined not only by societal norms, but also by my own sense of security in any given circumstance. A boundary, according to psychotherapist Charles L. Whitfield, is "how far we can go with comfort in a relationship."[20] If someone is telling you how you *should* feel, for example, your boundaries are not being respected. Confident people clearly define their boundaries and respect those of others.

An awareness of boundaries also fosters a healthy sense of independence. While I can enjoy the gratification of my relationships with others, I don't *need* others to be happy. When problems arise—especially in my relationships—I am aware that it's up to me to find ways to restore my sense of well-being and that I have those tools at my disposal.

Self-acceptance – Healthy self-regard is necessary to be able to esteem others as well. Accepting myself does not mean having to deny the reality of my relational "warts;" however, nor does it mean having to pretend to have everything all together. The authors of *The EQ Edge: Emotional Intelligence and Your Success*, Steven J. Stein and Howard E. Book, explain:

> Because individuals with healthy self-regard know their strengths and weaknesses and feel good about themselves, they have no trouble openly and appropriately acknowledging when they have made mistakes, are wrong, or don't know all the answers.[21]

Being able to accept myself means realizing that perfection is an illusion, while allowing myself and others to release their full potential.

How self-aware are you? What are your values, and are you living true to them? Are you comfortable with emotion? Do you avoid it as a sign of weakness, like Katie? Are you just emotionally tuned out, like Frank? Are you aware of your strengths and weaknesses, and are you setting goals accordingly? Are you truly confident—self-assured but humble—or playing a role?

SELF-REGULATION

Once we have greater awareness of who we are, we can begin to more skillfully apply this self-awareness. Self-regulation is the adroit management of our abilities, emotions and impulses in such a way that we actively align our lives with our personal values and standards. Briefly put, it's being conscientious.

SELF-CONTROL

Not every impulse should be followed. For the most part, our correctional system deals with people who lack self-control and have acted on impulse. Impulsive behavior can bring punishment and other kinds of consequences including property damage, unwanted pregnancy, financial reversal, addiction, alienation of loved ones, physical injury and even death.

Impulsive behavior, not the emotion behind the behavior, is what can get us into trouble. We may feel angry when an inconsiderate driver cuts us off on the freeway. Anger itself isn't wrong. But anger turned into violent road rage is clearly extreme and inexpedient. Goleman says, "One of the signs that feelings have veered over the line into the pathological is that they are so intrusive they overwhelm all other thought, continually sabotaging attempts to pay attention to whatever other task is at hand,"[22] such as driving. That's when you definitely *don't* want to be distracted or veering off course.

Anger is an easy example to point to, but what about more benign emotions like worry, sadness or irritation? Unchecked, worry can turn into full-blown debilitating anxiety or even paranoia. Sadness or melancholy can be fed such that depression ensues. We can choose to let irritation build to the extent that we fixate on a problem rather than focus on finding a solution.

While there are underlying medical conditions that often explain cases of chronic anxiety, depression and other mental illness, we have more volition when it comes to our emotions than we often exercise. When we are worried, do we ask ourselves if the worry is even valid or rational? Do we immediately look for ways to alleviate the concern? If we are experiencing sadness, do we proactively seek solace in the kindness of a friend or optimism from uplifting music? If we're annoyed by something our spouse said, do we question if it's worth stewing over? Do we go to him or her to discuss the issue? Sometimes we are powerless to change our mood, but most of the time we can influence and ultimately alter our emotional state if we are intentional.

Consider how much energy we expend on negative emotion, especially when it's unwarranted. It's not hard to see the effects of a foul mood on our outlook, motivation and productivity. Loehr and Schwartz point out: "From an energy perspective, negative emotions are costly and inefficient. Much like a gas-guzzling car, they draw down our energy stores at a rapid rate."[23] But on top of that, negativity is highly contagious: "For leaders and managers, negative emotions are doubly insidious, because they are so infectious. If we are prompting fear, anger and defensiveness in others, we progressively undermine *their* ability to perform effectively."[24] CEOs who care about their people and want passion and performance from their employees would be wise to manage their own emotions well. On the positive side, marshaling optimism or perseverance and other powerful, positive emotions, instead of simply repressing the negative ones, can enhance productivity and make life a lot more fun.

CONSCIENTIOUSNESS

Conscientious people are dependable and responsible, and follow through with their commitments—all without needing to be recognized or credited. They can also humbly admit when they make mistakes. Robert Cooper, who helps leaders excel in applying emotional intelligence, highlights the power of these admirable character traits:

> New research indicates that many of the individuals who make the greatest difference in the world combine the paradoxical qualities of personal humility and unwavering resolve to do what is right: personal accountability when times are hard and a great willingness to credit others when things go well.[25]

Because they value integrity over image management, conscientious people are trustworthy. We trust others when two important requirements are met: we feel understood and we feel valued. If your subordinates know you are invested in them as people and are concerned about the problems they encounter in their work, they will gladly follow your lead and offer their full support. Their hearts will be in their work and they will be on your side. Because trust requires such vulnerability, it is easily breached and, once lost, it is regained only with considerable effort and commitment. Trust is a high-cost investment.

A trustworthy person is truthful, forthright and authentic, even in the most trying of circumstances. "Faking it," manipulating or appearing to be one way while acting another gets results for only so long. Once the truth is uncovered and trust is lost, the poseur is left virtually powerless. Earning and keeping the trust of others gives us freedom and opens doors in ways that nothing else can. Think of your business reputation. Repeat business and long-term customer relationships are built on trust. Imagine what would happen to the marketability of your business if you were deemed untrustworthy? What might it mean to our business if we were more conscientious? How might our personal relationships improve?

ADAPTABILITY

In a windstorm, the tallest tree stands secure because its roots go deep and its trunk and branches are resilient. Though not moved from its base, the tree is flexible. Its flexibility makes it strong. In the same way, human beings can face storms if they have the deep roots of purpose and confidence, and can adapt and respond with resilience.

Emotional resilience has three characteristics:

   Responding appropriately to the situation – Different encounters require different emotional responses. If my response is too rigid (perhaps to someone who has a valid criticism about a decision I made) or too lax (perhaps in the case of an employee whose reckless behavior needs to be checked), my personal credibility is in jeopardy. I'm more a weak sapling than a mighty oak. If I lose a big client, I can choose to surrender to defeat or learn from what went wrong and refine my business strategies and practices. Resilience is necessary for growth.

   Understanding emotional "rhythm" – Muscles are strengthened through a cycle of stress and recovery—use and rest. Our emotional muscles, and therefore our relational health, are built up in the same way. After a heightened emotional experience, say a deadline crisis at work or a death in the family, we need to step back and give room for emotional recuperation and renewal. If we fail to pull away as necessary, we'll burn out, "explode" or succumb to depression. If we fail to engage when our full emotional presence is required, we will miss the mark, set our relationships adrift, or lose focus.

   Keeping momentum – You can't grow by standing still. If you stand still, you quickly get stuck. Resilience means moving on even when it's difficult to do so. This may entail accepting circumstances you can't change and finding a way to keep going. To forgive, for example, is a decision we make, sometimes with the benefit of reconciliation, sometimes not. Where resolution is impossible in a relationship or where a solution to a problem cannot be found, resilient people accept what they cannot change and get past it.

Adaptability, put simply, is the ability to deal with inevitable stressors with perspective, poise and grace.

INNOVATION

One way to adapt is to innovate: creatively apply new ideas to achieve results. Creativity, seeing connections and patterns where to most they would be unapparent, is the impetus behind innovation. But great concepts aren't enough. Great ideas have no practical value until they are executed. That's when they become truly innovative.

Finding a new way to do the same thing is also innovative. The Schwinn Bicycle Company began in the 1890s, survived the Depression era and dominated the market for years. Schwinn bicycles came to represent *the* select cycling machine through the mid-twentieth century and into the 1970s. However, management made a strategic error and chose to disregard the new trends of employing foreign labor, using foreign parts and building lighter frames, and the rising interest in BMX and mountain bike styles. By the time they realized the market had shifted, it was too late. Jay Townley, industry consultant and former Schwinn executive, reflecting on their product at the time, said of their bikes: "Durable? Yes. Lasts forever? You bet…. What the customer wanted? No."[26] Schwinn couldn't adapt or shift their thinking about bicycle making. They couldn't innovate. The company declared bankruptcy in 1993.

Innovation is problem solving. A single man or woman might complain of having serially dated commitment-phobic people. However, if he or she talks about wedding plans or a minivan full of children as a standard part of first-date repertoire, commitment phobia isn't likely the real issue. Perhaps a change of approach—a more casual one-day-at-a-time dating philosophy—would foster longer-term relationships.

Are you an agent or a reactor? Do you exercise self-control, managing your emotions, doing the right thing even when you don't feel like it and looking for ways to meet challenges positively and resolutely? The answers to questions like these can tell you a lot about your ability to self-regulate.

MOTIVATION

Personal standards, having goals to reach and the commitment to make steady progress are signatures of successful people. Motivation that translates into results comes from a drive to achieve, the commitment to see things through and the pluck to take strategic risks.

DRIVE TO ACHIEVE

Beyond merely setting goals, highly motivated people get ahead because momentum, achievement and personal growth are fundamentally gratifying. The inner conviction that comes from a sense of purpose and a visceral connection to personal values drives people to achieve and get what they most want for themselves—physically, relationally and financially.

COMMITMENT

The Microsoft empire isn't known for being shortsighted. Still, in 2002, they realized that they had missed the boat when it came to the Internet search engine market. Google and Yahoo had outstripped them by a mile. On top of that, the search engine revenue the company had realized to date was beginning to fall off. Ironically, Microsoft, though known for innovation and domination in anything that requires booting up, had its own search engine, MSN, powered by other companies.

Instead of licking their wounds, executives launched a new project, determined to build a brand new search engine from scratch to catch up to and hopefully surpass the competition. Square footage, personnel, machines and capital were earmarked to see the project through. Still, in the years that followed, there were unanticipated problems with search engine setup, technical difficulties and changes in the way users searched the Internet. And Google and Yahoo weren't just sitting on their hands in the meantime. Microsoft wanted to deliver a top-notch product, but success was a moving target. Sixteen-year veteran software developer for Microsoft, Ken Moss, said that he had never seen such a challenge. "It was the hardest thing I'd ever looked at, technologywise."[27]

After two years and a lot of perseverance, the team realized their goal of five billion pages searched and a faster rate of growth than Google in the first quarter of 2005. Christopher Payne, who headed up the project, remarked, "We knew... that this was three, five, 10 years of innovation.... Our focus was on the long-term from day one."[28] That's commitment.

Long-term gains come not only from commitment in business, but in relationships, too. Most psychologists and relationship counselors agree that a high level of commitment in any relationship is a good predictor of that relationship's life span and degree of intimacy. Commitment level can have more influence over the quality of a relationship than many other factors. In fact, a study by University of Virginia sociologists W. Bradford Wilcox and Steven L. Nock determined the following:

> Women who share with their husbands a strong commitment to lifelong mar-
> riage—who, for instance, think that marriage is a "lifetime relationship and
> should never be ended except in extreme circumstances"—are much more
> likely to report that they are happy in their marriages, and that they are happy
> with the affection and understanding they receive from their husbands, com-
> pared to women who do not have such a commitment to marriage.[29]

When the going gets tough, committed people keep trying, keep
working, keep at it. They don't hope fleetingly that things will work out.
They *make sure* things work out—whatever it takes.

OPTIMISM

Commitment requires optimism: "an inclination to put the most favor-
able construction upon actions and events or to anticipate the best possible outcome."[30] Hopeful optimism, unlike glib denial, sees reality for what
it is; it is often a way of framing negative realities. Optimistic people see
every circumstance, positive or negative, as an opportunity. Peter Urs
Bender, Canadian "presentation guru" and communication expert, says,
"It doesn't matter if your glass is half full or half empty, as long as it holds
more than you can drink."[31]

Happiness and contentment are chosen states of being. A "can do"
attitude that sees opportunity more than adversity and that takes obstacles in stride is at the heart of optimism. Goleman points out the difference between optimists and pessimists: "People who are optimistic see
failure as due to something that can be changed so that they can succeed
the next time around while pessimists take the blame for failure, ascrib-
ing it to some lasting characteristic they are helpless to change."[32] That's
why optimists are such high achievers; they believe problems can always
be solved somehow and that change and growth are always possible.
Drive, dedication and expectancy translate into motivation, an attitude
that says, "I refuse to quit," "I refuse to settle" and "I refuse to accept anything less than my personal best." People who possess this quality are perpetually hopeful, leaning into life and unafraid to initiate or spearhead
change. They will have the necessary motivation to look at and improve
their physical, relational and financial wellness.

Frank liked his new resolve to improve his life. He enjoyed the way it
felt. He had found his backbone and was beginning to use it, setting goals
to improve his health and reconnect with Katie. His renewed determination reminded him of the young executive he had been, hungry to reach
his full potential. Frank felt hungry again, even though he wasn't that
young anymore. It was a welcome relief to the dull dissatisfaction he had

grown accustomed to. For the first time in years, he was hopeful and excited about what the future held.

Do you have drive and determination, or are you just counting off calendar days? Do you have hope for your future? How are you investing in your personal tomorrow?

EMPATHY

Empathy is the ability to think or even feel from another's vantage point. It is the foundation of the biblical Golden Rule: "Treat others the way you want to be treated." If we have a large capacity for empathy, we will be able to readily anticipate and gauge how our words and actions will impact those around us.

UNDERSTANDING OTHERS

You don't often hear empathy touted as a good marketing strategy, but it is. Good leaders will demonstrate empathy in the way they manage their teams by staying connected to what motivates their people and by providing attentive customer service. Successful companies intuit and empathize with the needs of their customers and are thereby better able to meet those needs, providing a product or service the client really wants—and will buy.

A lack of empathy can be devastating. People leave their jobs if they don't feel understood, despite excellent pay and benefits. Clients can become disillusioned by firms that fail to accurately "read" what they need, and they may take their business elsewhere. Relationships can falter or even dissolve where empathy derails; we stop caring or feeling cared for.

The judicial system exists for lack of empathy. Civil and criminal violations occur when individuals favor their own potential for gain no matter what others might lose or who might get hurt. The key players in the Enron scandal and the company's eventual bankruptcy in 2001 were apparently bankrupt in empathy as they defrauded and lied to shareholders and employees. The shortsighted actions of a few "resulted in the loss of $60 billion in market value on Wall Street, almost $2.1 billion in pension plans and 5,600 jobs."[33]

REACHING OUT TO OTHERS

While empathy can elicit positive behavior, it can also transform destructive impulses. More and more, bullying among school-aged children is being recognized and addressed as a serious epidemic. School bullies are notorious for their lack of empathy and their ability to inflict grievous acts of violence and verbal cruelty on their victims. Yet helping the bullies develop empathy is possible.

"Roots of Empathy" is a kindergarten-to-middle-school program being used in many districts in Canada with remarkable results. The program has at its core a neighborhood infant and parent, along with a certified Roots of Empathy instructor, who visit the classroom every few weeks during the school year. Students follow the baby's development, learn about his or her needs and have the opportunity to interact with the child. The results are often amazing. Evaluations conducted at the end of the program consistently show empirical evidence that children are improving their social behavior, increasing their emotional awareness and curbing formerly aggressive behaviors. Within these classes, 88 percent of students who demonstrated some proactive aggression in a pre-program test showed a reduction in aggression at post-program testing.[34]

Empathy inspires us to respond to the needs of others. As we feel compassion, we want to reach out. As it turns out, helping others can have tremendous self-benefit. Altruism makes us feel good about ourselves, but it may also improve our health. Stephanie L. Brown, a researcher at the Institute for Social Research at the University of Michigan, says that "among a group of 423 elderly couples followed for five years, the people who reported helping others... were only about half as likely to die as those who did not."[35] Researchers wonder if the phenomenon might be due to stress reduction. No matter how it works, giving is good for you—both physically and emotionally.

Would you describe yourself as caring? Would others describe you that way? Are you giving something of yourself to others? How might it feel to reach out more or in a different way? How open are your eyes to those around you?

COMMUNICATION SKILLS

Relationship coach Dr. Susan Campbell says, "Unclear communications and unexpressed discomfort about them are a major source of stress in our lives."[36] Ever walk away from a meeting feeling like things went sideways somehow? Ever chew on a breakfast table discussion for the rest of the day? Communication, or the lack of it, dominates our inner world.

Good communication happens when you and the person you're speaking with both feel understood. That kind of connection facilitates good relationships both in and out of the office. A conversation will be effective when both expressive and receptive skills are used well. Remember that communication is only partly verbal. We also send messages through our tone and body language—with our eyes, our posture and our gestures.

EXPRESSIVE SKILLS

These are the skills you use to send your message. How well the message you send actually matches the message you *intend* to send is an indicator of how skilled you are at expression.

> *Getting the other person's attention* – How you open a conversation sets the tone for the rest of it. An "Excuse me, Sue, can I speak with you for a few minutes?" demonstrates respect—by mentioning the person by name, acknowledging that she might be busy and making the subtle but important distinction between talking *at* and speaking *with* her. Checking your emotions going in helps you to use an appropriate tone of voice, an aspect of conversation especially important if you are about to raise a contentious issue and need to be direct, while tempering your remarks.

> *Convey the information* – This seems simple enough, but we all have experienced occasions where something was lost in translation and our message was completely missed. This might be the result of poor listening skills on the receiver's part, but it might have something to do with how we are expressing our message. Are we using emotionally loaded words like "should" or exaggerations like "always" or "never"? The wrong words used at the wrong time can cause our listener to get mentally stuck right there and miss what we're trying to say.

> Does our body language match our words? Are we anxious, but it's coming across as terseness rather than nervousness? Albert Mehrabian's often referenced "7%-38%-55% Rule" says that the literal words spoken convey only seven percent of the meaning in face-to-face communication, while the rest of the message comes from the speaker's tone of voice (38 percent) and his or her nonverbal communication (55 percent). Mehrabian cautioned that the results shouldn't automatically be extrapolated to all communication settings, as participants in his study were conversing about things they liked and disliked—subject matter with high emotional

content.[37] Nevertheless, personal experience tells us that what we *don't* verbalize often comes across more than we realize.

🗐 *Check for understanding* – Strategic questions such as "What do you think?" invite feedback and opportunity to see if the listener received the same message you intended to send. Clarify if necessary and check again.

RECEPTIVE SKILLS

Listening, or receiving the message, seems straightforward enough but usually isn't at all. Much of the time when we think we are listening, we are really distracted, or we are rehearsing our next remarks. In some cases, we might even be "reloading" for the next round.

🗐 *Acknowledge the speaker* – Maintain eye contact. Keep your body turned to the speaker. Give verbal cues or nods to show that you're engaged.

🗐 *Attend to what's being said* – Resist the temptation to prematurely frame your response, and dismiss mental distractions. Listen empathetically, looking for the emotion behind the words, then evaluate the supporting facts (words and body language). This is where the real impact of the message is. *Don't interrupt!*

🗐 *Check for understanding* – Reflecting, or paraphrasing, what you've heard—even mirroring the other person's body language while they speak—demonstrates a willingness to create understanding. If you're not sure you've understood, ask questions to help clarify the message.

COMMON COMMUNICATION PROBLEMS

Why do we so often miss each other's messages? Several factors can trip up effective communication:

🗐 *Filling in the blanks* – The average rate of speech is about 150 words per minute, while the average rate of hearing is about 500 to 750 words. We can listen faster than we can speak. When we're listening, we're prone to boredom and often to coloring in details inaccurately. If we're coming to a conversation with prejudice or emotional baggage, we'll fill the gaps with things that really aren't there and could potentially lead to misunderstanding and even conflict.

Railroading – When one person in a conversation wants more to be heard than to promote understanding, the usual two-way street of communication is roadblocked. The listener will feel dumped on, abused or ignored. If the listener is the one railroading, he or she will constantly interrupt, finish your sentences or act as though he or she already knows what you're going to say and you need not bother speaking. There's a huge difference between communicating to *control* versus communicating to *connect*.

Untimely silence – Sometimes we need to talk, the air needs to be cleared, and the relational garbage needs to be taken out. Avoiding uncomfortable conversations only causes issues to grow and allows our inner dialogue to steer us away from what might be the reality of the situation. Where we lack concrete information, we assume, and we are often wrong. Keeping the lines of communication open and clear is critical to maintaining forward momentum in any kind of relationship.

Manipulation – Almost 90 percent of all communication comes from the usually unconscious intent to control the other person or the situation.[38] This might stem from discomfort with vulnerability, anxiety about an undetermined outcome or other insecurity—not to mention the normal tendency to want things to go our way. When we *consciously* use communication to control, it becomes manipulation. Manipulation is motivated by feelings of superiority, disrespect or sometimes even contempt. These are not exactly the ingredients for connection, mutual understanding or a healthy relationship.

Communication skills are indispensable, whether in the boardroom or the bedroom. How are you at expressing yourself? At listening? What's your communication style? Would those closest to you agree with your assessment?

We'll discuss the unique communication dynamics of intimate relationships in the next chapter.

CONFLICT MANAGEMENT

Good communication goes a long way in preventing disputes, but there are as many ways of looking at the world as there are people in it. Disagreement is inevitable. Few of us relish dealing with disagreements or the conflict that may ensue, but when relationships clash—and they will—having good conflict management skills can make all the difference between good resolution and emotional escalation.

Some CEOs have a hard time knowing how to deal with relational conflict in their personal lives. In business, it's appropriate to compete: to outsmart and out-argue rivals. Dealing with conflict is about securing a "win." However, when conflict arises in personal relationships, the goal needs to be "win-win." It's not easy for every CEO to shift gears and meet the demands of their personal relationships in this way. It requires a different skill set.

DIFFERENT APPROACHES TO CONFLICT

- *Denial or avoidance* – Some people avoid conflict altogether. They tend to lack the communication skills necessary to promote mutual understanding in the first place. Preferring to keep everything pleasant on the surface, even if it means denying reality, which is entirely different from optimism, conflict avoiders would rather let issues go unresolved than risk having to deal with a potentially messy situation. Frank would rather pretend nothing was wrong than risk running into an obstacle he couldn't overcome. Over time, small problems both with his health and in his relationship with his wife had become critical issues simply because he hadn't wanted to face them sooner.

- *Surrender* – People who feel threatened by conflict or who lack self-awareness or confidence may simply give in no matter what in order to "keep peace." This lack of integrity will usually lead to resentment on the part of the person giving in and ultimately contributes nothing to resolving issues or staying relationally connected.

- *Passive aggression* – This is another form of avoidance, but it deflects rather than denies the issue. The passive-aggressive person might make someone "pay" in subtle ways like giving them the "silent treatment," rolling their eyes, deliberately making the other person's life difficult or using manipulation, such as taking on the role of the "victim." If the other person isn't aware of this dynamic, he or she might take undue responsibility for the entire problem or be tempted to drop the matter entirely in an effort to restore peace. But not facing what's really going on only allows the conflict to go underground and continue to fester.

- *Escalation* – This is closely related to railroading, which we discussed earlier in terms of communication. When faced with conflict, some people will unleash their emotions—anger or hurt, for example—in an overblown and unwarranted fashion in an attempt to intimidate, manipulate or even provoke the other person enough to dominate them or make them back down. Katie would usually let Frank know pretty clearly if she was angry. Some of it was through passive-aggressive door slamming and large doses of the cold shoulder. Other times, she would vent. She would yell at him, resorting to name-calling at times, and blame him for her upset. In her mind, if she was angry, it was his fault, so he should have to pay the price.

Conflict and emotions like anger go hand in hand, but effective conflict resolution requires that we manage emotion in favor of addressing the issue head on, without causing the other person injury—emotional or even physical. Expressing anger or frustration about someone's behavior or comments is legitimate, while taking shots at them personally never is. This is where self-control and self-awareness are critical. Where is our anger coming from? Dr. Phil McGraw, psychologist and television talk show host, maintains that "in the vast majority of cases, anger is a sham, a superficial covering for something else. It is expressed when we are afraid to express what we are really feeling, which almost always, in some combination, is hurt, fear and frustration."[39]

Yet, we often get a bit of a thrill from venting our anger. Goleman reminds us:

> Unlike sadness, anger is energizing, even exhilarating. Anger's seductive, persuasive power may in itself explain why some views about it are so common: that anger is uncontrollable, or that, at any rate, it *should not* be controlled, and that venting anger in "catharsis" is all to the good.[40]

But this cathartic effect is an illusion. Researchers Diane Tice and Roy F. Baumeister conducted a study to investigate whether or not venting anger had any benefit. What they discovered goes against conventional thought. They found that "when people told of times they had taken their rage out on the person who provoked it, the net effect was to prolong the mood rather than end it."[41] This was the result when people shared their anger with a third party, too.

Angry outbursts are not just bad for your relationships; they're bad for your heart, too:

> Hostility and anger have been shown to enhance activation of the sympathetic nervous system, fostering frequent and prolonged blood pressure and heart rate responses to stress—i.e., "cardiovascular reactivity"—which may contribute to later hypertension and atherosclerosis [thickening of the walls of the arteries].[42]

What do you do with your anger? Do you acknowledge but diffuse it, or do you fuel it?

Resolution – People focused on conflict resolution have the courage to face issues head on, but do so carefully. There exists underlying goodwill—an attitude of wanting to invest in the good of the relationship, caring for the other person and seeking understanding and reconciliation—more than a defensive spirit that needs to get its own way. When overwhelmed by anger, those seeking resolution will step back long enough to regroup and come to the clash with perspective and calm. That doesn't mean the anger can't be acknowledged, just that it won't control the discussion. Keys to effective conflict resolution include the following:

- finding the appropriate time; waiting for or even scheduling a time when there won't be distractions

- focusing on areas where there is already agreement

- assuming the best intentions from the other person in what is said and what they want for the relationship

- managing negative emotions

- practicing good communication skills

- committing to a positive outcome for both

- desiring to reconnect more than to "win," with a posture that says "I can agree to disagree even if we don't come to see eye to eye"

- deciding to forgive and move on if the best attempts at reconciliation fail

Forgiveness is also a form of resolution. Katie couldn't make peace with her dad, since he was no longer living. But she could choose to forgive him and carry on with her own life without the burden of bitterness or resentment.

How are you at conflict management? Can you think of issues at work or in your personal life right now that are unresolved? What will you do about them? We'll look at conflict resolution, as it pertains to intimate relationships, in the next chapter.

So how are you doing in your overall relational capacity? In self-awareness, self-regulation, motivation, empathy, communication and conflict management? Remember that these are all skills you can learn, practice and hone to improve your relationships in every environment. Don't minimize the importance of these qualities in your ability to not only relate better, but also perform better at work, and to get more pleasure out of the everyday.

We can begin to *behave* our way into greater relational capacity. It is a choice we exercise. New ways of thinking and behaving may at first seem foreign, and they are not enough as an end in themselves. Maslow says, "We must try to make a particular kind of people, of personality, of character, of soul one might say, rather than try to create particular kinds of behavior."[43] However, we can have a change of heart and calibrate our behavior accordingly. With a new attitude and progressive action steps, our commitment to relate better can transform new behaviors into instinct and integrated character. Where we need assistance—and often we do—we can get help from experts with further knowledge and experience with relational wellness.

What's love got to do with it? Who needs a heart? We all do. We could all stand to live with a lot more heart. Will you?

"So, why did you want to speak to me?" George asked. Frank had requested this meeting with George, chair of the board, the man who had witnessed his collapse on the green and ordered him to get straightened out.

The previous week, Frank had sent out a memo to his direct reports asking them to give him performance and personal feedback. It was unprecedented. It was brazen. Frank was scared out of his wits, but he did it anyway. He had given them a list of questions to comment on, either in meeting with him directly, or anonymously via a return envelope to be delivered to the mail room. In the days following, two of those people had invited him to lunch.

The conversations had been surprisingly enlightening. His office manager, Rose, had asked him to give more detailed evaluations of her work versus a simple "nice job." Doug in accounting had expressed frustration that none of the systems improvements he had suggested were being implemented, even though Frank had promised more than once to follow through. Doug had shown him again, with the hard evidence of numbers, ample reason to get moving on the initiatives. Frank had apologized and started making the requested changes. He couldn't believe how Doug's countenance had changed in a few short days. The guy was on fire, working hard and... humming. It was happy humming. Both Rose and Doug had expressed thanks at being invited to share their thoughts.

Now he needed to deal with George. "I haven't been up front with you, and I need to be. When you pitched the Chips Corp. campaign to their guys in April, you threw out a curve ball you hadn't run by me first." George's brow furrowed as he tried to remember. "The mail-outs, George. The flyers. They didn't like it and I knew they wouldn't. It's old school. If you'd talked to me first, I would've told you right then."

Frank took George's silence as permission to proceed. "It left a bad taste in their mouths and cost me some of their confidence, too, because they thought it was my idea as much as yours. I was solid with them before that, George. Solid. I didn't make a fuss in that meeting out of respect for you, but I resent you blaming me for the deal taking a downward turn when you've had your own hand in messing things up."

George put his hands on his hips and turned to look out the window. "OK."

"What?" Frank asked.

"OK. You're right. I should've checked with you first. I handled it badly." Frank knew George was being straight with him. "Can I buy you lunch tomorrow? Maybe we can discuss how to make up the ground we lost. How's that sound?"

"That sounds good," Frank replied. "Thanks." George gave him his slightly corny but forgivable salute.

Frank walked out, closing the office door behind him and breathing a huge sigh of relief. He had rehearsed that scene for days and worked himself up for, well, he had to admit, a fairly anticlimactic result. George was really just a tame, friendly house cat.

Now, he'd leave the office and go home to an entirely different animal. The tigress. She was beautiful and wild, in no sense declawed—but that's what he loved about her. "Rowwrrrr!" he thought, and went home to his wife.

5 *Your relational wellness:*
Knowing each other

The meeting of two personalities is like the contact of two chemical substances: If there is any reaction, both are transformed.

Carl Jung, Swiss psychologist

"Frank? Is that you?"

In an instant, all the hairs on the back of Frank's neck stood on end, though it took him a few moments to place his ex-wife's voice. He turned around. "Lois?" He hadn't seen her in over 12 years. She was a yellow sunflower, he thought, in a bright yellow dress, with yellow heels, a wide-brimmed yellow hat—trimmed with a big white silk daisy—and elaborately coiffed shoulder-length blonde hair. Her family was originally from Texas. Everything was big and bold in Texas, Frank mused. A big sunflower, standing in his favorite deli. It struck Frank as odd, but funny. She looked pretty good, he thought. Overwhelmingly yellow, but good.

Lois grabbed and pumped his arm. "How are you?"

"Married—I mean fine," Frank stammered. Geez, get a grip on yourself, Frank thought. What's your problem?!

Lois smiled at his gaffe, sensing his nerves. She still knew him. He resented that. "Yes, I heard you remarried," she said coolly. "Some girl from Colorado, right?"

"Yes," Frank replied. "Katie. We've been married a little over eight years now. How about yourself?" Club and bag anyone? he wanted to say, but didn't.

"Oh, yes," she postured. "Antonio. We live in San Antonio now. Isn't that precious?" she said, laughing. Frank just nodded.

They continued to make small talk, but Frank's mind wandered to how this woman could still jangle his nerves, but couldn't (what a happy relief!) touch his heart; to how she had been like a perfect wax doll, but how Katie was flesh and bone and hot-blooded; to how Lois had lined up the bathroom towels almost hourly, and how Katie left her towel on the floor every time she showered; to how this yellow woman had only been sunny on the outside, and how Katie, so cool and collected on the surface, smoldered and burned inside with regular fury for her work, for life—for him. How could he have married such different women? Yet somehow they both were familiar: one giving him a false sense of security, the other offering vitality by proxy. Where did he fit in? What was his very own? Not what these women, or maybe even his parents, had bestowed upon him—but what was his own substance, what made him solidly real? What did he have to give that was real, that was his?

Damn that Healthy CEO, Frank thought. Things had been simpler when he didn't have so many questions. But he couldn't just shut the door on this new journey. It was an uncharacteristically courageous thing for him to embark upon, he realized. But he liked the challenge— and the vigor it quickened in him.

"Lois, it was very nice to see you again." Frank shook her hand, collected his Mediterranean sandwich and orange juice and got ready to leave. "Give my regards to Antonio... San and the man. I best be moving on."

And he did.

In the last chapter, you learned how to assess your relational capacity— the intrinsic skills you possess to maintain your emotional health and allow you to relate well with others. Now you'll explore how to assess the dynamics of your most significant personal relationship, likely a marriage or other committed romantic partnership. To better illustrate key relational principles, this chapter will focus on your relationship with a spouse or partner, but most of these principles can be applied effectively to other kinds of relationships.

Knowledge of relational wellness:
Our most significant personal relationship

What key factors contribute to a successful romantic relationship? The four Cs to assess in your relationship are as follows:

- Consciousness

- Commitment

- Connection

- Cooperation

CONSCIOUSNESS

Our relational capacity for *self-awareness* is applied in our most significant personal relationship as our ability to recognize what we contribute to the dynamics of the relationship. *Other awareness*, or empathy, makes us conscious of our partner's contribution to and his or her experience of the relationship. Both partners can use their *motivational, self-regulatory* and *communication* capacities to bring expectations and desires to a level of mutual consciousness. Once these expectations and desires are expressed, couples can make decisions about how the relationship will function. Partners can then begin to flow with, instead of against, natural relational dynamics.

What are some of the personal and relational dynamics that we need to bring to consciousness?

FAMILY-OF-ORIGIN DYNAMICS

Marriage therapist Harville Hendrix, Ph.D, developed Imago Relationship Therapy, a process to help couples create a "conscious marriage." After years of practicing what he felt was largely unsuccessful and disillusioning couple's therapy, he stepped back to perform in-depth research into relational dynamics and current counseling strategies. He discovered that people are attracted, mostly unconsciously, to individuals who resemble their childhood caregivers, in both their positive and negative traits. An unconscious pull to replicate and thereby "fix" first-family dysfunction—given the assumption that no family is perfectly functional—or to meet the unmet needs of childhood seems to govern the way couples come together and how they then try to function.

In the first flush of romantic love, according to Hendrix, four connections occur between people: a sense of familiar ease and comfort with each other, a sense that they've known each other for years, a sense of becoming complete and a sense of needing the other person in order to be happy.[1] Hendrix posits that although some individuals may have awareness of these sensations, they occur inevitably—consciously or not. As the relationship continues, it becomes easy to take for granted that this person who makes us feel so alive and complete should continue to do so. We place responsibility for our happiness squarely on his or her shoulders, transfer associations with traits or experiences from our childhood caregivers to our partner and become disillusioned when the relationship reopens old wounds rather than heals them. Hendrix says:

> It is especially easy for people to transfer their feelings about their parents onto their partners, because through a process of unconscious selection, they have chosen partners who resemble their caretakers. All they have to do is exaggerate the similarities between them and diminish the differences.[2]

The problem is not necessarily that we've chosen the wrong partner, but that we are allowing our unconscious needs and desires from the past to invade our current relationship. Incidentally, this influence of the past holds true for past romantic relationships as well, since the dynamics that contributed to the demise of those relationships are the same ones we imported from our family of origin in the first place. Frank's first wife, Lois, had been very nurturing, like his mother, but she had looked to him for constant validation. Frank soon went from feeling well cared for to feeling smothered and pressured to keep Lois's self-esteem intact. She seemed to be a bottomless pit of emotional need, and nothing he could do was enough for her to feel secure. Soon he began to resent her care, which he had first associated with happy memories of his mother but really had many self-centered strings attached.

Latent desires, needs and dysfunctional tendencies themselves are not the problem; the problem is that we fail to bring them to a level of consciousness where we can use our rational and intentional thought processes in examining the validity of our impulses, emotions and expectations, and what we project onto our partners. For example, Katie had brought emotional guardedness as a self-protective strategy into her marriage with Frank. She had learned at an early age that emotional displays could trigger angry outbursts from her alcoholic father, and her mother would discount, minimize or mock her daughter's feelings, if expressed.

For Katie, anger was the safest emotion; it was a preemptive strike and a way to mark territory. Tender emotions were more volatile, unsafe and ultimately foolish. Even though Frank was more comfortable with emotion than Katie's parents had been—and he often wished his wife was more vulnerable with him—Katie had never looked at her emotional modus operandi. She had never challenged her basic assumption that to express vulnerability to Frank would be as futile, painful or threatening as it had been with her parents. If Katie became more conscious of her emotional defaults and challenged them, she might experience new fulfilling ways of relating to Frank.

Conversely, Frank didn't have an aversion to emotion so much as he was content to be invisible. Being "flat" emotionally allowed him to remain unnoticed and not rock the boat. In his family of origin, while Frank had always felt loved and cared for, there had been constant stress and preoccupation on the part of his parents with making ends meet. His mother had been responsible for the care of six children, while his father had worked sporadically, but many 12-hour days as a laborer. Frank, a middle child, learned that to blend in, to accommodate and to not make any demands helped alleviate some of the pervasive tension in the home. His own professional rise and eventual corporate success as a result of his talent, intelligence and work ethic had been spurred mostly by a fear of poverty and his equating money with peace and security.

Part of Frank's attraction to Katie was that she was so free to express the intensity of feelings like anger. He could experience her fervor and feel emotionally alive through her. Without actually having to own those intense emotions himself, Katie's passion was a way for Frank to connect to his own emotion and feel more visible than before. If he was willing to own some of his own emotional vitality and express his feelings to Katie, Frank might feel more present in their relationship—and discover that, ultimately, Katie would respect him if he stood up to her or met her "on the mat" rather than if he simply acquiesced.

Consciousness is particularly important when conflict arises. Many arguments occur over missed signals or wrong assumptions, or because we give our history too much power in the present. Author of *Saying What's Real*, relationship coach and speaker Susan Campbell says, "If someone's present circumstance reminds him of a frightening or painful situation in his past, this will cause a knee-jerk negative reaction."[3] We often react without looking at what lies beneath our response. How often do we ask ourselves in the heat of the moment, "Why am I feeling threatened by what's happening here?" "Do I have the full picture?" "How might my partner be feeling after what I just said?" "This reminds me of the way my father handled my concerns. Is my anger at my partner a legitimate response in this case?"

Along with examining and maybe even challenging our thoughts, reactions and emotions, it is helpful to be aware of our "triggers." If my father was impossible to please and repeatedly made me feel inadequate, I'm likely to hear criticism where it may not be intended at all. If my mother leaned on me inappropriately for emotional intimacy and support, I need to be aware that I may be suspicious of people wanting to swallow or consume me and that this could surface with an individual who is genuinely and respectfully trying to get to know me on a deeper level. If I was given the role of surrogate parent when my father or mother left the family, I need to be aware of my tendency to feel overly responsible for the well-being of others.

We can and need to practice consciousness in our relationships. How aware are you of the "baggage" you have brought into your current relationship? Have you unpacked it to see what's really there? What are your triggers? Where are you relationally weak or vulnerable? What are your flaws, and do you acknowledge them with your partner? Where might you be projecting your own suppressed emotions or characters from your past onto your partner?

EXPECTATIONS

We come into every relationship with expectations, our own set of unwritten rules for what the relationship should look like, including who is to fill specific roles and what priorities will factor into the relationship. Identifying and voicing our expectations to our partner helps dispel many underlying assumptions on both our parts, assumptions that may later contribute to significant conflict if they aren't fully acknowledged early on. Our expectations for our most significant personal relationship revolve primarily around our past experience, our values and our beliefs about the roles we are each to fulfill.

> *Past experience* – Though Frank and Katie both celebrated Christmas, their first holiday season together was anything but straightforward. On December 1 of that year, Frank pulled out a box of decorations he had inherited from his parents and began hanging them around his and Katie's apartment. Katie walked in the door from a visit to the store and Frank immediately asked when they would be going to get a tree and why she hadn't started addressing Christmas cards yet. An argument ensued, in which

Katie told Frank she felt like he was bossing her around and trying to make decisions for her. She hated Frank's "trashy" decorations and resented the "fact" that he was trying to make her into his mother. Frank was put off by his wife's Scrooge-like insistence that even the holidays be devoid of any sentiment. It was the season of "goodwill toward men," and they were ready to kill each other.

Once they were able to cool down and look at what was happening more objectively, Frank and Katie shared how their families had celebrated Christmas and discovered how their past experiences were coloring their expectations for the present. Frank's family, though poor, had made a big deal of the holidays. It was time to pull together as a family; decorate their small, simple home with school crafts, tinsel, lights and baubles of all kinds; travel together to their uncle's farm to search for the "perfect" tree; send out personal greeting cards to everyone they knew; and gather around a turkey dinner with the best home cooking Frank had ever sampled. Those were some of Frank's most cherished memories, even more significant since it was the one time of year when no matter what else was happening, the family relaxed, enjoyed each other and put their problems and stresses aside.

For Katie, the holidays had always been a nightmare. Christmas Eve was the anniversary of her paternal grandmother's death, her father's best excuse for his libations. He would drink more than ever during the holidays, grow sickly sentimental (though ever more insincere) and buy his wife and children expensive gifts. But, inevitably, he would "crash" and succumb to grief and churlishness. Katie came to resent the gifts her father gave because once he hit bottom, there would be no end to his caustic remarks about how ungrateful and undeserving she was of everything he gave her and all the things he did for her. Christmas was still intensely painful for her, and it was all she could do to wait it out and avoid as many hallmarks of the holiday as possible.

Once they understood each other's frame of reference, Frank and Katie were able to compromise on how they would celebrate the holidays, and they committed to establishing their own brand-new traditions.

In your relationship with your spouse or partner, it's critical to uncover how your past experiences are impacting the way you believe your relationship "ought" to function. It's unrealistic to expect that everything will proceed the way you're used to or that makes you feel most at home. You now have a new "home," with your partner and in this relationship.

Talk about what you want to carry forward from past experience, what you're willing to let go of and ways you can uniquely mark your relationship *now*. It's never too late to have this discussion. You could be married 40 years and still benefit from talking about the ways you continue to bring the past forward into your current relationship. Work collaboratively, recognizing that you can't expect your partner to let go of more of his or her past culture than you're willing to deny yourself. Think positively about the ways you are shaping the new culture of your relationship. Accept the reality of relational dynamics you've imported that you can't avoid or "fix," and work intelligently and consciously with what you have. Remember that it takes time for each of you to make changes and for your relationship to adjust to them.

Values – In Chapter 4, we learned how our values—those things we hold as important to us shape our lives. They also shape our expectations in relationships. If we value family, we might want to have several children and favor one parent staying home to care for them, versus both parents pursuing heavy-hitting careers. If we value personal accomplishment, we may not want to have children at all so we can have the time and energy necessary to focus on our goals. If our values are at odds with our partner's, we're vulnerable to conflict.

In choosing a life partner, it makes sense to find someone whose values align with yours, and it's wise to discuss your values before committing to a long-term relationship. Some couples fall in love and get married, only to discover that their individual values differ significantly.

Some value shifts, or even reversals, can happen for either or both individuals over time. For example, a couple that has a deep desire to have children may shift their priorities from wanting to conceive a child naturally to looking at adoption. Or they may decide to adopt a new value of caring for other families or social causes. A stroke or heart attack may cause someone to abruptly reprioritize his or her values of professional success and physical health. Our partner threatening to walk out of the relationship may incite us to renew our commitment to the value of intimacy. Sometimes our values themselves don't change, but rather we become more aware that we're not really pursuing what we most deeply care about after all. We can lose our consciousness of what we want and what gives our life purpose.

Having different values doesn't have to be a deal breaker, as long as each partner is willing to compromise where necessary. Most importantly, couples need to bring their values to a level of mutual consciousness, identify where there is agreement or areas of potential discord and define how the relationship will function. Practically speaking, some matters that couples should determine include the following:

• whether or not to get married and what it means to be married

• where they will live and what kind of home they will have

• whether or not to have children and, if so, how many

• how money will be spent and how much is enough

• how time will be spent—at work, in hobbies or with each other

• the place in-laws and other family will have in the relationship

• their individual goals and their goals for the relationship

Assumptions about roles – Closely linked to our past experience and our values are our assumptions about the roles each partner is to play in the relationship. Some of our assumptions come from what we saw in our family of origin: Mom stayed home to raise the children while Dad worked, Dad fixed things around the house, or Mom took care of money management for the home, for example. We come into relationships with often unconscious ideas about who is "supposed" to do what in the relationship. These assumptions are neither right nor wrong, but we need to be conscious that they are, in fact, assumptions and not hard and fast rules. Committed relationships can function successfully and with mutual satisfaction when partners take on any combination of roles. The right definition of roles for your relationship will be the one that works for you.

If you're experiencing chronic conflict in certain areas, it may be because you've never uncovered your unconscious template for relationship roles. Discuss and negotiate roles for your relationship. Your discussion might cover any or all of the following:

- Who is responsible for the care of the children (and in which aspects)?

- Who is responsible for the care of the home (and for which tasks)?

- Who is responsible for generating income (in what proportion and in what amounts)? How much will be shared or individually controlled?

- Who will administrate the home (pay the bills or maintain the calendar, for example)?

- Which tasks will be performed by each person (and which tasks will be jobbed out)?

RELATIONSHIP MYTHS

Much of the time, disappointment in our relationships springs from having implicitly bought into common myths.[4] See how aware you are of some of the common misconceptions about romantic relationships:

We need to have mutual interests and perspectives – Common interests are constructive in your relationship only if you can enjoy participating in them together. Many couples relate in satisfying ways while maintaining very separate interests. Partners who enjoy golf may not be able to tolerate golfing together if one sees golf as a highly competitive display of skill and the other sees it as a leisurely way to spend a sunny afternoon. You may share congruent perspectives on many things in your relationship, but you may also have differing views on many things. It is more important that you agree to disagree than be aligned in all your thinking. In fact, two distinct individuals contributing their views and allowing each other's influence can form very healthy relationships.

We should be making each other happy – Many couples become disillusioned with their relationship when the early, almost worshipful, stage of the relationship evolves into something quite different. A partner who once declared his or her rapt devotion and made it a life mission to ensure the other's unending happiness has turned into a fixture on the couch, become attached to the computer or begun toting a permanently hip-holstered child.

While it is true that your partner can give you real and powerful emotional gifts in word or deed, he or she cannot maintain your self-esteem, sense of identity or positive mood. When we approach relationships with a sense of security, personal responsibility (for our own actions and our own mental state) and purpose—each independent of what our partner may or may not contribute—we can more freely give to and experience the benefits of the relationship.

We need to feel romance – Couples can always build more romance into their relationship, but this is more an action-based than a feelings-based reality. Psychologist and talk show host Dr. Phil McGraw points out, "Being in love is not like falling in love."[5] The addictive, giddy high of the early stages of love wanes predictably. But mature love and less-heady emotion don't mean the relationship is in trouble or that it can't be satisfying. To expect the relationship to deliver a constant emotional high is unrealistic.

We need to carefully maintain a reciprocal relationship – While a good relationship should involve healthy give and take, some relationships can become stifling, competitive or filled with resentment when there is a sense that one or both partners are keeping score.

We need to be able to vent all of our feelings – Emotional catharsis or exhaustively rehearsing every issue we have with our partner can be more destructive than constructive. Nitpicking is not the same as raising pertinent issues in an effort to create increased understanding or find solutions for solvable problems. Nor does venting negative feelings necessarily make you feel better or give your partner the picture he or she needs of what you're feeling. Sex and marriage therapist Dr. David Schnarch points out that "the stability of your relationship depends more on soothing your feelings than on expressing them."[6] Ill-timed, overly impassioned remarks can quickly become relational A-bombs; we often regret words unleashed in the heat of the moment. But the words and their impact are irrevocable.

We need to avoid conflict – Conflict in any relationship is inevitable. Two individuals with two different perspectives and two sets of experiences cannot possibly see eye to eye at every turn. Conflict is not an indication of a troubled relationship; conflict avoidance and unhealthy ways of dealing with conflict are.

We need to solve all of our problems – According to relationship expert John Gottman, whose marriage lab studies and findings have made significant contributions to current marriage therapy practice, 69 percent of any couple's relational problems will never be solved.[7] Couples can commit to navigating their areas of conflict with good-natured humor, coping skills and the resolve to not let problems derail their commitment to each other and to staying connected.

We need to work together in order for our relationship to improve – A decision to improve the relationship is usually made by one party before and sometimes independent of the other. Can any real change occur? Absolutely. Hendrix says, "A relationship is like a balloon filled with air: you can't push on one part of it without affecting the shape of the whole."[8] Later, this chapter will cover the role an individual can play and the responsibility he or she must take in transforming and being happy in a relationship.

RELATIONSHIP WARNING SIGNS

Beware of dynamics in your relationship that would indicate relational illness. If you see any of the following signs in your relationship, take heed:

Extramarital affairs – An "affair" is more than the literal illicit relationship that may arise between a committed man or woman and someone outside the relationship. Affairs might be anything that routinely draws us—in time, energy or focus—away from our partner when we should be turning, instead, toward him or her. This might be a friendship, a job, a hobby, watching TV or even focusing too much on the children. None of these pursuits is wrong in and of itself, but when it becomes a way to escape our partner (and relational issues we should be dealing with more constructively), it can slowly drain the relationship of its life blood. If your spouse seems more like a roommate than a romantic partner, that's a clear sign that you've been meeting your emotional and relational needs outside the relationship.

Criticism – Criticism, different from complaint, carries with it implicit personal attack. Where complaint focuses on the specific behavior ("I feel ignored when you watch TV all evening"), criticism is leveled at the person's identity ("I can't believe how lazy and self-ish you are, watching TV all evening"). Regular criticism slowly chips away at a partner's self-esteem and erodes his or her good-will. The critical partner, in turn, withdraws more and more from the relationship, interpreting everything his or her partner says or does through negative lenses.

Contempt – Closely related to criticism, contempt is an attitude of disdain and disgust. Marked by sarcasm, cynicism, name-calling and mockery, contempt sends the message that "I have given up on you. I don't value you and I don't have any hope for you." Relationships in which there is contempt quickly unravel: one or both partners have come to negative conclusions about their partner, and their relational stance has become one of turning away and rejecting, versus turning toward and embrac-ing, their partner. In the extreme, contempt is displayed through belligerence, abuse and violence.

Extreme responses to conflict – If you respond to conflict with your partner by shutting down and withdrawing or by over-whelming him or her with a deluge of words and emotion (or even destructive behavior), you're likely headed for trouble.

Failure to attempt relational repairs or rejection of your partner's attempts – Not giving or acknowledging goodwill in a relation-ship closes all avenues of connection and growth. You ultimately get stuck, and your relationship begins to lose cohesiveness.

Sexual dysfunction – Couples can engage in sexual activity with a wide range of frequency, physiological responses, duration of en-counters and so on, and be mutually satisfied with their physical relationship. What works well for one couple may not work well for another. At the same time, what is functional for one couple may be dysfunctional for another. Communication of sexual needs and desires and a mutual commitment to help fulfill them is what counts. Some happy couples have sex very frequently and others, hardly at all.

Research shows that when a marriage is going well, sex contributes only 15 to 20 percent toward the relationship's overall satisfaction. However, when the couples are unhappy, their sex lives impact 50 to 75 percent of their happiness.[9] Sex, then, is a barometer for the rela-tionship as a whole, more than a determining factor for relational harmony. When sexual dissatisfaction is present, especially when it's not out in the open, the relationship needs attention.

How "conscious" is your relationship? Are you aware of how your past impacts your relational style and how you perceive your partner? Are your expectations for the relationship—how you and your partner work with each other's values and perspectives, how you make decisions and how you fulfill various roles—out in the open? Are they reasonable? Are you aware of your partner's expectations? How vulnerable are you to common relationship myths? Are there areas where your relationship is prone to disease or is even in "critical condition"? Foundational to creating intimacy with your partner and avoiding and dealing with conflict is having increased awareness of the dynamics at work in your relationship. Hendrix says, "In an unconscious marriage, you believe the right way to have a good marriage is to pick the right partner. In a conscious marriage you realize you have to be the right partner."[10]

COMMITMENT

In *Getting the Love You Want*, Hendrix looks at ways to create a more loving and ultimately more satisfying relationship. One of those ways is to commit. He says:

> Ironically, the more I have become involved in a psychological study of love relationships, the more I find myself siding with the more conservative proponents of marriage. I have come to believe that couples should make every effort to honor their wedding vows to stay together "till death do us part"— not for moral reasons, but for psychological ones: fidelity and commitment appear to be conditions dictated by the unconscious mind.[11]

The ultimate relational commitment is marriage. Studies show marked differences between couples who live together and those who share marriage vows, in terms of their relational satisfaction and longevity, as well as their physical health. Haltzman wrote *The Secrets of Happily Married Men* to inspire married men to feel good about the commitment they've made, in part by comparing it to the focused determination to succeed they have at work. Haltzman maintains that marriage requires a different level of commitment than cohabitation does, especially for men, and so must be viewed differently:

> You'd be surprised at the statistics which demonstrate that marriage and cohabitation are horses of different colors. The level of expressed and implied commitment is dramatically stronger in marriage, particularly on the part of men. To treat these two entities as though they were the same robs

the married couple of the chance to use the greatest tool at their disposal, their devotion to each other.[12]

The results of a Centers for Disease Control and Prevention study published in 2004 showed that married adults were about half as likely to be smokers or heavy drinkers as single, divorced or separated adults. The study also indicated that even unmarried couples don't reap as high a level of health benefit as those in a good marriage.[13]

So what does commitment "look" like?

KEEPING THE FAITH

Commitment, essentially, is sticking with your partner by keeping the relationship exclusive, but also by deciding in advance to weather inevitable storms and stay invested in the health of the relationship. This inner conviction to hang in there no matter what is possible only when we realize that our feelings are often fickle. Feelings follow behavior; we can perform loving acts that actually cause us to think and feel more romantically about our partner.

There are times when commitment to a partner may be unwarranted, such as when he or she "cheats," is abusive, abandons the relationship or succumbs to addiction. But many times we are tempted to bail well short of such crises—when we aren't getting our way, when the relationship isn't as exciting anymore, when our partner becomes less attractive to us or when we start looking for greener grass over the fence.

See if you practice the following measures to keep faith with your partner:

> *Show acceptance* – Determine to always be "for" your partner, regardless of things he or she may do or say that annoy, frustrate or even hurt you. Deal honestly and directly with your partner's behavior, bringing up honestly and forthrightly the things that concern you, but make sure your partner knows unequivocally that he or she has your love, regardless of what he or she may do. It cannot be earned or lost. Dr. Phil says it this way:

>> When you exhibit a spirit that indicates that you accept your partner, you're saying that even though you may not like everything your partner is doing, things are still okay.... You're saying that despite our differences in personality and temperament, despite all the things I sometimes wish you were or weren't, the bottom line is that I accept you for who you are, and will always be there for you.[14]

Acceptance believes the best of the other person. Where you can't clearly discern your partner's intentions in something he or she has said or done, check in for understanding, but try to assume the best. Instead of being tuned in to your partner's faults, can you identify and begin to appreciate his or her gifts, contributions and admirable traits?

Though she knew Frank didn't always agree with her, Katie was sure he accepted and was committed to her. This helped her to relax and feel free to be herself, something she never felt liberty to do as a child. Sometimes she felt guilty for not showing Frank as much acceptance in return. The way he honored her was like a mirror held up to her heart. Experiencing Frank's respect made her aware of ways she didn't—but needed to—respect him. His acceptance inspired her to want to give him more.

Eliminate "exits" – The "affairs" we discussed previously, those things that steer us away from instead of toward our partner, kill intimacy. Hendrix describes these affairs that take us outside of healthy focus on our relationship as "exits."[15] When we soothe ourselves with relational placebos instead of making efforts to connect with our spouse, our relationship will drift, each partner becoming more and more isolated, widening the distance we will need to bridge to get back to each other. Having interests outside the relationship is healthy, but ask yourself, "Am I using this activity or relationship to avoid my spouse?" If you are, that may be a door you need to close, at least until you can achieve a greater level of connectedness with your mate. Ironically, where one partner feels smothered or chased by the other, if he or she eliminates exits rather than seeking them and draws near emotionally to his or her partner, this can cause the "chaser" to relax and allow his or her partner ample psychological space. Alcohol or drug abuse and other addictive behavior are often relational exits.

Make your partner a priority – How do you treat your best client? Now think of the way you treat your spouse. Does he or she feel like a priority to you? Does the way you spend your time indicate that you're invested in your relationship with your spouse? Does he or she get your undivided attention for significant periods of time? Does he or she feel valued, heard and understood? Would your spouse say you are dialed in to his or her world of interests, thoughts, feelings, goals, concerns and so on?

CREATING SHARED MEANING

Gottman says, "In the strongest marriages, husband and wife share a deep sense of meaning. They don't just 'get along'—they also support each other's hopes and aspirations and build a sense of purpose into their lives together."[16] These couples create their own culture.

Relationship goals – You have targets for your business. Do you have relationship goals? Where do you and your partner want to be next year, in five years, in ten years? What are some things you want to accomplish as a couple—for yourselves, for your family, for your community? Many couples have never discussed what they hope for their relationship or what they envision coming out of it. They may not even have discussed their life purpose or their key values with each other, which is unfortunate, since many partners have individual life purposes that complement each other well. Working together, partners can combine their inner resources to help each other realize their individual and collective goals sooner and in more fulfilling ways.

Rituals, symbols and stories – The things that make one culture distinct from another are the unique practices, symbols and stories that make it meaningful for those who belong to it. Marriage is a "microculture" between two people. Tremendous bonding can happen between partners who have regular rituals (like morning coffee in the sunroom or planting a tree with the birth of each child or grandchild), symbols (like artifacts collected from shared holidays and displayed) and stories (about the day they met, their honeymoon or how they survived one partner's cancer treatment together) told again and again. These are the markers that make the culture of our relationship unique and special—the things that make us "us."

Gottman reminds us:

> Developing a culture doesn't mean a couple sees eye to eye on every aspect of their life's philosophy. Instead there is a meshing. They find a way of honoring each other's dreams even if they don't always share them. The culture that they develop together incorporates both their dreams. And it is flexible enough to change as husband and wife grow and develop.[17]

PROTECTING THE RELATIONSHIP

Honor your spouse by putting healthy boundaries around your relationship. Couples with flimsy boundaries can become overly involved in outside activities or other relationships. They tend to find their relational fulfillment outside the relationship and have difficulty enjoying true intimacy with each other. However, partners who have walled in their relationship with rigid boundaries become enmeshed, losing their identity in their partner and becoming isolated from having relationships with anyone else. They feel that they cannot exist apart from each other. Healthy boundaries allow each party to be an individual, with his or her own interests, activities and satellite relationships, but healthy boundaries should also set clear limits that honor the commitment each person has made to his or her partner.

Choose friends who support your commitment to your spouse. If you're out of town on business, check in with a phone call that says, I'm thinking of you, even though you're not here. As much as possible, keep your relational issues between the two of you. Affair-proof your relationship by guarding against emotional exits.

TAKE RESPONSIBILITY FOR YOUR PART IN THE RELATIONSHIP

One of the most significant ways you can commit to your partner and to your relationship is by taking responsibility for your own happiness, personal growth and contribution to the relationship, regardless of what your partner chooses to do. In relationships where both partners look to the other to fulfill all of their emotional needs, love becomes commodified and they become relational consumers, wholly dependent on each other for a sense of value, of significance and of being loved. When you don't come through for me, I then feel justified in withholding love from you. If you won't give, I won't give either. Many relationships reach a stalemate and then begin to disintegrate. This is a picture of unhealthy codependence, where identity and sense of self is so enmeshed between partners that they depend on each other for their happiness. They relinquish their power and abdicate responsibility. Standing on your own two feet emotionally gives you the freedom to connect with your partner; if you recognize that your happiness is up to you and that only you have the power to define who you are, you can receive feedback without feeling threatened, and you can give love genuinely without ulterior motives.

Most couples enter marriage with the unconscious agenda of healing themselves through their relationship. Dr. Phil is adamant that there is always something you can do *by yourself* to make your relationship work better and become more fulfilling. Even when your spouse seems the bane of your existence, "whatever it is your partner is doing, you are either eliciting, maintaining or allowing that behavior."[18]

Schnarch cautions not to equate taking personal responsibility with letting your partner off the hook:

> Don't confuse shouldering your rightful responsibility with constantly adapting to your partner's weaknesses, limitations and immaturities. In some situations... collaboration requires refusing to continue the accommodation and anxiety regulation you've been doing up to this point.[19]

Sometimes the most loving and relationally responsible thing you can do is confront your partner's behavior, not tolerate it. It wasn't long into their work with The Healthy CEO that Frank realized he needed to "step up" emotionally in his relationship with Katie. He had allowed her to become the keeper of his emotional keys. When she was happy, he was happy. When she was angry, he became angry—although he often didn't know why. Frank knew he needed to become responsible for his own emotions, expressing his own joy and his own anger, even at the risk of upsetting Katie.

As he counsels couples who are struggling, Hendrix encourages them to let go of the sense that the relationship needs to be "fair"—that both parties need to be equally invested in improving the relationship for it to "work" and that there ought to be mutual back-scratching. Instead, he tells them,

> You have to stop expecting the outside world to take care of you and begin to accept responsibility for your own healing. And the way you do this, paradoxically, is by focusing your energy on healing your partner. It is when you direct your energy away from yourself and toward your partner that deep-level psychological and spiritual healing begins to take place.[20]

The best way to become more personally fulfilled and whole is to invest in someone else. This doesn't mean an investment in *changing* your partner; it's a decision to love him or her simply because everyone is worthy of love—and because the decision to love others brings growth to your own life. Whether or not your efforts are recognized or received, you can realize the benefit of a better you, your own healing and growth in emotional capacity and character. That becomes a gift you give yourself as well as your partner. While you improve yourself on the inside, you may also offer your best self to your partner on the outside. Simple things can easily be overlooked, like your grooming and how well you are taking care of your body.

How committed are you to your partner? To the health of your relationship? In how many ways are you practically demonstrating your commitment? Would your partner agree with your assessment? Look at ways you might better invest in your partner, your relationship and, ultimately, yourself.

CONNECTION

Other words for connection are "intimacy" and "closeness," the sense that you and your partner are bonded and relating well, and that there are no barriers between you. Connection is not the same as feeling engulfed by your partner or losing yourself in him or her. Rather, it is a heightened awareness that both of you are fully present and participating mutually in the relationship.

FUN AND FRIENDSHIP

In a study of 300 couples married for between 15 and 61 years, the happiest couples agreed on the importance of play and humor in their relationships. In fact, both husbands and wives ranked play above sex as being a vital aspect of a successful marriage.[21] For men especially, recreational bonding can create more powerful intimacy than deep conversation. Satisfied couples are those who find ways to enjoy being together. Their emotional bond is intensified as they associate pleasure with their partner. Partners can engage in fun activities together, such as sports or watching a comic movie, and feel more connected without hardly sharing a word.

FONDNESS AND APPRECIATION

It's often very easy to see and become focused on our partner's faults. Before we realize it, we begin to see everything our partner says or does through negative, or "dirty," lenses. In the previous chapter, we talked about the emotional capacity of *optimism*—the ability to envision and work toward a positive result. Optimism can be a powerful tool for good in our most significant personal relationship. Trade in your dark lenses for some rose-colored glasses for a while. This is not the same as denial; it's not turning a blind eye to your partner's faults. Rather, it's not allowing your partner's flaws to blind you to the great qualities he or she possesses. Practice noticing your partner's positive traits and verbalizing appreciation. Research has shown that the ratio of positive interactions to negative interactions must be at least five to one for a spouse to stay emotionally invested in the marriage.[22] Looking for the good in our partner not only helps us feel more positively about the relationship, but it also inspires our partner to continue positive behaviors and improve on others, working toward the image we have of him or her.

KNOWING AND BEING KNOWN

Keeping up to date with what your partner is thinking and how he or she is feeling, and communicating the same about yourself, maintains connection. Gottman calls this intimate familiarity with your partner's world a "richly detailed love map."[23] Do you know what your partner's favorite dessert is? His or her favorite way to spend a free day? What about his or her deepest dreams, longings or fears? Does your partner know yours? Demonstrating that you want to know someone communicates that you care about them. Think about how you relate at work. How do clients respond when they realize you've done your homework and researched the way they do business, what their needs are and what makes them unique? When people know you care, they're more willing to invest with you. The same is true in your most significant personal relationship.

This level of self-disclosure is a risk we sometimes shrink away from. Our mind plays out all the possible outcomes of being that transparent: What if my partner uses this piece of information to hurt me? What if he or she doesn't really acknowledge or care about what I share? The best predictor of what will happen when we risk vulnerability is how *we* respond to our partner's vulnerability. If you are a "safe place" for your partner to leave his or her most prized possessions—his or her innermost thoughts and feelings—that care and protection is likely to be returned. Your relationship can be a place of security and solace for both of you.

Focusing on the negative "what ifs" can keep us from considering the rewarding "what ifs." What if you could create a powerful ally in your spouse by communicating your anxieties? What if, in getting a fuller picture of your partner's inner world, you found new ways to come together?

COMMUNICATION

In Chapter 4, we looked at the components of effective communication applicable to any relationship. A relationship between partners can be more fulfilling when they recognize the unique ways they can communicate with each other.

> *Love languages* – Author, speaker and director of Marriage and
> Family Life Consultants Inc. Gary Chapman says there are five
> main ways you can communicate love to your partner, what he
> describes as "love languages":
>
> > • *words of affirmation* – verbal compliments or words of appreciation: "You are so good at problem solving," or "I appreciate how patient you are with the children."

- *quality time* – giving your undivided attention: turning off the TV to talk or making it a priority to share evening meals together

- *gifts* – bestowing a visible expression of love: a favorite coffee beverage, a new ball cap or a piece of jewelry

- *acts of service* – doing things for your spouse: washing the car, taking on an extra chore (even hiring someone to do it) or preparing a favorite dinner

- *physical touch* – sex and other forms of physical affection: prolonged and attentive lovemaking, a back massage or holding hands while sitting or walking together[24]

Writing to married men who understand financial statements and how to deliver the goods at work, Haltzman says, "In your marriage, you need to determine what currency your wife values; then you'll know what she's looking for in her paycheck."[25] When we're tapped into the language our partner speaks, we're better able to communicate love and we eliminate the frustration felt when we speak the "wrong" language and don't get the results we were hoping for.

When we travel to a foreign country, we get farther by communicating in the native language, rather than insisting the locals speak ours. We are in their domain, so we adjust. In the same way, while it might (especially at first) feel awkward and unnatural to communicate in your partner's love language, you'll connect better by entering his or her world.

Differences between men and women – In general, men and women are socialized to prefer or excel at different things, but there is an abundance of evidence pointing to the ways in which men's and women's brains develop and function differently, apart from environmental influences:

- The typical male brain devotes much more brain area to spatial skills—things like mechanical design, manipulation of physical objects, and abstraction. Male brains usually have less area for word use and word production.[26]

- The male brain usually produces less of two powerful chemicals, serotonin and oxytocin, than the female brain does.

Serotonin tends to calm us down, while oxytocin may be related to bonding behaviors.[27]

• Using PET (positron-emission tomography) brain scans, author of *What Could He Be Thinking* Michael Gurian demonstrates that men have less involvement of the emotive centers of the brain than women do when both groups are shown a picture of a sad person and are asked to identify what emotion they see.[28]

In terms of communication, women are generally more verbal than men and may be more emotionally astute in reading people. Research shows that the average woman uses 7,000 words a day, using many gestures and up to five tones, while men use about 2,000 with only three tones.[29] While these tendencies are not hard and fast rules—some women have more "male" brains and some men have more "female" brains—the disparity between men and women in how they communicate and respond emotionally is noteworthy.

John Gray, author of *Men Are from Mars, Women Are from Venus*, may be on to something. He points to some of the distinct ways men and women tend to communicate:

• Women communicate verbally primarily to express emotion, while men communicate verbally primarily to convey information.

• Women communicate verbally to solve problems, while men typically solve their problems by working them out in other ways.

• Women use verbal communication to create intimacy, while men typically look to other avenues to feel connected (recreation or sex, for example).[30]

Asking for what you want – Often our disappointment with our partner lies in the conviction we feel that he or she has let us down. We feel neglected and put out because, surely, the other person must be deliberately denying us. Much of the time, our partner really has no idea what would make us feel loved or happy. Even the most willing and intuitive partner can't read our mind. We don't get what we want or need from our partner sometimes just because we don't ask. Expressing what you would like from your partner (making requests and not demands) gives him or her the satisfaction of knowing that what he or she does and says means something to you. That can be very affirming. At the same time, we need to be careful not to *require* that our partner deliver. We might express disappointment if our requests are denied, but again, we are responsible for our own happiness and shouldn't try to control our partner's behavior.

True listening – As we discovered in the last chapter, listening is an active, not a passive, process. You and your partner need to feel that what you have to share is received, acknowledged and validated, whether you agree or not. To accomplish this, couples can do the following:

- *Mirror* – Confirm understanding by paraphrasing what your partner has said, expressing back to your partner in your own words what it is you heard to make sure you've understood his or her meaning correctly.

- *Validate what has been expressed* – This is understanding and appreciating your partner's point of view without necessarily agreeing with it. It is saying, "I can see why you think or feel that way," with sincerity. Mirroring helps you arrive at a level of understanding where true validation can occur.

- *Empathize* – Offer compassion and understanding for your partner's emotional experience. "Given that you think that way, I can see how you might be hurt."

From there, couples can work toward clarity where there has been misunderstanding, reconciliation where there has been a rift in intimacy and compromise or acceptance where partners are at an impasse.

SEX AND OTHER PHYSICAL TOUCH

Feeling emotionally connected to your partner can lead to great sex. Great sex, in turn, contributes to your sense of connection to your partner. For men, higher testosterone levels usually create a higher sex drive than most women have. In terms of feeling emotionally connected to their partners, men also "need" more sex. Oxytocin, the "bonding chemical," is released in men more during intercourse and orgasm than during any other activity. Haltzman points out that in women, oxytocin is released more variably and is usually at a level 10 times higher than the normal oxytocin level in a man's brain. Only at orgasm do men's levels of oxytocin match the levels in women.[31] Sex is a mind-body experience.

Sexual problems

Schnarch maintains that it is *normal* for couples to have sexual problems. He rues the fact that many couples continue to struggle with bedroom issues because they are too embarrassed or afraid to disclose them. He says, "The constant barrage of sexual information, advertising, and sex-laced entertainment in mass media makes it feel somehow inappropriate to have sexual problems in our liberated times."[32] Yet "anywhere from 10 percent to 52 percent of all men and 25 percent to 63 percent of all women have sexual problems."[33]

Sexual satisfaction (or dissatisfaction) correlates with the following factors, alone or in combination:

    Sensory stimulation – This refers to the kind of touch transmitted (and how the other senses come into play): light to more intense touch; how much and what kind of foreplay; sexual positions; oral, hand or genital contact; accoutrements such as lotions, feathers or electronic devices; lighting; music; scented oils; and so on. Good "technique"—what turns each of you on and keeps you turned on—falls into this category. Satisfactory sensory stimulation may or may not include intercourse. Physical bonding, especially for many women, occurs in powerful ways through other forms of touch.

    Physiological factors – These may include any of the following:

        • *Physical health* – How fit you are, what you eat, medical procedures you've undergone and any medical conditions you may have.

        • *Hormones* – Pregnancy, menstruation and menopause cause hormone variations in women. Women can lose 90 percent of their hormones over a two-year period once they enter menopause.[34] These hormones directly affect a woman's level of sexual desire, arousal and response. As men age, they lose testosterone, which is intrinsically linked to their sexual functioning.

        • *Stress and fatigue* – These are desire killers. They rob the body of the energy required to engage in sexual activity and they impair performance.

        • *Medications* – Prescription drugs such as those used to treat depression, anxiety and hypertension can impair sexual satisfaction.

More than 80 percent of people who take SSRI antidepressants experience some sexual impairment.[35]

These factors, alone or in combination, can inhibit our body's ability to respond to even the best sensory stimulation. If you wonder if one or more of these factors may be influencing your sex life, be sure to talk to your doctor.

Psychological factors – A couple's sexual experience may have more to do with psychological factors than they realize.

- *Mind noise* – Stresses from work, money problems, distractions from children and other preoccupations can get in the way of sex.

- *Unresolved relational issues* – Sex is a consummation of intimacy. If you aren't feeling emotionally connected, physical intimacy isn't likely to ring true. For some couples, sex provides a release of tension in order to be able to face their problems more rationally. For others, sex exacerbates problems. Better connection outside the bedroom usually leads to better lovemaking. Schnarch says, "Profound emotional connection during sex can bring your stimulation to all-time highs." Conversely, "the more unresolved personal issues you are dodging, the more you have to tune out during sex and the more vulnerable you are to sexual problems."[36] Sometimes unsatisfying sex is the result not of a lack of good physical stimulation, but of good verbal stimulation—compliments or words that express love and care.

- *Fear or anxiety* – Performance-based anxieties about sex can become self-fulfilling prophecies, resulting in premature ejaculation or erectile dysfunction for men and failure to lubricate or to reach orgasm in women. Self-esteem-based anxieties centered around poor body image or feeling unworthy of love or pleasure can impede sexual response. Experience-based anxieties, such as those arising from memories of past abuse or shaming messages about sex from childhood, can block sexual arousal and pleasure if allowed to invade the present. Don't allow past experience to block your sexual pleasure unnecessarily. Invest in your relationship now, with therapy if required. And don't be hemmed in by stereotypes, such as the misconception that deeply religious people aren't having heady sex.

The 1992 National Health and Social Life Survey, when analyzed in terms of religion, showed that women who reported some religious affiliation were more likely to have orgasms than those who didn't.[37]

Sex for a lifetime

While the physiological changes of aging can sometimes make sexual arousal and performance more challenging, the *psychological* aspects of sex can greatly improve as a couple share and go through life's seasons together. There are manifold remedies, therapies and treatments to assist couples with physiological problems, including products like next-to-natural lubricants, medications such as Viagra, and hormone replacement therapies to address testosterone or other hormone deficiencies. Help is available. But what is a couple to do in the earlier years of their relationship, when they are dealing with the professional pressures of advancing their careers and securing job stability or the family stresses of infant-induced sleep deprivation and the reality of being on call 24/7 to older, but dependent, children? Even if their bodies are "all systems go," many young couples barely have the time, energy or even privacy to undress, much less make passionate, orgasmic, soul-moving love to one another.

As couples age and their relationship matures, a deeper sense of connectedness, combined with their children being more independent, can lead to a deeply fulfilling sex life. When partners mature relationally as individuals and experience greater emotional connectedness, they can share intimate moments that would likely have been impossible for their younger, busier, more stressed-out selves. With more maturity, partners can express what they would like from each other sexually and meet each other's sexual needs with the confidence that comes from seasoned trust and companionship. A couple's sexual relationship can be fulfilling and even exciting, albeit sometimes in different ways, from the first to the golden anniversary.

All touch, including sex, should be framed within wanting to connect with your partner as two souls who are much more than just physical bodies. A major characteristic of couples who have a happy sex life is that they see lovemaking as an expression of intimacy, but they don't take any differences in their needs or desires personally.[38] Remember that only you and your partner can determine the quality of your sexual relationship. If neither of you perceives any problems, there aren't any. If just one of you does have some concern, it's an issue for both.

Are you aware of your partner's sexual wish list? Are there physiological factors affecting your sex life that you can look into? Sex can be blissfully or excruciatingly vulnerable. Where do you have anxiety or fear? Have you allowed your partner to share his or her thoughts and feelings about your sex life with you? There may be medications, new techniques or other steps you can take to increase your level of sexual stimulation and response—and it's important to examine these—but perhaps the best approach to creating a more fulfilling sex life with your partner is to look for non-physical ways to connect: recreation, exploring each other's inner world and effective communication. Are you contributing to relational closeness or allowing relational drift?

COOPERATION

Cooperation between partners is evident in their aim to always let the *relationship* "win," versus gaining a competitive advantage over their partner. Intimate relationships are not competitive; if our ultimate goal is to always be right or to "win," we will lose our partner somewhere along the way.

ACCEPTING INFLUENCE

If you have a business partner, you know how often you consult each other on day-to-day operations, on decisions that have to be made and to get perspective on how to deal with issues as they come up. Your relationship with your spouse can be a great partnership. Wherever possible, include you partner in your decision-making processes, seek his or her opinion and communicate that his or her opinion matters to you. You can choose to disagree if you like, but including your partner in your world and accepting his or her influence builds cohesiveness in the relationship and communicates that "your thoughts and feelings matter to me."

DEALING WITH CONFLICT

Dr. Phil believes that in relationships, it's more important to be happy than to be "right." Success in the relationship is whatever keeps the relationship "working," whether or not every problem gets solved.[39] Remember that 69 percent of the problems in a relationship will never be solved, and problems in a relationship are not necessarily a sign that there's anything wrong with it. Haltzman reminds us, "No couple is compatible all the time.... Research studies make it quite clear that both happy and unhappy couples have just about the same number of arguments and, in fact, tend to argue over the same issues."[40] The hot buttons for marital conflict for most couples are money, domestic roles, sex, children and in-laws.

Not letting problems derail intimacy is far more important than finding solutions. Getting *through* sometimes matters more than getting things *right*. For couples to better survive conflict, says Gottman, they need to identify which problems are solvable (and solve them) and which are unsolvable (and compromise, or resolve to move on anyway), and make acceptance of their partner non-negotiable.[41]

> *Solvable problems* – Just because a problem is solvable doesn't mean it will resolve itself. Many couples lack the skills and insight they need to master these kinds of difficulties. You can usually recognize solvable problems because they don't get you as upset as perpetual problems. Your focus is on the immediate issue or situation itself, and underlying dynamics don't usually come into play. Perpetual problems often start out resembling solvable ones, but they usually mask more deep-seated issues.

When they were first married, Frank would get a phone call from his mother, Dorothy, at least twice a week. She wanted to call to chat and see how he was doing. Unassumingly, Frank would give a run-down on his and Katie's week. Inevitably, Dorothy would find fault with Katie, especially with the lack of domestic support she was providing her new husband. Dorothy had been the quintessential housewife, focused on her husband and home, and she took great pride in her devotion. She had also sanctioned Lois, Frank's first wife, because she was also very domestic. Frank would deftly change the subject, finish the conversation and then often share what his mother had said with Katie, never as a criticism, but more with a sense of humor. Katie would still become angry. She would disappear out the front door or into the bedroom sometimes for hours. Frank didn't understand Katie's response, and Katie couldn't believe Frank's insensitivity.

When Frank finally mustered the courage to ask Katie what was wrong, she told him she resented her mother-in-law's comments, but that she was even more hurt by Frank's tolerating them. Frank pointed out that he didn't agree with his mother's point of view— that Katie should dote on him as his mother (or his ex-wife) had— and that he actually found her independence refreshing. Frank wasn't able to fully understand Katie's hurt feelings until she told him that she wanted him to respect her and their marriage enough to make it clear to Dorothy that Katie was now the most important woman in his life—that Frank would defend her and keep their relationship private. Once he saw Katie's point of view, Frank felt honored that their relationship meant that much to her and that she looked to him to protect her honor, even in smaller ways.

Frank felt inspired by her comments and began to affirm his wife to Dorothy on the phone and in person. He didn't allow his mother to make disparaging remarks. In fact, he asked his mother to stop calling, promising that he would call her at least twice a month to see how she was doing, asking her to respect his time with his new wife. Katie was thrilled, and Frank was happy to oblige.

Frank and Katie's problem, in this instance, was entirely solvable. All that was necessary to "fix" things was clear communication and an honest attempt to understand and be understood. With this understanding and a desire to resolve the situation, they were able to find a good solution.

Gottman offers these five steps as the way to solve solvable problems:

1) *Soften your start-up* – Wait until emotions diffuse, if necessary. Introduce your concern without criticism, accusation or blame.

2) *Learn to make and receive repair attempts* – Stop the argument if it's getting overheated and ask for a break. Verbalize your acceptance of your partner and your commitment to a positive outcome. Give and accept apologies, where warranted.

3) *Soothe yourself and each other* – Don't try to solve your problem until each of you is calm.

4) *Compromise* – Most of the time, like it or not, compromise is the only viable solution to relational problems. You don't have to agree with your partner's opinion, but you should at least consider it.

5) *Be tolerant of each other's faults* – Let go of the need to change your partner. The only person you really have the power to change is yourself.[42]

If either of you feels devalued, misunderstood or rejected by your partner, resolving any kind of conflict will be difficult. Again, demonstrating *consciousness, commitment, connection* and *cooperation* is more important than being "right." In reality, in all arguments, whether solvable or perpetual, no one is ever completely right. "There is no absolute reality in marital conflict, only two subjective realities," says Gottman.[43]

When couples don't find a way to compromise, they can become resentful and entrenched in their positions, transforming a solvable problem into a perpetual one.

Perpetual (unsolvable) problems – Perpetual problems are often the same issue with different faces. If one partner views the other as irresponsible, arguments might arise over the way that person drives, takes care of the home or yard or handles finances. If mistrust keeps resurfacing as an issue, it might show up as arguments over not showing up on time or "never" communicating. Perpetual problems show up in relationships as the same argument occurring over and over again, covering the same ground without making any headway. These surface arguments are often really about big issues like insecurity, selfishness or betrayal.

Again, the spirit with which you handle perpetual problems is key. If your partner is always late to functions and isn't bothered by it, you can accept that you will also be late to most functions, or arrange alternate transportation if you value promptness over showing up together with your partner. Being good-natured, having a sense of humor wherever possible or devising coping strategies can keep the relationship on the right track. If you can accept that your partner isn't perfect, as you hope he or she would accept you, your connection to each other can be maintained.

However, many couples encountering perpetual problems reach a state of gridlock where each partner is blocking the other's goals and the relationship gets "stuck." More talking doesn't solve these kinds of issues because the problem doesn't lie in not having enough information. It's more the perception that their basic personhood is at risk. Schnarch doesn't despair, however, when he encounters gridlocked couples: "Gridlock is either an irresolvable impasse or a pivotal turning point, depending on how you deal with it."[44] The solution he offers can seem counterintuitive. When you and your partner are more adversaries than allies, you feel fused together by anxiety and the spoken or unspoken invalidation you've each communicated. Your instincts may tell you to pull away in order to protect yourself and to punish your partner. Schnarch says:

> The solution isn't getting further away from your partner; it's regulating your own anxiety and developing your own sense of identity and self-worth. This allows you to get closer to your partner, in more pleasant ways than you are now: This is closeness *with* separateness.[45]

Are you and your partner cooperating in your relationship? Are you working together as allies, building intimacy and investing in the long-term good of your relationship? Or are you pulling in opposite directions, through neglect or conflict?

Look honestly at how *conscious, committed, connected* and *cooperative* your relationship is with your partner. Where are there potential areas for growth? Where are there obvious problems? What are the things you can celebrate?

Consulting a relational expert

This relational review is a summary of the dynamics in our most significant personal relationship. Relationships are extremely complex because human beings are extremely complex. You may be able to note areas of concern and even begin to address some of your relational issues on your own or together with your partner. However, it can be helpful to consult experts to help you identify your unique personal makeup and the distinct dynamics within your relationship. Sadly, for many couples, it takes a crisis before they consider therapy or counseling, even though there are many benefits they could reap from expert help well short of relational breakdown.

To maintain physical health, routine visits to your doctor can help you enjoy wellness without the untimely or unnecessary onset of illness or disease. While there is no relational equivalent to the yearly physical exam, feedback and training from relational experts can be extremely valuable. Couples therapists, marriage counselors, sex therapists and clergy can all provide help. There are also marriage and relationship seminars offered by various agencies—sometimes in the form of weekend getaways—to give couples relational tune-ups from time to time. For purposes of this program, we recommend that you consult a relational expert to give you the benefit of his or her objectivity, experience and expertise—especially in the case of significantly disruptive relational or emotional issues.

FINDING A RELATIONAL EXPERT

It's easy to become confused when trying to find a relational expert suited to your unique situation. First, you need to determine if the issues you're facing are individual (such as mental health, substance abuse, professional or self-esteem) or relational (such as communication, conflict resolution, sexuality, parenting, infidelity or family breakup), involving you and another person, most likely your partner. Finding a therapist who is a good fit for you and your situation can be difficult, but here are some of the best methods:

- *Word of mouth* – In confidence, consult a friend who may have seen a therapist before. Especially if he or she went to therapy for reasons similar to what you're dealing with, your friend may be able to point you to someone he or she found helpful.

- *Your primary health practitioner* – Your doctor can refer you to someone he or she knows has been helpful to other patients.

- *A local professional body* – Go through the medical association, psychologists' association, association of social workers and so on. You can ask for the names of three or more therapists qualified to deal with your particular concern.[46]

When you first visit a relational expert, you don't have to commit to carrying on therapy with that individual. You have every right to be referred to someone else. Furthermore, if the therapist you meet with recognizes that he or she is not qualified to deal with your specific concerns, he or she is obligated to refer you to someone who is. You need to feel comfortable and safe with your therapist. It may take initial visits with two or three relational experts before you find someone you feel is a fit.

WHAT TO EXPECT

When you do find someone you feel comfortable working with, you should experience sessions similar to what is outlined below:

- The therapist will be pleasant but professional, easy to talk to, a good listener and interested in you and the problem you are bringing.

- He or she will ask questions that deepen the level of conversation appropriately, that demonstrate he or she is knowledgeable about what you're dealing with and that are focused on the concerns you would like to have addressed.

- The therapist will be most interested in fully understanding the nature and severity of the problem and how it is affecting you, rather than being quick to give advice.

- He or she will eventually ask for your ideas as to possible solutions or strategies, versus simply championing his or her "favorite" approach.

- At some point—often before you come to your first session—you and the therapist will discuss fees and payment options.

- You will leave the session with a sense that the therapist will likely be helpful to you and will work *with you* rather than doing therapy *to you.*

- At an appropriate time, often not until after the initial visit, the therapist will offer problem-solving solutions for you to consider; the solutions will depend on the therapy approach he or she uses.

- Whatever strategies are employed, you will feel that you are fully informed about them, your questions about them have been answered and you have given informed consent to them. You will feel like an active participant and in control of your experience.[47]

Your most significant personal relationship is worth significant investment. Working toward a more intimate, fulfilling relationship has many benefits: a more gratifying connection with your partner, a more personally developed you, a sense that someone has your back as you go out into the world and the chance to become a more loving person in general. Haltzman, again writing to men, encourages us:

> Be clear about your priorities. If you care about your work and ambition but know that none of that kind of achievement can happen, nor would mean a darn thing, if you didn't have your wife and family as the number one reason to be alive, helping you establish who you are in the world and providing the home base for everything you do, then keep that attitude at the very front of your mind....[48]

The theater was cool and dark, and the mingled aroma of "butter" topping and nacho cheese sauce filled the air. Frank was sitting very close to her—you couldn't fit a popcorn kernel between them—and he was holding her hand.

Katie remembered their first date, nearly 10 years ago, when Frank had taken her for dinner and then a movie, some shoot-'em-up gangster film. Then, the theater air had probably been filled more with pheromones than the smell of edible oil product. It hadn't been a great date movie, but Frank had learned a lot since, Katie mused. On their first date, he had been too shy to hold her hand, though she could tell by his attentiveness and the way he watched every move of her lithe frame that he had probably wanted to do that—and more. Looking back, now well schooled in all his little tics and mannerisms, she knew that he had been nervous. He had fiddled with his fork at dinner, "ahemmed" frequently and picked imaginary lint off his pants. She had been nervous too, but Frank had missed seeing that, apparently. He said months after that night, "You were so poised and together and... 'perfect'.... I thought, 'What the hell is this girl going to think of me?'"

What had Katie thought? She had felt a sense of peace. Frank was steady, quiet, solid... safe. And he hadn't been put off by her brashness, or even her cynicism. He had been a captive audience. He had really seen her, he loved to watch her—and she got a thrill out of that.

Tonight, they were part of the audience at a Spanish picture, part of the yearly foreign film festival. Frank had come somewhat reluctantly, but here he was, snuggled up beside her, his strong hand tenderly around hers. He shifted a little and rested his head on her shoulder. She could smell his shampoo and feel his hair brush her jawline. "How sweet," she thought. Frank wasn't always such a romantic. But here he was, watching a film he probably hated for her sake, cozied up on her shoulder. He was her leading man, for sure. He was... snoring! Katie couldn't help but feel a little disdain... at first. But then she let it go and let him sleep. He was here. With her. That was enough. She rested her head on his and got lost in the subtitles.

6 *Your relational wellness:*
Making relationships work

" It is our choices... that show what we truly are, far more than our abilities. "

J. K. Rowling, from *Harry Potter and the Chamber of Secrets*

Katie and Jude, her assistant, were sharing a rare moment of quiet in the lunchroom. The last batch of cakes for tomorrow's event was in the oven, and the kitchen hands had been set free early.

"I would like you to consider something, Jude," Katie ventured.

Jude took off his apron and laid it on the table in front of him. He wiped a patch of flour from his forearm. "Sure, what's up?"

"I'd like you to consider taking on some more responsibility with Organic Delights, if you're interested." Katie watched his response. Jude leaned in and waited for her to continue. "I've never been great at delegating, and it's hard for me to let go...." If you only knew, she thought, that this business is my dream, and I've been gripping so tightly ever since it became real. "I think you're very talented and competent, and I've maybe kept you from using some of those abilities because I've been a bit of a control freak. I mean, really, I have been." She laughed a little. Jude let it go.

Katie thought about the way she had felt threatened, initially, by Jude's abilities in some areas. He could plate a dish with more artistic flair than anyone she had ever seen. His palate was impeccable, and he wasn't afraid to experiment. He was an artist. If it were possible, his standards were even higher than hers. Once, after a batch of caramel had gone to crystals, he had cursed himself, gone outside to have a cigarette and then been silent for an hour. But he had started the new batch right away, and it had come out perfect—amber and smooth. For Katie it felt like a risk, on the one hand, to unleash any more of his talent. She had always been the Queen of Cuisine—her staff the loyal, admiring subjects. Now she smiled at the thought. You're still a little girl, playing dress-up, Katie.

As she had been revisiting her priorities and getting more tuned in to her relationship with Frank, she realized she wanted more than just a successful business. She wanted time and freedom to enjoy her life, to enjoy her husband. And, she thought, giving Jude more responsibility and opportunities to make decisions would allow him to use his gifts even more. That could only help her business in the long run and make her look good—and make Jude happier. She didn't want to lose him.

Katie looked Jude in the eyes. "Do you want to have more responsibility and creative freedom here, Jude? I'd compensate you, of course, and I'd want your input on how to set that up."

Jude grinned and offered her what resembled a little bow, his palms pressed together. "Thank you," he said. "Thank you for thinking of me that way. I'm curious to know what you're envisioning. I have to be honest: I do have some ideas that you might be interested in... or not."

"I'm sure I would. Why don't we set up a time to get together and talk about this in more detail?" They proceeded to schedule a meeting where they could explore these new possibilities. Afterward, Katie told Jude he could leave; she would pull the cakes out of the oven when they were done. Jude got up, shook her hand ceremoniously and went out the back.

Katie laid her head on the table and cried. It was hard to let go. Why? she wondered. But the tears also came out of sheer relief. She knew this decision, as hard as it was, was good for her—and for her marriage. It felt like a milestone, and she let herself feel some pride in having grown, even just a little. Simply being able to weep freely felt like a milestone.

The timer dinged cheerily and Katie rose, tested the cakes to make sure they were done and pulled them from the oven, setting them out to cool. They were golden-brown, level and aromatic with real vanilla bean—perfect. Her life was like this cake: a beautiful whole, but made up of many ingredients. She realized she couldn't be both eggs and sugar. I'll be sugar, she thought, and breathed in the vanilla.

How do we become more relationally healthy? To improve our physical wellness, we can get enough exercise, follow a healthy eating plan and take supplements to replace missing nutrients. But what is the relational equivalent of drinking six to eight glasses of water a day? Is it giving six to eight hugs or compliments? Is there a relational parallel for getting enough physical exercise? While an active sex life might seem an obvious choice, is that a fair equivalent? It's one thing to define and assess areas where we can improve the way we relate at work and at home, but how do we actually make discernible and effective changes?

It's easy to live in denial. Because relational maladies can't be measured quantitatively, they're often sloughed off as immaterial. We ignore symptoms like communication breakdown or remain ignorant about how people truly experience us. Who needs the burden of meticulously deciphering every verbal exchange? Who always has the guts to tell a colleague that his or her persistent negativity is like a dripping faucet? Do you really want to risk hearing from your direct reports that they think your business acumen is lacking in some areas? Is it really worth telling your spouse what you feel you need, but aren't getting, from the relationship? Facing truth or risking uncovering something about ourselves that's hard to face can feel like putting our very identities on the line. Confronting someone whose opinion really matters to us is frightening for many of us. Sometimes it feels easier not to face these problems at all.

Changing our relational approaches or learning new social skills can seem more daunting than changing our appearance or physical health. It's one thing to change our body physiologically, but quite another to grow as a whole person. Many of us are terrified that we'll be risking who we are, especially in trying to improve our most intimate relationship. Someone else is involved—someone with a whole other set of motivations, perspectives and personal goals. These are variables we simply cannot control. In addition, we often fear we'll have to give up what we want and need, or that we may be rejected. However, improving your emotional intelligence and learning to relate better with your partner—with or without his or her cooperation—doesn't change who you are fundamentally or put your identity at risk. In fact, evolving into a more relationally astute person is about being who you really are—more honestly, more fully and more freely.

There are still stigmas to overcome in business, though the new millennium and resulting shifts in cultural paradigms have made it more socially acceptable to discuss health and even corporate performance more holistically. Many who seek coaching or therapy do so in secret. CEOs in particular tend to be hesitant to reveal any need they have for outside help with emotional or relational issues, even the ones that play out at work. Yet, at the same time, there is mounting pressure on CEOs to draw on an ever-widening range of personal resources. Michelle Conlin, writer for *BusinessWeek Online*, points out, "The global economy has stretched the CEO skill set." And what counts the most in the long run? "Ask board members," Conlin says, "and they'll tell you: CEOs get hired for their skills but fired for their personalities."[1]

But management or human resource consulting, executive coaching, counseling and other therapies are gaining more and more credibility in the professional world. Some organizations are proactive, encouraging their top brass to get this kind of support. John Donahoe, CEO of Bain, the global management consulting firm, says, "Contrary to being a sign of weakness, it's now perceived as a strength if people are getting help and investing in themselves."[2] More and more companies are getting their executive and management teams involved in human resource workshops, emotional intelligence seminars and other relational capacity training.

Making changes in our character seems so daunting. How do we do it? While relational wellness must be approached differently from how we approach our physical wellness to experience real change and greater relational vitality—and we'll see some of the reasons in a moment—we must actively apply what we learn about ourselves and our relationships. Channeling our *knowledge*, recalibrating our *attitude*, *preparing* ourselves for growth, taking deliberate *action* steps and *evaluating* our progress are still the means to a healthier end. In the previous two chapters, we summarized and then assessed our emotional or relational raw materials and how we currently employ them in our relationship with our partner. We've got the knowledge piece. Now, what do we do with that knowledge?

Your attitude toward relational wellness

Have you ever lost a big account or been fired from a job? As you reflect on what happened, are you sure you know why things went wrong? It's easy to point to someone else on the team who dropped the ball, a difficult client, downsizing or an implacable colleague or board. In your personal life, what has contributed to fallout in your love life or friendships? Our ego or the need to protect ourselves from pain may tell us it was all the other person's fault, but is that really true?

ASSUMING RESPONSIBILITY

Even if you've been the victim of underhanded business tactics, a belligerent colleague or board, or an insensitive lover, try to note the ways a different approach on your part may have staved off disaster. If you had fostered greater *self-awareness* in your work life, perhaps by gleaning feedback from colleagues, you might have discovered some blind spots or unanticipated issues you could have addressed. Could better communication skills have uncovered misunderstandings between you and your boss or created greater goodwill? Even if your relationship with an ex faltered and fell apart because he or she was seriously relationally challenged, or even pathologically selfish and cruel, are you *conscious* of why you chose that person in the first place or why you remained with him or her as long as you did? As you look back on past relationships, were you fully *committed* to a positive outcome and invested with a *cooperative* spirit? If you currently harbor resentment or carry your wounds into each new relationship, have you really taken responsibility for your emotional and relational world, or are you abdicating that authority to the mere memory of someone from the past? We often have more power to create fulfilling relationships than we realize.

In his work with The Healthy CEO, Frank had become more conscious of the ways he had leaned on the women in his life for a sense of identity and well-being. His mother was very nurturing, but with her husband gone or busy much of the time, she had used her son as a confidant and tried to meet many of her emotional needs through Frank. Without necessarily being aware of what she was doing, her behavior was inappropriate in that it caused Frank—only a child—to feel responsible for his mother's happiness. Frank also became her way to "exit" her marriage.

Frank's first wife, Lois, was very nurturing, too. This familiar scene created a sense of safety for Frank. Wanting to keep her happy was a learned impulse. But after a while, nothing he could do made Lois happy, and she left him.

Partly in reaction to his experiences with these nurturing women, Frank had married Katie, who he had never thought of as nurturing. She was bold, brash and intense. But she still fostered Frank's inclination to allow someone outside himself to define him. He didn't have to feel anything. Katie felt for him. He didn't have to make any decisions. Katie was happy to make them. And since he was a leader every day at work, this opportunity to be passive was often a welcome relief. Now he realized he needed to take responsibility for his own happiness, feelings and opinions. He was slowly beginning to express these things to Katie, telling her what he wanted in their relationship. They were actually fighting more lately, but they were getting to know one another better in the process. Somehow, they always landed on their feet. The fact that Katie was respecting his ideas and initiative was giving him more and more courage to keep growing—as an agent in his own life, not just someone who responded to his environment.

Even at our best, we can't avoid some relational problems or make people we have to work with or even live with any easier to be around. We are only one part of the relational equation. Still, we are a very significant part. Whatever other factors may be at play, we can still choose our response and perspective. Our happiness and fulfillment are ours to guard, but also our responsibility to maintain. There is mutual benefit to you and your spouse when each of you takes individual responsibility for him- or herself in the relationship. This isn't selfishness or withdrawing from intimacy. It's standing on your own two relational feet such that you are able to contribute your best self to a relationship with your partner. Yours becomes a union of interdependence, an intimate relationship where you're free to meet your partner's needs and have many of your own met without either of you becoming *needy*. Sex and marital therapist David Schnarch says this individual ownership of the relationship guards against becoming "fused" with your partner, or losing yourself, and creates true intimacy. He asserts, "That means taking 100 percent responsibility for *yourself*, 100 percent responsibility for things you haven't done and for things you can still do—regardless of what your partner has or hasn't done."[3]

In our relationship with our partner, taking 100 percent responsibility can be incredibly difficult. We may choose to treat him or her well and not have our care reciprocated. If our relationship has reached a critical stage, such as emotional gridlock, we may feel we are only setting ourselves up to be hurt or made a fool of if we are the first, or perhaps only, partner to try to relate more constructively. When we feel so intensely at risk in this way, like our relational gestures may be mocked or our best intentions spurned, taking full responsibility can be counterintuitive.

It's imperative to remember that any intentionally loving behavior on our part, and not our partner's response, is what defines us. We can lose sight of the gift we also give to ourselves as we commit to being more loving. If you change your behavior, it is as much for your sake as for your partner's—perhaps more so. You are investing in becoming a more relationally healthy human being, claiming dignity and honor for yourself whether or not your partner has the insight or capacity to respond in kind. Couples therapist Harville Hendrix goes so far as to say that partners who reach out in this way, by the very act of loving someone else, are loving themselves. "The love that they are sending out to each other is touching and healing their own wounds."[4]

CEOs who take responsibility for their people skills at work or even for their personal problems, by getting the help of executive coaches or therapists, for example, find not only that they are received more positively at the office, but also that they feel personally rewarded as they work at growing relationally. Scott Flanders, CEO of Columbia House, went to weekly therapy for five years in his thirties. He says that if it weren't for psychotherapy, "I wouldn't be married today, wouldn't be happy" and might not have become a CEO.[5] Michael Levin, chairman and CEO of US Franchise Systems, Atlanta, which owns three hotel brands, says therapy earlier in his career helped him recover from depression and anger over debacles at work. He realized his ability to relate in the office was impeded by his mental state. "As a leader, you have to jump on ideas and provide an environment where employees can be creative and take risks," he says. "It's difficult to do that when you're not in good psychological shape."[6] Because of their unique challenges at work, CEOs are often some of the best candidates for therapy. Furthermore, "CEOs have the same relationship problems and life stage issues as the rest of us," says Robert Michels, a psychiatrist and psychoanalyst at Cornell University's Weill Medical College in New York who has treated top executives.[7] More and more business leaders are taking full responsibility for their relational wellness.

As Katie began to explore some of her deepest fears, she realized she had tangled her identity and sense of self-worth together with being in control and highly competent. She kept her emotions in check and did everything she could for herself, by herself. What better way to protect herself from being hurt by others?

Slowly, she was learning to trust that she was worthy of love and respect just by virtue of being human, not because of how she might perform. Frank was able to help her with this. In beginning to relinquish some control over areas of her business and over some vulnerable places in her heart, she was gradually creating a margin to relax and experience what it was like to be cared for. She was having a hard time adjusting to not always having to be "on," but it felt good to be moving in what felt like healthier directions.

The way we relate to those around us ultimately defines us. Our words and actions are our personal marketing campaign: we can deliberately create our own identity. No one else can brand us. Does the way we relate represent our idea of our best self? Have we taken full responsibility for our own relational health?

FINDING MOTIVATION

The authors of *Primal Leadership*, emotional-intelligence icon Daniel Goleman, Richard Boyatzis and Annie McKee, point to changes in the way today's generation of leaders look at being the top in business, as compared with previous generations. Emotional intelligence seems to be growing in value. The authors say:

> Many young leaders, roughly defined as those under 40, have learning goals that are more holistic—addressing many aspects of their lives rather than just their work—than was the case in previous generations of leaders.... Not willing to make some of the sacrifices that they watched their parents make, they are seeking a balanced life along the way.[8]

What people want out of life seems to be changing. For others, what they thought they wanted becomes disillusioning. Goleman et al. say that the older generation seems to arrive in this same place eventually: "Many of their older colleagues are coming to the same conclusions, but for them it is part of aging, midlife and mid-career crisis."[9] What motivates us changes as what we value changes.

SETTLING THE "WHYS" OF RELATIONAL CHANGE

When we're in touch with our values and who we are, we begin to observe how our relationships, both at work and in our personal lives, align or clash with how we want to define ourselves, what Goleman et al. call our "ideal self."[10] If our relationships are in trouble, there's a good chance we're not on course with our life purpose or our personal values and goals after all. In his typical hard-hitting fashion, Dr. Phil McGraw says it this way:

> If you are in a relationship that has gone awry, a relationship that is laced with pain, confusion, or emptiness, then by definition I know you have lost touch with your own personal power, your own dignity, your own standards, and your own self-esteem.... You've lost touch with that part of you that I call your core of consciousness—that place where you are absolutely defined, the place within you where your greatest strengths, instincts, values, talents, and wisdom are centered.[11]

How do you get back to that "core of consciousness," from which you can draw greater relational capacity? Goleman et al. say we need to compare our "ideal self," or the person we most want to be, with our "actual self," the person people encounter when they interact with us, and then work to bridge the gap through greater self-awareness and intentional steps toward greater relational wellness.[12]

Motivation to start making relational changes can come when we realize that our people skills or our relationships don't reflect our ideal self. It becomes an issue of integrity. Dr. Schnarch points to other negative motivators that stem from no longer being able to tolerate the status quo: emotional gridlock reaching an intolerable impasse, a sense that what or who we love is at stake, or getting to a point where our fear that things will stay the same exceeds our fear of change.[13] This fear of change is very real. It leads people to lose hope, and emotionally check out of relationships—sometimes through infidelity—until they become numb and complacent or irritated and wanting an escape hatch. Without hope, there is no possibility that a relationship can turn around. But hope can come from surprising places.

We can be spurred to hope by positive motivators, like the prospect of greater intimacy once we face and deal with our relational issues, or negative ones, like a midlife crisis, a job loss or an impending divorce. Faced with such crises, our options seem to narrow significantly. Will we regroup, reengage, "fold" or try to move on without heeding where things have gone wrong? Can we anticipate and safeguard against such crises before they happen? Isn't the hope of something better than humdrum (or worse) worth being more vigilant in our relationships? If your relational capacity just needs some fine-tuning, take the time and make the effort to grow in your "weaker" areas. Consider it a relational insurance policy. If you have a great relationship with your spouse, you know so because of the regular and intentional ways you stay engaged with your partner. If you have some real problems to face, harness hope as a motivator.

Preparing to improve relational wellness

While our relational health is more subjective than our physical health, there are practical steps we can take to improve ourselves and our relationships. The first of those steps is to increase our *self-awareness*, an important relational capacity we discussed earlier. Hopefully you gained insight from Chapters 4 and 5 that helped you identify your relational strengths and weaknesses, and areas where your relationships, including the one with your partner, could be improved. Harnessing your *self-regulation*, specifically through *innovation*, along with your *motivation* can help you set and start working toward your relational goals.

SETTING GOALS: THINKING IN THE LONG AND SHORT TERM

If you'd like to increase your capacity to relate well with others or improve your marriage, you're not likely to see any real change without setting some shorter-term goals. In relationships, there's no such thing as coasting. Inevitably, we are either intentionally moving toward greater connection, or we are drifting toward greater isolation. Part of becoming more intentional with our relational wellness is setting goals, similar to the way we set goals for our physical wellness. Let's look at the go-**FAR** principle we discussed in Chapter 3 in context of relational wellness.

FOCUS YOUR RELATIONAL WELLNESS GOALS

Make them specific

If empathy is one of the relational capacities in which you'd like to grow, becoming more regularly involved in building your community—say by offering 10 hours or a fixed donation every month to a charitable organization—is a great longer-term goal. In the shorter term, your more specific action steps might include the following:

- List areas of need—in your community, city or even globally—that you see or that stir you to want to respond; consider how your interests or skill set might mesh with a particular organization.

- Make phone calls to various non-profit agencies to get more information on how they function, what needs they address and how volunteers can help or how contribution dollars are spent.

- Designate a set number of hours each week or month to help, or commit to a regular donation schedule.

You may even want to explore ways your business could help others. Even as you begin to take these action steps, there's a good chance you'll expand your ability to empathize, just by exposing yourself to the realities of those less fortunate.

If you'd like to create a greater sense of *connection* in your most significant personal relationship, some more immediate action steps might include the following:

- Schedule a fun activity with your spouse this week, something you can both enjoy and where there is no agenda other than having a good time together.

- Get an update on your partner's "love map" by asking what he or she identifies as your relationship's greatest strength and greatest weakness. Focus on communicating that you care about your partner's perspective; set aside any urge you may feel to counter his or her point of view or to fix what might be wrong. Just listen and acknowledge your partner's inner world.

- Ask your partner what his or her primary "love language" is. Some couples are actually surprised to find out that they've made the wrong assumptions about what communicates love to their partner.

- Ask your partner to give you a list of 10 things you could do to show him or her appreciation or devotion. When you get the list, do three of the items listed this week.

- Spend an evening exploring new ways to relate sexually, talking through what each of you wants, what feels good and what doesn't.

- Go to a marriage therapist with your partner.

- Go to a marriage therapist by yourself.

There are many other ways you can work on your goal of greater *connection* in your relationship, but these examples give you some idea of the possibilities. You know your relationship and the action steps that would be most helpful. Where you aren't sure or if you don't know where to begin, ask a relationship expert for help. If you are facing a crisis, however, seek outside help as soon as possible.

For our relational goals, setting benchmarks isn't always straightforward. If you want to lose weight, you can count lost pounds. If you want to quit smoking, you can count your nicotine-free days. For many of your physical wellness goals, you can count the hurdles you cross. Creating the same significant markers in your growing relational wellness requires *self-awareness*. This is where journaling or some other way of documenting your progress is particularly effective. The very act of journaling exercises your *self-awareness* and is a valuable tool for seeing how you're making progress. You can compare how you're doing now with earlier legs in the journey by reviewing your journal entries. If, under the capacity of *self-awareness*, you want to improve your ability to *self-assess*, you might conduct a survey of your direct reports or staff at the office, asking specific questions about your performance or how people receive you. To better assess yourself, you might compare the results of the same survey taken six months from now. Aim at producing very different results between now and then. The second survey, though still a qualitative tool, would be a powerful way to measure your progress.

Similarly, you can set benchmarks for creating a more *conscious* relationship with your partner. Start with a list of things you don't know about your partner but are determined to learn—from interests, to opinions, to thoughts and feelings about your relationship—and let your benchmark for success be when you have collected and internalized all of that information. Frank and Katie both realized that they hadn't bothered to explore much of each other's inner world, Frank because he had lost touch with it and Katie because she had so fiercely guarded it. Another benchmark in creating greater consciousness could be the point at which you, together, have discussed and more intentionally defined your respective roles in the relationship or in running your home.

CREATE A MENTAL PICTURE

As a CEO, meetings are a regular part of your business itinerary. You can probably remember in vivid detail one or two that were painfully dull or during which you or someone else made a "fatal" remark. If one of your goals is to improve your *communication skills*—or maybe the communication skills of your whole office—what kind of meetings would you like to see in the future? Try to "see" them now, through visualization. Picture yourself and the usual attendees. Let's say you're chairing this one as a more emotionally intelligent version of yourself. What looks different? Imagine yourself sitting up straight, making eye contact and including everyone in the room as you speak. You're calm, prepared, attentive and tuned in to the comments and the body language of everyone around the table. Picture their responses as you speak with more authority (or empathy) and listen more actively. Are they more alert, more engaged? Inspired? Maybe even laughing? Create a picture that you want to work toward as a way to begin to realize those images.

Imagine your spouse coming home from work to a candlelit dinner that you've thoughtfully prepared. What does the scene look like? What are you serving? Picture the steam rising off the plates. Take in the aroma and let the music you've selected wash over you. Observe your partner laying down his or her briefcase and the expression of gratitude or delight. As you survey the scene, note the sense of fulfillment or joy in having put together such a gesture of care and honor. Feel how your heart and your capacity to demonstrate care and commitment to your partner have expanded.

Remember that visualization does not guarantee results. This is why it's so important to primarily visualize your own behavior and responses; other players in your scene will "improvise." However, the pictures you create in your mind before the actual events will determine what they become. If you imagine episodes that have negative outcomes, you almost always guarantee that result. If you imagine positive outcomes, your chances of experiencing pleasing results are very good.

Golf professionals don't make every shot, but they still win tournaments, thanks in part to the practice of visualization. Gio Valiante, a professor at Rollins College in Winter Park, Florida, has done visualization work with Davis Love III, Chris DiMarco, David Duval and Chad Campbell. He helps players form a selective memory so they think only positive thoughts during their game. He tells Masters competitors to "expect the best and prepare for everything."[14] You can do the same in your relationships.

ADD VALUE TO YOUR RELATIONAL WELLNESS GOALS

DO A COST-BENEFIT ANALYSIS

The estimated average cost of a divorce is $15,000[15]—and that's just the monetary cost. Broken homes leave heartbreak in their wake, especially when children are involved. Yet more than half of all marriages in North America end in divorce. What do *you* stand to lose if you don't realize your relationship goals? Even if your relationship with your partner is functional, how do simple misunderstandings or parallel schedules keep you from enjoying true intimacy? If you consider your relational wellness in context of your professional life, how might you build in relational supports, both from within and from those around you, to prevent burnout, rather than trying to revive your career or tourniquet a nervous breakdown later? Your mental and emotional health is worth taking care of now. As with your physical health, prevention is the best cure.

When you increase your relational wellness in one area, a remarkable phenomenon occurs: you automatically improve in several others. For example, as you improve your *self-awareness*, perhaps in noticing that you habitually reach an inner boiling point when interacting with one particular colleague, you can begin to better *self-regulate* and find ways to manage your anger. Alternatively, with greater *empathy*, you may discover that this difficult person struggles under a chronic stress load from caring for a mentally ill parent. That empathy *motivates* you to interact with that person differently, and you kindle increased *optimism* about the future of the relationship.

With your partner, as you become more *conscious* of dynamics in your relationship, such as projecting past issues with your parents onto your spouse, you can better communicate with your partner about what's really going on. When you harness hope and courage and begin to verbalize your sexual anxieties or unexpressed desires, you can bring the feelings you've been hiding into the light. That's *connecting*. As you become more connected, you create a strong friendship that steadies you both while you more *cooperatively* address areas of your relationship that are in atrophy or are hot spots for conflict.

IDENTIFY POTENTIAL BARRIERS

If you've lived with a back injury where your spine has become crooked, all of the muscles in your body compensate for that misalignment so you're able to walk upright. You keep your balance, but your muscles and joints are strained in ways they were never designed to be. Headaches and neck, back, shoulder and leg pain may result. After treatment by a physiotherapist or chiropractor, our spine is realigned. We're straightened out. But for a time, we will feel strangely off balance. Our muscles must relearn how to perform properly, to transform from dysfunction—even if it feels normal—to proper function. Your physiotherapist or chiropractor will assign you exercises to help retrain and build the muscles in atrophy to balance off the way your other muscles have become stressed from overexertion. Deliberate care must be taken to get the muscles in shape to support the spine, or the vertebrae will not be able to stay in place. It takes time and effort to get things straight and to keep them that way. The same is true of our relationships.

Expect resistance, even if you begin giving your partner what he or she has asked for and even if he or she opts into the plan to transform or improve your relationship. Freud said that underneath every wish is a fear of having that wish come true.[16] Your partner may not be able to accept your overtures at first. It's human to be suspicious of our partner's motives when he or she begins to behave in new or uncharacteristic ways. Especially if you've made such attempts before only to retreat at the first sign of difficulty, it'll take your partner some time to trust your sincerity.

As you draw from your motivation and begin to take deliberate action steps, you will experience some anxiety. After all, you're not just starting an exercise routine; you're exercising a new you, building relational muscles that you may not have even known you have. When trying to turn a relationship around, Schnarch says, "You have to tolerate some anxiety before your anxiety goes down. You can't get comfortable doing something new until you do it repeatedly, and that involves being uncomfortable for a time."[17] Dr. Phil even suggests facing your fears by playing out worst-case scenarios in your mind to their end: "If my partner does do something negative or hurtful when I open up and let myself care again, I won't like it, but I will survive."[18] Fear can incapacitate us such that we guarantee our own discomfort, but if we were to actually face our fears, we might never even experience what we most dread. We're afraid to risk in case there's an awful outcome. So we often settle for "safe" malcontent instead.

Realize before you even begin that you are likely to experience resistance and anxiety as you make relational changes. Discern the difference between taking breaks from working on your emotional wellness—following the principle of taxing and then resting your muscles—and simply checking out using any of the relational exits we identified in Chapter 5. Don't create new roadblocks that don't need to be there.

RELISH YOUR RELATIONAL WELLNESS GOALS

TAILOR YOUR GOALS TO FIT YOU

Doing what works for your relationship is more important than following a prescribed plan for relationship building. Each romantic partnership is its own culture and won't look exactly the same as any other. The dynamics will be different. The challenges will be different. The solutions will therefore likely be different, too. You can use the principles of building a healthy relationship, both in capacity and in function, in ways that suit you and your partner's needs and personalities. If you're very verbal, leave yourself inspirational messages, perhaps quotes from this chapter, where you'll run into them often—on your computer, bathroom mirror or PDA. If your partner "hears" love communicated through gift giving, focus on finding small tokens to bestow, perhaps once a week. This can be a great way to begin what may seem like a daunting task: changing the way you relate to others.

MAKE THEM REALISTIC

For some people, the thought of going to a therapist—a perfect, though well-meaning, stranger—to reveal their most private thoughts and feelings can be tantamount to emotional torture. The anxiety it creates for some is simply too extreme. Dr. Scott Haltzman, author of *The Secrets of*

Happily Married Men, says that some traditional therapy can exacerbate a couple's relational problems by ignoring the differences in the ways men and women process emotion. Women's left and right brain hemispheres typically link better than men's, which facilitates listening and the spontaneous communication of feelings. Men, on the other hand, don't access both sides of their brains at the same time as readily. Quiet time alone allows them to better process their feelings.[19] As a result, loosely structured talk therapy might be very frustrating for a man. Haltzman writes:

> Despite this evidence demonstrating that men can't communicate like their women, therapists urge men to do so and set them up to fail. By trying to generate equality where there is a relative lack of brain ability, therapists increase a man's sense of incompetence, leaving the wife even more disappointed.[20]

The frustration with not feeling competent to "fix" what's wrong can become just one more problem in the relationship. And many women resist therapy, as men do, worried that it won't "work" or that they'll feel exposed, either in the personal nature of the exercise or in feeling open to their spouse's rebuke, or both.

There are many forms of therapy, including male-friendly practical tools that are specific, action based and highly effective. The good news is that many therapists are more knowledgeable about a wider spectrum of therapeutic approaches and aware that different therapies will work for some couples and not for others. Still, if you're not willing or ready to go together, there are many other things you can do: go to therapy alone, read books that offer insights and practical tools, or begin to engage more proactively in behaviors you already know work for you and your relationship. It's better that you do something to move toward relational wellness than set lofty goals without being able to gather yourself enough to achieve them.

BUILD IN FUN

If one of your goals is to increase your confidence, an attribute of *self-awareness*, consider joining a public-speaking club or signing up for martial arts classes. You can work on your relational capacity in a social setting and even work on your physical wellness at the same time. Not surprisingly, as you go after physical, relational and financial wellness more deliberately and watch as you achieve those goals, your confidence will grow too.

Perhaps your goal is to enrich your relationship with a greater sense of significance. Take an evening together and try to capture what you love about your relationship in a creative form. If you like to write, write your love story. Take yourselves on an amazing adventure together. Maybe you're artistic. Paint, draw or use photographs to create a collage or storyboard of your relationship. When you're finished, frame it and hang it on the wall over your bed. Write your own personalized lyrics to a favorite song. Be creative. Play together. Have fun!

Relational wellness in action

Since 1988, sportswear and sporting goods empire Nike has been using the slogan "Just do it." What separates those who successfully achieve their goals from those who do not is often that they "just do it." As you've learned in business, the best goals are useless if they aren't implemented.

GET MOVING

For your relational wellness goals, look at the ones you can begin today and dive in. Which action steps can you take immediately? One of the best ways to begin may be to pick up a book from the recommended reading list at the back of *The Healthy CEO* and begin improving your emotional intelligence a little every day. Or perhaps a significant relational action step for you is to get home today in time to sit down with your whole family for dinner and to put your kids to bed. Some of the simplest steps are the most powerful.

Remember to pace yourself. When you watch a marathon runner achieve his or her goal, you may become inspired to set your own goal to run a marathon, and you likely can achieve it. But "just do it" in this case, especially if you've never been a runner, doesn't mean going out and running 26 miles in one shot. For all your enthusiasm and dedication, you'd fall dismally short of your goal and become disillusioned with your original pledge. A beginning marathoner trains for the big goal by pacing him- or herself with smaller, incremental goals to build endurance and slowly improve the body's capacity for the physical toll running the actual marathon will take.

In the same way, one intense conversation with your spouse is not all it takes to make you a better communicator. Furthermore, your sudden and overwhelming gusto may only alienate your partner, working against your ultimate goal. Start with the smaller steps that will build your relational "muscles" and improve your overall emotional "conditioning." This training will allow you to accomplish greater relational feats later without feeling the same strain, anxiety and exhaustion you might have felt had you just jumped in without being ready.

ENLIST SUPPORT

One of the benefits of seeking professional help is that you find an automatic ally for your relationship or your pursuit of increased relational capacity. As you begin to practice new behaviors or techniques, getting feedback on how you're doing and regular encouragement for your efforts may be the difference between quitting prematurely and realizing tremendous results. Especially if you're working on a troubled relationship with your spouse, you will need someone in your corner. We all have relational needs and finding emotional support from someone who also supports your marriage will help keep you going while your partner can't or won't help meet your emotional needs.

Allies, coaches and accountability partners can help you stay on track with your goals and maintain and improve *self-awareness*. For example, if one of your goals is to better understand your relational strengths and weaknesses with a view to improving areas where you lack some skills, list in two columns—strengths and weaknesses—your character traits as you perceive them. Then find two other people, a colleague at work and a personal friend, perhaps, to provide the same list from their perspective. Or have these individuals look over your "relational wellness plan"—one you create using the same framework you would use to draft a good business plan, with vision and mission statements, capital investment considerations (what it'll cost you), short- and long-term projections and so on—and have these same individuals give you feedback. Again, this kind of insight is invaluable. Just remember to appeal to people whose opinions you respect and who will sincerely support what you're trying to accomplish.

REFRAME SETBACKS AND REENGAGE

Changing the way you relate to others or the quality of your most significant personal relationship will not follow a straight cause-and-effect or input-equals-output formula. There are other people involved, adding several variables, no matter how solid or sincere your efforts may be. There will be surprising successes, but there will be disappointing setbacks as well. As we learned in Chapter 3, when you initiate changes that move you toward improved wellness in any area, you will experience some failures. It's inevitable, so take the pressure to be perfect or to always get positive results off yourself right now. In regard to making changes, relationship expert John Gottman says it's key to find ways to soothe yourself when necessary, to be able to step back from what's happening—especially from emotional triggers or any heightened conflict you may be experiencing—to regain perspective, confidence and calmness. Sometimes what Gottman and others call "flooding," feeling overwhelmed both emotionally and physically, can shut you down. He says:

> I have found that in the vast majority of cases, when one spouse does not "get" the other's repair attempt, it's because the listener is flooded and therefore can't really hear what the spouse is saying. When you're in this condition, the most thoughtful repair attempt in the world won't benefit your marriage.[21]

Instead of allowing things to escalate, it's wise to self-soothe, stepping away from the issue temporarily to calm down and regroup. People can self-soothe in any number of ways: by listening to music, exercising or meditating, for example.

If you understand in advance that flooding may be likely, or if you realize what your emotional triggers are (this goes back to becoming more conscious, as discussed in Chapter 5), you will be better equipped to take these setbacks in stride and deal with them more effectively. Remember that perceived setbacks may actually be evidence of real growth. If you're arguing more with your spouse, it may be because you're just now getting to the heart of some important issues or identifying misunderstandings that you can begin to resolve as you move forward. Step back, process what's happening, do what you need to do to soothe yourself or remind yourself that your identity is not at risk. Keep taking steps toward relational wellness.

Haltzman says:

> To make both your job and your marriage work, you'll haul your butt out of bed on the good days and the bad ones. You'll master certain management strategies, apply due concentration and diligence, and take each opportunity you find to improve your performance and stay at it for the long haul.[22]

Evaluate your progress

TAKE STOCK REGULARLY

As with our physical wellness goals, it's important to check in with ourselves and look at how we're doing compared to the goals we set in the beginning. Doing so at regular intervals will help us to see where we're making real progress so we can celebrate, or to see where we may have dropped the ball. If we're doing a bang-up job in one area because we've become more self-aware, doing a regular assessment of how we're doing in other areas can help us to shift our focus to where it's most required.

REASSESS AS NECESSARY

Recognize and change what's not working. Don't feel constrained by the principles in this book or any other. Use the principles you see here as tools you can use in whatever way works for you. What works *works*, whether it follows some prescribed formula or not. Dr. Phil writes:

> The litmus test for you should be whether or not what you and your partner are doing is generating the results that you want. It's not important that you follow particular principles. It's important that the two of you are comfortable with the principles that work, and then write your own rules.[23]

Psychologists, executive coaches and others, through research and dealing with hundreds of couples or individuals in improving their relationships and people skills, have gained some helpful insights and developed generally useful rules of thumb. But if they aren't working for you, thumb the rules. Adapt them, or abandon them, as necessary.

BUILD IN REWARDS

Making relational improvements or learning new skills can be hard work, and you should reward yourself for your efforts! Each time you reach a goal, celebrate—even if only in a small way. (You may be surprised at the way others begin to celebrate you, too!) If morale around your office is improving, celebrate with a company golf tournament on a Saturday. If you and your spouse are making real progress in your relationship, make a big deal of it. Go away for a weekend, get a massage together, or try some of these suggestions by Haltzman:

- Take a bath together.

- Have sex.

- Have a party.

- Renew your vows.[24]

The added benefit of most of these rewards is that they continue to build into the relational wellness you're trying to develop. Again, be creative, have fun and personalize your rewards.

We might try to minimize the importance of becoming more relationally fit, but research and our own experience can clearly point to the ways better relationships and increased emotional intelligence help us to think better, perform better and even become healthier. Our relational wellness contributes directly to physical wellness and vice versa. And while for ease of presentation relational capacity and the actual functioning of our most important personal relationship have been separated into different chapters, relational skills and capacities are useful in any context, in any relationship. One of Hendrix's counseling clients ("Greg") found that better strategies for relating to his wife ("Anne") also helped him at work. "I've gotten quite adept at spotting hidden agendas," he says. "I know that the issue that people are talking about is not always the real issue. I look for the underlying problems." Greg says he's also become better at empathizing:

> I say to myself, "If I were that person, what would I be wanting or needing at this moment?" Being able to empathize with Anne has given me that skill. My marriage has also made me a better communicator and able to withstand more pressure. If someone at work has a problem or becomes angry, I am able to keep from getting defensive. I am able to get things done.[25]

Perhaps one of the best ways you can invest in the success of your business is to invest in a successful marriage.

Don't wait for your circumstances or your partner to change. Remember, you control your happiness. Your relational behavior defines who you are. You navigate your own destiny.

The supermarket was crammed with shoppers, the aisles dense with carts. Instead of playing elevator music, maybe the store should be giving traffic reports, Frank thought. "Traffic is backed up on aisle nine. Travelers are rubbernecking in the frozen food section, overcome with morbid curiosity about a toddler screaming for ice cream...." This is why Katie usually does the grocery shopping, Frank thought. He, the big CEO, couldn't handle the stress. Katie had sent him a text message at work earlier saying she was stuck at a dinner she was catering. She asked if he could grab some groceries on his way home and said she would have a list to him by the time he reached the store.

Frank found home base in the store—the organic fresh foods section—and looked for Katie's list on his Blackberry. There were only seven items listed: baby back ribs, new potatoes, bib lettuce, baby corn,

Baby Ruth chocolate bars, pickles and ice cream. Had Katie lost her mind? What was she doing asking for chocolate bars? That would mess with their health goals.... Then it hit him. "Baby... new... bib...? Pickles and ice cream?" Oh Lord, Frank thought. He steadied himself on the avocado display. Then he dialed his wife's cell number.

"Yes, honey?" Katie answered, with sappy sweetness. She knew he was on to her.

Frank tried to keep his voice down as shopping carts continued to circle around him. "What are you trying to tell me, Katie? Are you...?"

"Yes."

"You're sure?"

"The line in the little window was blue, Frank. Both times I tested."

"So, this means..."

"Yes."

"And are we OK with this? Are you OK with this?" Frank was still in shock, but he felt himself warming around the edges, thinking about what this new reality would mean.

"I think I am. I think we're ready.... Do you?" Katie asked. She sounded more tentative, softer. Different from the Katie he was used to.

"Yeah... I think so." Frank paused for a moment. "Katie, I love you. You know that, right?"

"Yes. I do," she answered. "I love you, too. But I have to run now. We're setting up the dessert table. Let's talk when I get home, OK?"

"OK. But wait a minute. Was this one of our relational goals?" Frank asked.

Katie laughed, "Nope. Just a performance bonus." She added, "Would you mind picking up some soy milk? We're out." And she was gone.

7 Your financial wellness:
Making sense of your personal finances

> If we command our wealth,
> we shall be rich and free;
> if our wealth commands us,
> we are poor indeed.

Edmund Burke, statesman, author and philosopher

"Your financial wellness is like your golf game," said The Healthy CEO, ready to tee off on the tenth hole. Frank and Katie looked on nonchalantly. By now, they were used to the sage's obtuse illustrations and wellness meditations. "Just like there are nine holes on the back nine, there are nine factors in your financial wellness—savings, investing and estate planning being three. On every hole, you're working with variables: your swing, the course and the elements. With your money, you're dealing with your spending habits, interest rates and investment risk. Some holes are more challenging than others, but you're always operating within the parameters of certain constants: momentum, gravity and resistance, or compound interest, IRA rules and federal taxes. You can compete with your colleagues if you want to, but the real thrill of the game is in lowering your handicap—in improving your own game. And when you hit the ball flush...," said The Healthy CEO before hitting a beautiful, big, gentle draw around the dog's leg, "...there's nothing like it."

Katie was more impressed with his swing than his speech, but she indulged him. She was in her sixth week of pregnancy and starting to feel some nausea, which was becoming more and more of a distraction. She gnawed at a piece of gingerroot, which helped ease the queasiness some. Here they were, hashing out the ABCs—or, rather, the tee, approach and putt—of financial wellness, and Junior was already competing for attention. While she didn't enjoy the physical effects of being pregnant, she was surprised at the way she was enjoying having something—or someone—to think about other than her business. The sentiment surprised her. This is all pretty self-aware of me, she thought, amused. She looked at Frank. It was his turn to take his shot, and he was addressing his ball at the tee box. He doesn't have a care in the world, Katie thought.

Frank's mind was racing. Estate planning.... We'll have to make a will. Tuition.... What does it cost to put a kid through college these days? How much are diapers? He couldn't think about anything other than the new baby. Could they handle this new responsibility? The stress? The cost? He and Katie were in an adult-only condominium high-rise right now. They'd have to move. Where would they live? What could they afford? Should they already be thinking about proximity to schools? There was so much to do to get ready....

"Frank, are you going to take your shot?" Katie asked.

"We have to be ready," Frank said out loud.

"You're already ready, Freddy," she said, teasing him.

I don't feel ready, he thought. He wound up and sliced the ball into the brush.

The Healthy CEO laughed good-naturedly. "Ah, yes," he said. "And, as in golf, if you get yourself into some kind of financial difficulty, there's always a way out."

Katie stepped up and hit a long, straight drive. Right on the money, she thought. She spat out some well-chewed gingerroot.

You have achieved success in the world of business. Maybe you're a high-ranking executive at your company, like Frank, or the owner of a booming small business, like Katie. You may read detailed balance sheets and complex income statements the way other people read the arts section of the *New York Times*. You may have no trouble deciphering the often-arcane language of corporate accounting, distinguishing EBIT from EBITDA, operating income from net operating income, and so on. But has this wealth of financial knowledge and business acumen carried over to your personal life, or do your personal finances need serious attention?

In his now-classic *7 Strategies for Wealth & Happiness*, business coach and motivational speaker Jim Rohn says that even entrepreneurs, CEOs and well-educated professionals often "don't seem to understand everyday economics, the economics of becoming financially independent on a steady, ongoing, ever-predictable basis."[1] The United States may have the world's largest and most powerful economy, but many Americans are flirting with financial ruin. Between 2001 and 2004, the share of U.S. families with any kind of debt rose to 76.4 percent.[2] In 2005, one in every 60 U.S. households filed for consumer bankruptcy.[3]

Previous chapters have demonstrated that wellness in one area of your life inevitably affects the other areas. For example, increasing your physical activity and sticking to a healthy diet will boost your energy levels, improve your mood and reshape your body, all of which will build your self-confidence. These efforts can also improve your relational wellness. In a similar way, your financial well-being will impact your physical and relational wellness.

Financial matters are a common source of stress, anxiety and depression. At their worst, financial difficulties can push people to such relational dysfunction—hopelessness, isolation, lack of perspective—that they feel they have no options. In Japan, the world's second-largest economy, 2003 statistics showed all the signs of a suicide crisis. The numbers were startling: every day, nearly 100 people took their own lives, at a rate of almost one every 15 minutes. What was the cause of all this despair? Officials attributed over 25 percent of all Japanese suicides that year to money problems, linking the despair to unemployment, bankruptcies, accumulated debts, corporate restructuring and other economic problems.[4]

Many CEOs feel financially secure—with enviable salaries, healthy benefits packages and even stock options—but they often create financial stresses equal to their resources, sometimes with adverse effects on their family life or their relationship with their partner. A recent survey commissioned by credit-scoring company Fair Isaac (originators of the FICO score) found that problems paying bills matched in-law troubles as the top source of stress in relationships.[5] While it's difficult to come up with a quantitative measurement of the major causes of marital breakdown, anecdotal evidence from family law experts and relationship counselors suggests that financial matters are a major cause of divorce.

Why are so many of us in an adversarial relationship with our own finances—not commanding our wealth, but allowing it to command us?

Some of the challenges *are* due to factors beyond our control. One such factor is the rapidly increasing cost of living. When home values climb 14 percent in one year, as they did in the United States in 2004 (in some coastal cities, it was 20 percent or more), even high-income earners may struggle to be able to afford the home they want.[6] And mortgages aren't the only expense weighing us down. A U.S. Census Bureau report from 1998 found that "even the highest-income households sometimes had problems meeting basic needs"[7]—that is, essential expenses such as utility bills and dental and medical care.

Another factor beyond our control is the pervasive social pressure to consume. North Americans may feel this pressure more than any other population on earth; the drive to consume in our society is inescapable. Without always realizing to what extent, many of us define ourselves by what we buy—the home we live in, the car we drive or the clothes we wear. And what we can't pay for with our own money, we buy on credit—credit that is easy to get. According to Jean Chatzky, one of America's most popular money experts and author of the bestselling book *Pay It Down!*, "There really is no credit score... at which you can't qualify for a credit card."[8]

The fact that over 75 percent of U.S. households have some kind of debt is a strong indicator that we as a society are living beyond our means. Chatzky sees it this way: "We've forgotten what it means to live on what we make. By not paying off our credit cards, we're living on borrowed money. By not saving, we're living on borrowed time."[9]

What about you?

How does your own financial picture look? Do you have a handle on every aspect of your finances, or is there room for improvement? Do you really know how much money you have, where it's going and how accessible it is? Are you planning for the future, or are you like the grasshopper in the fable of the grasshopper and the ant—living the good life today at the expense of tomorrow? For many of us, practices like spending less, saving and investing are not second nature. Unless you were raised by parents who talked openly about money matters at home and taught you the importance of saving and planning for the future, you probably had to school yourself in matters of personal money management.

In the same way that your physical and relational wellness depend on your increasing knowledge in these areas, there is always more to learn and new ways to grow in your finances. Friends and colleagues can be sources of useful information, and there's no shortage of books, television shows, CDs and the like aimed at teaching the basics of good financial planning. But be warned: like any goal worth pursuing, successful wealth creation and management require an investment of time and energy. You may handle business finances like a pro, but if your work consumes your days (and sometimes nights), you may not be giving the required attention to your personal finances.

Knowledge of financial wellness

FACTORS OF FINANCIAL WELLNESS

You've already committed to assessing and improving your physical and relational wellness. Just as you need the help of a doctor to fully assess your physical wellness, you will need to follow up your financial "check-in" by consulting a financial expert. Once you've gathered all the information you need, you can do a meaningful overall self-assessment of your financial wellness and identify and prioritize areas that require change.

So what constitutes good financial health, and what exactly will you be assessing? These are the factors of financial wellness over which you have control:

- net worth
- household budget
- debt management
- saving
- investment
- tax efficiency
- insurance
- estate planning
- philanthropy

Given your business experience, you likely already have a solid grasp of several of these factors. The goal is not to test your knowledge of financial concepts, but rather to "check in" on your personal finances and identify areas where you are doing well and others you may need to address.

NET WORTH

Understanding net worth

If you went into a store looking for shoes or clothes without knowing your size, chances are you'd have some trouble finding just the right fit. You'd probably get the desired results eventually, but not without expending excess time and energy. Knowing your net worth is a lot like knowing your shoe size: if you don't know your net worth, you will find it difficult to develop a saving and investing plan that fits you just right. In financial planning, there is no such thing as "one size fits all."

Your net worth is not a measure of your worth as a person. However, it is the best measure of your current financial status, and it should be the starting point for your financial self-assessment. Your net worth is the amount by which your assets exceed your liabilities. Typical assets include the balance in your bank accounts and retirement accounts, any real estate you own (home equity), the net worth of your business (if you have one), any vehicles you own, mutual funds, stocks, bonds, the cash value (not the death benefit) of any life insurance policies you have, any money owed to you and any valuable artwork, jewelry, antiques or collectibles you may possess. Typical liabilities include credit card balances, the principal remaining on your mortgage, any taxes you owe, car loans, business loans and personal loans. Simply put, your net worth is the dollar value of what you *own* minus the dollar value of what you *owe*.

The U.S. Census Bureau defines net worth as "the level of economic resources that a person or household possesses at any given time,"[10] and the last part of that definition is key. When you calculate your net worth, the results will be a snapshot of your personal finances *at that particular moment*. If you recently got married and your wedding and honeymoon costs far exceeded what you had originally budgeted, you may find that your net worth at this time is negative. On the other hand, if you receive a sizable inheritance from one of your relatives tomorrow, your net worth might be back in the black in no time.

Many of us make the erroneous assumption that a high income equals high net worth. In fact, there is no simple correlation between income and net worth: your annual income may be in the six-digit range or higher, but if you are weighed down by credit card debt and other loans, your net worth will suffer. The list of celebrities who found themselves in bankruptcy court at least once in their careers, despite having incomes well above six digits, includes animation pioneer Walt Disney, filmmaker Francis Ford Coppola, boxing champ Mike Tyson, Oscar-winning actress Kim Basinger and real estate tycoon Donald Trump. Thomas J. Stanley, author of *The Millionaire Mind*, describes this phenomenon as the difference between being "income-statement affluent" and "balance-sheet affluent." According to Stanley, those who are income-statement affluent have "big incomes, big homes, big debt, but little net worth." In sharp contrast, those who are balance-sheet affluent "focus upon accumulating wealth. Their assets greatly exceed their credit liabilities. Often they have little or no outstanding credit balances."[11] In other words, what you make is less important than what you *do* with what you make.

Despite the dire statistics about national debt, the average household has actually seen an increase in its net worth in recent years. According to the Census Bureau, the median household net worth in the United States in 2000 (the most recent year for which figures are available) was $55,000. This is an increase of about 10 percent from 1998, when the median household net worth was $49,900 (in 2000 dollars).[12]

Most people know the amount of their monthly paycheck or how much money they have in their checking account, but they don't know their precise net worth. And yet, without this crucial number, any attempt at personal money management will yield ill-fitting results at best. Your net worth is your personal bottom line. Knowing where your finances stand now is an important first step toward financial wellness.

WHERE DO YOU STAND?
Do you know what your personal balance sheet looks like? If you know your net worth is negative, resist the impulse to panic or despair over your situation. Whether you are in the red or in the black, you can take positive steps to increase your net worth through smart investing and money management. Not knowing your net worth is worse than having a negative net worth. Remember that this is a fluid number that you have the power to change with every financial decision you make.

HOUSEHOLD BUDGET
WHO CONTROLS THE MONEY?
Frank and Katie had a system for handling their personal finances. It boiled down to this: Katie took care of everything. Both were business

leaders in their own right, but Katie had always been the financier of the two. She liked to be the one in charge, she thrived on stress, and she had a talent for crunching numbers, so it seemed only natural that she would manage the couple's finances. Frank couldn't recall ever formally agreeing to this arrangement, but he hadn't objected to it either: if Katie wanted the added stress of paying the bills every month, he was glad to let her have it. Or so he thought. Now that he was becoming more assertive and more present in his relationship with Katie, Frank found himself wanting to know more about their money—about what was coming in and what was going out of the household. Perhaps Katie had not done so intentionally, but Frank felt she had left him out of the financial loop. Now he wanted back in.

If you and your partner are living together, do you have a system in place for tracking and paying bills? The consensus among financial advisors is that there are no hard and fast budgeting rules and that every couple should stick to the system that works best for them. However, both participants need to know what's going on, and bill paying cannot take care of itself.

In a corporation, the chief financial officer is responsible for managing the financial risks of the business and handling financial planning and record keeping. Some couples find it most efficient to manage their personal finances in the same way—with one person handling most money matters as CFO of the household. This is fine, as long as the designated CFO keeps his or her partner fully informed. After all, if your company's CFO were keeping pertinent financial information from you, would you stand for it? When you go from being a single person managing your money alone to being half of a couple managing your money together, your approach has to change. In her book *The Road To Wealth*, Suze Orman writes: "No matter who pays the bills, it's important that you both be familiar with everything about your finances.... This is the only way for you to be respectful of the money you have in common—and respectful and protective of each other in your essential role as partners."[13]

In Frank and Katie's case, Katie thought she was doing Frank a favor by sheltering him from the stress of mounting credit card bills and the hassle of household budgeting, but she was actually doing them both a disservice. From a purely practical perspective, their arrangement left them open to all kinds of problems. For example, if Katie were incapacitated by a sudden illness or accident, Frank would be left to sort things out, perhaps without knowing where Katie stored their financial documents, what recent transactions she had made or even what (if any) health and disability insurance they might have and the parameters of such contracts.

For couples, this kind of arrangement is also risky from a relational wellness perspective. We may not like to admit it, but holding money is like holding power. When one person controls the finances and the other is left in the dark, this disparity is likely to upset the balance of power in the relationship. In other words, you may create an unhealthy dynamic in which the person holding the purse strings exerts real or perceived control over the other person. Orman writes, "Ideally, you should both think about, touch, and manage your money."[14] As you go through your financial self-assessment, think about the system you have in place for tracking and paying bills. If either you or your partner manages the finances alone, are you having regular, open conversations about your money? Would you consider the possibility of handling the household finances together every month, or being individually responsible for them on alternating months?

MAKING A BUDGET MAKES SENSE

The fact that so many households are spending more than they earn is a sure sign that too many don't have a personal budget. For many of us, the word "budget" is about as enticing as the word "diet." Like tracking your calories, tracking your spending smacks of joyless deprivation. As discussed in Chapters 2 and 3, a good diet is not meant to limit you; it is meant to enable you to do *more*. A balanced diet helps you develop a healthy body. Likewise, a good budget should enable you to grow your wealth and do *more* with your money. A budget can help you develop your financial health. But if the word "budget"—like "diet"—has too many negative connotations for you, try calling it a "spending plan" instead.

Every household needs a spending plan. Even if you are blessed with a very comfortable income, you cannot afford *not* to have a plan. Do you know of any successful company that does not have a budget? Your professional experience has taught you the importance of keeping good books. The same basic accounting principles that apply to your business also apply to your household; tracking your income and your expenses— both fixed and variable—is the best way to ensure that you're using your money the way you really want it to be used.

KEY ELEMENTS OF A GOOD BUDGET

To develop a realistic budget, you need an accurate assessment of your household's fixed expenses (such as utility bills, mortgage payments and car loan payments) and your variable expenses. You may find that the variable expenses, the so-called "small things"—takeout dinners, movies, online purchases, treats for the kids—are taking a huge bite out of your monthly income, and yet they are the hardest to track. Financial advisors often recommend getting a small notebook and pen that you can easily carry in your pocket or purse and writing down *everything* you spend money on for at least a week. Even a pack of gum at the drugstore or a can of soda from a vending machine costs money, and that money can add up fast.

Many people find personal-finance software to be helpful for tracking all their spending—both fixed and variable—by category, drawing up reports that help them evaluate current spending and pinpointing areas where spending should be decreased or increased to meet their financial objectives. It might take a couple of months of actual spending for you to get used to tracking expenditures in this way, but the process will soon become automatic. Then the most gratifying part of developing a spending plan can begin.

Once you have a clear picture of where your money is going every month, you can eliminate needless, wasteful spending and start setting aside money for priorities such as your retirement, your health care and improvements to your home. Imagine being able to devote your money to what *really* matters to you and your partner: building a healthy nest egg, traveling the world, giving back to your community or, in Frank and Katie's case, planning for a new arrival. This is the true joy of budgeting, the part you seldom hear about. A budget tailored to your needs, values and goals won't weigh you down—it will give you wings, allowing you and your partner to develop what Orman calls "a shared vision for the future, and a means of getting there."[15]

DEBT MANAGEMENT

GOOD AND BAD DEBT

In 1989, *Forbes* magazine put Donald Trump at number 26 on the Forbes 400, its annual list of the wealthiest individuals in the United States. At the time, the magazine gave a generous (and much-disputed) estimate of Trump's net worth, pegging it at $1.7 billion. But what a difference a year can make: in 1990, Trump was off the list altogether, and his net worth was estimated at *negative* $900 million. By 1991, Trump was saddled with $3.4 billion in business debt, in addition to the $900 million in personal arrears.[16]

Debt does not discriminate; it can affect anyone—even those who own over 18 million square feet of prime Manhattan real estate.

For the majority of North Americans today, debt is a fact of life. The challenge is not to avoid debt altogether, but rather to understand which debt makes sense and which does not, and then to wisely manage money that is borrowed. There is bad debt, and there is good debt. Most people cannot afford to pay for a house in cash, but that doesn't mean they should never enjoy the security of having a home and the benefits that come with home ownership. A 20 percent down payment and a mortgage is the traditional way to purchase a home. Frank and Katie, for example, would have to purchase a new home soon, so they were considering what they could afford to put down, how much mortgage they wanted to carry and how they should price their executive condo. There were many decisions to be made. As long as the house you buy is within your means, a mortgage is one example of good debt. Student loans used to pay for college tuition are another example of good debt—one taken on as an investment. As Orman says: "Debt has a time and place in all our lives. But the debt you take on must be in alignment with the goals you've set for yourself."[17]

Generally speaking, good debt is debt that is taken on for a worthy cause and only after careful consideration. Bad debt, on the other hand, is usually symptomatic of our culture's "buy now, pay later" mentality. We tend to take it on recklessly, for things we don't need and can't afford. Too many people who carry credit card debt are dealing with bad debt—debt that might have been incurred to keep up with extravagant friends, appease a teenager with expensive tastes or try to please an unhappy spouse. Whatever the reasons behind it, bad debt is bad news, and too much of it can destroy your finances and your plans for the future.

COMMON DEBT PITFALLS

Research conducted in late 2002 by market research and consulting firm RoperASW found that while 88 percent of Americans had enough money to pay the rent or make their mortgage payments every month and nearly as many had enough money to buy their necessities, only 44 percent could afford to pay off their credit cards each month.[18] This is cause for concern. As a rule of thumb, financial advisors caution that if you can't pay your credit card bills in full at the end of every month, you are probably in trouble with debt and headed for worse if you don't change your habits.

How can you avoid falling into the debt trap? Here are five common mistakes to look out for:

Using credit instead of debit – Credit cards represent loans, and with interest rates often hovering around 18 percent, these loans don't come cheap. Unfortunately, too many of us are using this borrowed money to buy things that we really can't afford. One smart way to avoid debt is to use debit instead of credit. When you use your debit card, you can't spend money you don't have.

Making multiple visits to the ATM during the week – Remember the days when you used to have to stand in line at the bank for an available teller to be able to withdraw money from your bank account? Going to an ATM is certainly more convenient, but this convenience is precisely what makes ATMs dangerous. If you find yourself making multiple ATM withdrawals during the week and then asking yourself where all the money went, you need a better system. Decide how much cash you need each week, take it out on a Sunday or a Monday, and don't go back until the following week.

Not tracking your discretionary spending – The so-called "little things"—the variable expenses—do add up. You can easily spend several hundred dollars every month and not have a clue where the money went. That's why carrying around your trusty notebook and pen and tracking everything you buy for at least a month is a great way to rein in your spending. It will encourage you to cut back on the things you don't need and start either saving the money you free up or using it to pay off your debt more quickly.

Taking on large financial commitments that you can't afford – While the small expenses undoubtedly add up, it's the big-ticket, long-term expenses that push many people to the brink of bankruptcy. If your home is more expensive than what you can really afford, if you've committed to car or boat payments that you can't make easily, or if your children are in a private school that is beyond your means, it may be time to reevaluate. As Richard Jenkins, editor-in-chief of MSN Money, advises, "You can undo the damage by slowly unwinding the commitments you've made and choosing something less appealing but ultimately more appropriate."[19]

Not knowing how much you owe, to whom and at what rate – According to Chatzky, not knowing this information "allows you to spend as if the problem doesn't exist.... It leaves you wondering if you're making the right decisions about who to pay first. In other words, it gives you room to hang yourself."[20] If you have this problem, it's time to get real with yourself. Pull out all your bills and face your debt head on.

COMPULSIVE DEBT-ACCUMULATION AND GAMBLING

You stride into your favorite electronics store and feel exhilarated, alive. You didn't come here to buy anything in particular—at least, nothing you *need*—but as you check out the latest digital camcorders, MP3 players and handheld organizers, you feel a familiar tingle. You fiddle with the high-tech toys, you pick a few items that seem to call out to you, and you bring them to the till, your heart pounding with anticipation. You are in the throes of your shopper's high, and you love it. As you drive home, the exhilaration starts to wear off. By the time you pull into the driveway, you're not sure you even want to take your purchases out of their bags. "I charged *how much* to my Visa for this stuff?" you wonder. Now experiencing full-on buyer's remorse, you stuff the bags into the back of your closet and hope your partner won't notice them. With the thrill of the hunt now over, you agonize over how huge your next credit card statement will be.

Does any of this sound familiar? Your weakness may be clothing or fine wine instead of electronics, or you may prefer gambling with your friends in Vegas to hitting the Sony store, but if the broad strokes of this scenario resonate with you, this may be a red flag. Unfortunately, because we live in a society that encourages conspicuous consumption, the problem of compulsive shopping—which often leads to crushing debt—is tacitly encouraged, under-researched and widely misunderstood. It affects both men and women, and all socioeconomic classes, and it's no laughing matter. Studies estimate that as many as 17 million Americans—or more than one in 20—cannot control the urge to shop, even at the expense of their marriages, families, finances and jobs.[21] Compulsive shopping is in fact an impulse control disorder, and, as mentioned in Chapter 4, impulse control is tied to our ability to self-regulate, which is one of the factors that determines our relational wellness. Compulsive debt-accumulation shares many traits with compulsive gambling, and both are serious problems—like alcohol and drug abuse—that can have devastating personal and professional consequences if ignored.

Those in the booming gambling industry have identified CEOs as a key target market, declaring poker "the new golf" for CEOs and describing CEOs as "naturals" at high-stakes casino games because the games demand many of the skills executives use at work.[22] Unlike golf, however, gambling is not all fun and games. In 2001, according to the National Council on Problem Gambling, over 70 percent of adults in the United States reported gambling at least once in the past year. And nearly three percent (almost 9 million adults) met the criteria for either pathological gambling or problem gambling.[23] A survey of Gamblers Anonymous members reveals a strong correlation between suicide and pathological gambling: it found that an alarming 48 percent of GA members had considered suicide, and 13 percent had attempted it.[24]

YOU AND YOUR DEBT

You've read enough grim statistics. Now here's the good news: good debt or bad debt, small debt or huge debt, you still have every reason to feel optimistic and excited about your future. As Orman says, "No matter the size or the variety of debt, it is always ultimately manageable."[25] You *can* control your debt, instead of letting it control you.

SAVING

SAVING STRATEGICALLY

We sure like to spend, but when it comes to our personal saving rates, we always seem to come up short. In June 2006, CNN.com reported that the personal saving rate in the United States—that is, the percentage of disposable income saved—had slipped to *negative* 1.7 percent. It was the lowest saving rate since a hurricane-related record low in August 2005. The story quoted a chief economist at Standard & Poor's Ratings Services in New York, who observed: "We can't keep on spending and not saving. That's going to be a problem going forward."[26]

Federal Reserve statistics dating back to at least 1995 show that among families who *do* save, the most frequently cited reason for saving is retirement, followed closely by liquidity-related motives, such as the need for ready money and for funds in case of emergencies, unemployment or illness.[27] Because your main source of income once you retire will most likely be your personal savings, building a sizable nest egg is your most important long-term savings goal.

However, a comfortable retirement shouldn't be your only savings goal. If you take a strategic approach to saving, you can also set aside a healthy amount for various short-, medium- and long-term goals. Many financial advisors advocate some form of the "70-30 rule" as a saving strategy—the idea being that if you can teach yourself to live on 70 percent of your after-tax income, then you can devote the remaining 30 percent to saving and investing.[28] The first 10 percent should be devoted to saving for retirement (a priority), and the remaining 20 percent can be evenly split between emergency savings to protect your family in the event of unexpected financial hardship and some kind of "fun fund" to pay for anything from an exotic vacation to that coveted vintage motorcycle.

How is your personal saving rate? Is it as robust as it could be? Are you setting aside a significant chunk of your income to cover short-term emergencies *and* long-term goals like retirement income? Could you save even more if you put your mind to it?

SAVING FOR RETIREMENT

By now, you've probably heard countless stories about the changing nature of retirement: the average American worker today retires at 62, four years earlier than people two generations previous;[29] we are living longer, healthier lives and will require more money for expenses in these additional retirement years; and the government pension system is facing crisis and cannot be relied upon for income in the future.[30] When you assess your current retirement plan, you will want to keep these factors in mind.

What's the best approach to saving for retirement? It begins with the concept "pay yourself first." Paying yourself first means putting aside a set percentage of your income on a systematic basis and investing it for your future in a pre-tax retirement plan such as a traditional IRA or a qualified plan established by your employer, such as a 401(k). How much you decide to invest in your retirement account is entirely up to you—this is *your* financial wellness plan, after all—but financial experts recommend that you set aside at least 10 percent of your annual net income for retirement, which is in line with the 70-30 rule.

If you currently put only 10 percent of your income into a retirement plan, but your financial self-assessment reveals that you can afford more, you may want to speak with your financial advisor about ramping up your contributions. Remember, the advantage of paying yourself first through a pre-tax retirement plan is that the money you invest won't be subject to taxes—which means less of your income will be going to the tax man and more of it will be working hard for *you*. As long as the money is not withdrawn, you don't have to worry about paying taxes on any capital gains or dividends you earn. With an aggressive contribution strategy, that dream of early retirement may become reality sooner than expected.

Because every individual's retirement needs are different and because the rules and regulations surrounding retirement plans in the

United States are complex and dynamic, this book can only provide some general guidelines to inform your financial self-assessment. If you need more detailed information, you can easily find many resources exclusively devoted to the topic of retirement planning, such as those in the recommended reading list at the back of this book. To create a retirement plan tailored to your current financial situation and future objectives, you will want to work with an experienced financial planner.

Here are some general considerations to keep in mind as you evaluate your current retirement plan:

- *It's never too late to start, but you should start as soon as you can* – If you can afford it, the best time to become an enthusiastic saver and investor is in your 20s. If you get off to a flying start at the age of 25 and save 10 percent of your annual net income for 35 years at an interest rate of 5 percent, you will have a significantly larger nest egg at the age of 60 than an individual who saves at the same rate for just 10 years. However, saving later in life is still better than not saving at all.

- *Estimate what your spending needs will be at retirement* – Your first step in planning for retirement is figuring out how much you will need. What are your goals for retirement, your vision for the future? Do you want to buy a second home? Do you want to go back to university and pursue another degree just for the pleasure of learning? Do you want to travel the world? Your target retirement income will depend on your current lifestyle and the one you hope to have at retirement, but a reasonable target may be your current annual income (adjusted for inflation). Keep in mind that studies indicate people will need 80 to 90 percent of their pre-retirement income to maintain their current standard of living after retirement.[31]

- *If you own your own business, don't forget about a retirement plan* – Too many business owners make the mistake of not setting up a retirement plan, either because they think it will be too much of a hassle or because they assume they'll be able to sell the business for the "right" price when they're ready to retire. If you're counting on revenue from the sale of your business to provide your nest egg, you may be taking a huge risk. Everyone should have a retirement plan. If you don't have one and you are a business owner, look into plans such as Simplified Employee Pension (SEP) plans, Savings Incentive Match Plan for Employees (SIMPLE) IRAs and self-employed or "solo" 401(k)s. Consult your financial advisor for a detailed explanation of your retirement savings options.

◻ *Research all your options* – If you are a corporate executive, you may be able to take advantage of nonqualified plans in addition to the more common qualified plans. A nonqualified deferred compensation (NQDC) plan, for example, lets you defer the actual ownership of income you've earned and avoid income taxes on your earnings while enjoying tax-deferred investment growth. Although nonqualified plans have fewer restrictions on how much and who can contribute than qualified plans, they do have their drawbacks. For example, generally speaking, you cannot roll these plans over to an IRA, and when you take distributions, they are immediately taxable. Furthermore, if your company goes bankrupt, your nonqualified assets are not protected. Bottom line? Make the most of the opportunities available to you, but make sure any decision you make is an informed one.

◻ *Diversify, diversify, diversify* – When you put all of your savings into one form of investment, you run the risk of losing everything if the investment heads south, and you may limit your return on investment. Allocate a percentage of your retirement savings to conservative assets. That way, you help to guarantee a secure retirement, no matter what happens to your other assets. If portfolio diversification and proper asset allocation are concerns of yours, talk to your financial advisor.

◻ *Consider your partner* – If you are married or in a committed relationship, you will also have to consider your partner's retirement needs. Has he or she been saving? If the answer is no, can your retirement savings cover both sets of expenses? Can your partner establish his or her own retirement plan now? While the two of you can certainly share expenses during retirement, it is important for each person to have the financial independence and security that comes with having individual retirement savings.

SAVING FOR EMERGENCIES

Because life is full of surprises, both good and bad, we can all benefit from having an "emergency fund." This is a cushion of cash that you and your partner can build up to cover unexpected costs. In the event of unexpected financial hardships—anything from sudden job loss, illness, disability or a natural disaster to expensive car repairs and old appliances that need replacing—your emergency fund will offer a financial security blanket. If you dislike the sound of "emergency fund," think of this as an "irregular expenses fund" or a "peace-of-mind fund" instead. Again, following the 70-30 rule, you may want to set a target to put aside 10 percent of your after-tax income for this purpose.

How much money should you have in your emergency fund? Financial experts recommend having a cash reserve large enough to cover at least three, but preferably six, months' worth of household expenses. The actual dollar amount in your fund will vary depending on your monthly expenses, how much you can afford to set aside (if you can afford to save more than 10 percent of your income, you should) and the size of cushion you need to feel secure. However, as a general rule, you shouldn't need to save for more than 24 months' worth of expenses.

Where should you save your emergency fund? Most people will put this money in a checking or savings account at their local bank, but there are alternatives that provide better returns. Instead of letting your financial security blanket gather dust in a standard bank account, accruing a few nickels in interest every year, why not grow your money risk-free by putting it in an online bank with a high-yielding savings account? If the thought of entrusting your hard-earned money to a bank that exists only in cyberspace is guaranteed to keep you up at night, you still have options. Two of the top-yielding savings accounts available are at online banks with brick-and-mortar foundations: ING Direct (a subsidiary of the Dutch bank ING)[32] and Emigrant Direct (the online arm of New York's Emigrant Savings Bank).[33] Both offer FDIC-insured savings accounts with an annual percentage yield (APY) of four percent or more, and no fees, required minimums or service charges. If your emergency fund is sitting in a standard bank account earning one percent interest, consider moving to a high-yielding account and more than tripling your returns effortlessly.

SAVING FOR FUN

With his demanding job and her booming new business, Frank and Katie were always busy planning, goal setting, brainstorming and budgeting at work. But somewhere along the way, they had stopped planning, brainstorming and budgeting for the fun things they used to dream about doing together. They both felt overworked, spiritually and creatively undernourished, and out of touch with their authentic selves and each other. Their sessions with The Healthy CEO were opening Frank and Katie's eyes anew to the importance of rest, creativity and fun. They wanted to balance making a living with having a life, but would they have the means to make their dreams come true?

What about you? Do you and your partner have a "fun fund"? Have you forgotten what fun feels like? If you believe it's been too long since you shared your dreams with each other, make a date to sit down together and plan for something special, something wild, something enjoyable that you want to experience as a couple. It may be as simple as enjoying a day at the spa together or as ambitious as moving to a hot, sunny climate and owning your own vineyard. Not all dreams require money, but many of them do, and different dreams will have different timelines and saving targets attached to them.

The key is to make your dreams as specific and measurable as possible. If you tell your partner, "I've always dreamed of being a rock star...," well, you may have to settle for a raucous night of karaoke and leave it at that. If, on the other hand, you and your partner talk it over and decide that the dream you want to plan for is a second home somewhere near the Rockies so you can ski to your heart's content during winter holidays, then there are specific actions you can take within the next day, month and year to make that dream tangible.

Whatever you decide to plan and save for, make it a priority. Saving for unexpected car repairs may not fill your heart with anticipation, but saving for fun should. Channel that excitement into a focused, systematic investment plan. Commit to putting aside a certain dollar amount on a regular basis (weekly or monthly) into a specific investment with a respectable rate of return. Once again, this is your "fun fund," and you get to decide how much you need to make your dreams happen and how much you will contribute, but if your income allows it, you may want to follow the 70-30 rule and aim to save 10 percent of your after-tax income. Then watch your savings grow, and get your suitcases ready!

SAVING FOR THE NEXT GENERATION

According to a 2004 study by the Department of Agriculture, households with an annual income of at least $70,200 spend a total of $269,520 to raise a child to age 18.[34] Now that they were expecting their first child, Frank and Katie knew they'd have to revise their household spending plan and saving strategy to make room for Baby. They knew they had a healthy combined income—on Katie's end, Organic Delights would still be a moneymaker even if she worked less during the pregnancy and after the birth—and they weren't worried about the added costs of raising a child.

But Katie, ever the planner, was already thinking about another big expense: paying for their child's college tuition.

If you have children, are you saving for their college education? When your children graduate from high school and start applying to colleges, will you fret that you didn't do your homework and save enough money to pay for their tuition? Sending even one child to college could be one of the largest expenditures you ever face. The projected cost for four years of tuition and fees at a private college for a child enrolling in 2024 (approximately 18 years from now) is $281,100. Tuition for the average public college or university during the same period would be nearly one quarter of the cost—$72,700 for residents of the state where the school is located.[35] Needless to say, if you have more than one child, the costs will be much greater all around.

Fortunately, the government has a vested interest in encouraging an educated workforce. Families wanting to save for future college expenses now have more options than ever before. In addition to traditional investment vehicles—savings accounts, taxable investment accounts, annuities and U.S. savings bonds—they can also tap into new education-savings vehicles created by the government, such as Section 529 plans (also known as "qualified tuition programs") and Coverdell education savings accounts (formerly known as "education IRAs"). There are many federal tax breaks aimed at making your child's education more affordable. Do some research and take advantage of what the government has to offer.

While Frank and Katie knew they would have a variety of options to consider when it came time to save for their child's education, The Healthy CEO made it clear that one option should really be taken off the table: using their retirement savings to pay for college expenses. It wouldn't be wise for them to sacrifice their own hard-earned financial security to cover their child's costs. After all, if they didn't have enough saved to cover their expenses when it came time to retire, they might become a burden on their child, and they definitely didn't want that.

If you plan carefully and start saving early, you shouldn't have to make the tough choice between retirement and sending your child to college. Besides saving for college tuition in advance, there are always other financing options: student loans, scholarships and grants (the ideal financial aid), and money earned by your child through part-time work while he or she is in college. Clearly, some of these solutions are better than others, but if you use your retirement savings to pay for your child's college education, that money won't be there for you when you need it.

INVESTMENT

To the untrained eye, investing in the financial markets seems to be for risk-lovers only. The markets are volatile; bull markets come and go, and hyped companies can soar and then collapse on the strength of one earnings report. In truth, the markets can accommodate and reward investors of all stripes—even those who consider themselves faint of heart and weak of stomach. The key is to keep your emotions in check, maintain a long-term focus and ensure that your investing activity is in sync with your personality and investment objectives.

DETERMINING YOUR RISK TOLERANCE AND INVESTMENT OBJECTIVES

What type of investor are you? Are you someone who likes to take risks, whose eyes are glued to the ticker tape and whose only investment objective is growth? Is your TV always tuned in to the fast-paced banter of *Squawk Box* and the opinionated and frenetic shouting on *Mad Money*? Or do you see yourself more as a buy-and-hold investor with a penchant for safe blue-chip stocks and a preference for the kind of insight you'll hear on *The Suze Orman Show*? Neither one of these approaches to the world of investing is right or wrong; what matters above all else is that your chosen investment style suits your actual financial needs and objectives.

Investment objectives typically fall into three broad categories: safety, income and growth.[36]

- *Safety* – If you cannot tolerate any loss of principal and you want to be sheltered from the volatility of the markets, your risk tolerance is low, and you should probably pursue a safe investment strategy focused on maintaining the value of your portfolio. An investment portfolio tailored to this objective should include the safest fixed-income assets available, such as money market securities, government bonds and high-quality corporate securities with the highest debt ratings.

- *Income* – If your risk tolerance is low and your goal is to have investments that produce a steady stream of income during your retirement years, your portfolio should focus on safe fixed-income securities, such as high-quality dividend-paying stocks, preferred shares, and bonds with lower ratings (which provide higher yields).

▯ *Growth* – Younger investors with a long-term time horizon typically have higher risk tolerance (since they have time to recoup
their losses if some of their investments don't pan out). Their investment objective should be capital appreciation. Growth portfolios tend to emphasize common stock, mutual funds and
exchange-traded funds (ETFs).

When you assess your current investments, keep in mind that your
approach to investing should take into account your age, your risk tolerance, your investment timeframe and how far you are from your investment goal. Know your investing personality and allocate your assets
accordingly, taking care to periodically review and rebalance your portfolio as needed.

ALTERNATIVE INVESTMENTS
Are you in the happy situation of having enough discretionary income to
explore alternative investments? If you have a significant amount of risk
capital—capital you can afford to lose—you may want to explore non-
traditional investments such as hedge funds, commercial and residential
real estate, venture-capital-related projects and fine art, antiques or
other collectibles. Even your collections of mint-condition vintage base-
ball cards and comic books might be worth a tidy sum, so consider having them appraised by a professional.

Investing in alternative assets can provide an unexpected outlet for
your creativity, entrepreneurial spirit and passion (for art, fine wine, fixer-
uppers and so on); however, these assets do tend to be more difficult to
convert into cash than traditional investments. If you favor alternative assets, you will have to consider a very long investment horizon.

TAX EFFICIENCY
We all know what Ben Franklin thought about the unavoidability of death
and taxes, but you may find the pithy words of English economist John
Maynard Keynes somewhat more inspiring: "The avoidance of taxes is
the only intellectual pursuit that carries any reward."[37] While no one is
suggesting that you *evade* your taxes, finding perfectly legal ways to
lessen your tax burden and avoid giving nearly half of your income to the
government is always worth the effort.

Even the most patriotic among us will agree that, while we should
all pay our fair share of taxes to maintain our roads, schools, emergency
services and social programs, there is no need to pay *more* than your

fair share. In other words, make sure you take advantage of tax breaks; these are the incentives offered to you in exchange for your contribution to the economy.

When you evaluate your own tax efficiency, pay special attention to these four elements:

- *Tax deductions* – Ask your accountant to help you take advantage of every deduction to which you are entitled. As you know, those who own their own businesses can claim many deductions in exchange for their efforts.

- *Tax-efficient portfolios* – No one likes to lose money, but when tax time comes around, your capital loss carryforwards can be used to your advantage. According to the tax rules, they may be set off against capital gains or regular income to minimize your tax burden.

- *Entrepreneur-focused retirement plans* – If you are a business owner, you can preserve more of your income by increasing your contributions to entrepreneur-focused retirement plans such as SIMPLE IRAs, SEPs and individual or "solo" 401(k)s.

- *Charitable giving* – The government offers tax incentives—which often change over time—to encourage charitable giving. Of course, generosity is its own reward, but when you make a qualified charitable donation, there is no reason to not accept the tax benefits.

To the uninitiated, tax law can seem convoluted and arcane, and it often changes. If your financial self-assessment raises tax-related questions that you and your partner can't answer, put them in writing and be sure to bring them up when you meet with your financial advisor, accountant, tax lawyer or other financial expert.

INSURANCE

Like doing your taxes, buying the right insurance for your various needs can be a daunting and confusing task for even the most fiscally responsible person. If you feel overwhelmed by all the different types of insurance—health, home, life and disability, to name but a few—and the hundreds of different policy options out there, the desire to throw in the towel and forgo insurance altogether may be strong.

But if you fail to address your basic insurance needs throughout your adult life, you are putting yourself and your family at risk. According to Orman, making sure you're well-insured is "financial self-protection at its most fundamental," and it is a crucial part of planning for financial freedom.[38] You may have built up significant wealth through your job, your own business, your investments and so on, but if you do not protect yourself and your assets with insurance, it could all slip through your fingers.

HEALTH AND LONG-TERM-CARE INSURANCE
According to the Census Bureau, the likelihood of having health insurance rises with a person's income.[39] Are you and your spouse currently covered by health insurance? If not, make it a priority. Health insurance is becoming increasingly complex and expensive, but—as cliché as it may sound—you cannot put a price on your health and well-being. Health insurance is perhaps the most important insurance you can have: Without proper coverage, an illness or an accident can wipe you out financially. What took you years to build could be gone in a matter of months.

In 2004, nearly 60 percent of Americans had health insurance through their employer,[40] but if you are your own boss, or if your employer does not provide this insurance, you need to purchase your own. As you near retirement, you'll also want to consider long-term-care (LTC) insurance, which provides for any type of medical, social or support service you may need over an extended period of time. Standard health insurance typically does not offer long-term benefits. While it is true that LTC premiums can be very expensive, the cost does not compare to the exorbitant price tag of a nursing-home stay. Furthermore, one in two people who have LTC insurance will use it, yet it is the one type of insurance that most people don't bother getting.[41]

LIFE INSURANCE
If you are single and have no dependents, you do not need life insurance. However, if you have a spouse or dependents—relatives who depend on your current income and your future earning power—then you should consider life insurance.

Be aware that not all financial advisors see this type of insurance as an essential financial-planning tool or a must-have for people with dependents. Depending on your financial situation, your advisor may recommend that you forgo life insurance and instead provide for your dependents with funds invested in a good savings vehicle. Whatever you decide to do, the matter of life insurance should be looked at in the context of your overall estate planning.

DISABILITY AND CRITICAL-ILLNESS INSURANCE

During your working life, you're far more likely to require disability insurance than life insurance, yet this important form of self-protection is often overlooked. Many people take disability risk management for granted, assuming that the Social Security system will take care of them if they become disabled. In reality, qualifying for Social Security benefits can be difficult, and you may have to wait a long time before the benefits kick in. If and when you do get your benefits, Orman says, you won't be overwhelmed by the government's generosity: "the average disability benefit in the United States is $839 per month."[42]

If you and your spouse don't have disability insurance, there are good reasons to go to the private insurance market and get it—even more so if one of you is self-employed. Orman gives a compelling argument for why we should all make disability insurance an essential part of our financial wellness plan:

> In financial terms, disability is potentially more problematic than dying. Dead, you have no further expenses. Disabled, you not only can't work, but your expenses may be higher, depending on what kind of medical care and services you need to accommodate your disability.[43]

Introduced to the U.S. market in the late 1990s, critical-illness insurance is a relatively new type of insurance policy that pays you if you are diagnosed with any serious disability or life-threatening disease.[44] This is not to be confused with so-called "dread disease" insurance, which has been around for decades and is known for expensive policies that cover only one disease—such as cancer—and pay only small sums of money on a daily basis. Critical illness insurance offers a *lump-sum* payment immediately after the 30-day survival period from the date of diagnosis. If you are concerned about the expenses and lifestyle costs associated with health risks, critical illness insurance may be right for you. While this type of insurance is sometimes described as a cross between health insurance, life insurance, disability insurance and long-term-care insurance, it is not meant to act as a substitute for any of these other insurance vehicles.

HOMEOWNER'S INSURANCE

The home you own is one of your greatest investments. How are you protecting your personal property? Is your home protected from fire, weather disasters and theft? What about acts of terrorism?

Because your lending institution requires you to get some insurance on the building, you don't have much of a choice when it comes to deciding whether to be insured. However, you may not have enough coverage, or you may be paying too much for what you do have. Don't assume that the good people at your lending institution are looking out for you. Bottom line: you want homeowner's insurance that will allow you to replace your home and its contents should something catastrophic ever happen to it. You want replacement-cost coverage. Your financial advisor or a reliable insurance professional—not one who's just out to make a sale—can help you make choices that best suit the insurance needs of you and your spouse.

ESTATE PLANNING

In a recent study, Boston College researchers John J. Havens and Paul G. Schervish found that there is an astonishing level of accumulated wealth in this country, and that somewhere between $45 trillion and $150 trillion will be transferred through inheritance over the next half century.[45] Your own beneficiaries, current or future, may be among the fortunate group that gets to enjoy this abundance 50 years down the road.

THE IMPORTANCE OF AN ESTATE PLAN

There are many good reasons to make estate planning a significant part of your journey to financial wellness. Planning your estate is a continual process that goes far beyond just writing up a will. Not only can a well-constructed estate plan alleviate the financial impact of your death on those you leave behind, but it can also be used as an opportunity to impart your values to your heirs and teach them the importance of proper money management. Asked by *Fortune* magazine in 1986 whether he would bequeath his enormous wealth to his children, Warren Buffett—now known as the second-richest man in the world—replied that, in his opinion, the perfect amount to leave children is "enough money so that they would feel they could do anything, but not so much that they could do nothing."[46]

You can use estate planning as an opportunity to talk openly with your spouse, your children (provided they are old enough) and anyone else who will be financially affected by your death. Handled properly, the discussion doesn't need to be morbid or depressing, but neither should it be businesslike and devoid of emotion. Ideally, it will be freeing and empowering, and will address both practical and affective matters in relation to your estate. For example, if one of your daughters really wants to assume a leading role in your business after you die, this is the time to discuss succession planning; if one of your sons just wants to make sure he inherits the antique desk in your home office, you can make that happen too. Discuss your intentions with your family. Teach your heirs about the importance of money *before* they receive their inheritance and can no longer turn to you for guidance. See to it that they understand how to manage and preserve money instead of just spending it. Where there is open communication, there is understanding and, therefore, less opportunity for conflict.

Few things can stir up as much family discord as matters of inheritance. The emotions involved are complicated, and the bitter combination of grief and greed that sometimes comes up after a loved one dies can bring out the worst in people. Avoiding family conflicts is one of the most important objectives of estate planning.

Do you have an estate plan? Have you thought about how you will preserve your estate for your beneficiaries? Do you know what you want to distribute, when and to whom? If something happened to you tomorrow, would your beneficiaries be prepared for their inheritance, or would they squander it and squabble with others for a bigger piece of the pie?

As you evaluate your existing estate plan or devise a plan for the first time, you will also want to keep in mind three important documents: a will, a living trust and a power of attorney.

- *Will* – If you don't want the state to decide how your assets get distributed, you need a will. If you have young children and you want to name a person who will be responsible for their care when you die, you need a will. If you want to designate someone to handle your financial affairs (including taxes and debts) after your death, you need a will. Do you have one? Where is it filed? When was it last revised? Does it reflect your current situation? Who is the executor? Do you have guardians for your children? Who are your beneficiaries?

- *Living trust* – The most popular kind of trust is the revocable living trust, and it is becoming an increasingly common, cost-effective supplement to wills. With a revocable living trust, you can adjust the provisions of the trust and enjoy the benefits of your assets while you're alive, while having peace of mind knowing that, upon your death, your estate will be transferred without your beneficiaries having to go to probate court. Do keep in mind, however, that you still need a will—specifically, one known as a "pour-over" or "backup" will—if you have a revocable living trust.[47]

🗋 *Power of attorney* – This legal document ensures that someone designated by you will look after your financial affairs if you become incapacitated or if you can't be present to sign necessary legal documents for financial transactions. Be sure to appoint your agent wisely; he or she should be a trusted family member or friend, or a reputable, honest, time-tested professional.

Whichever approach you choose to take with your estate plan, be sure to seek the assistance of a certified estate-planning attorney to avoid errors, omissions or misunderstandings.

PHILANTHROPY

At the dawn of the twenty-first century, we seem to be witnessing not only a massive accumulation of wealth in the United States, but also an unprecedented amount of philanthropic activity. In late June 2006, Warren Buffett, who had vowed 20 years earlier to give the bulk of his astounding wealth not to his children but to charity, made good on his promise in a huge way. The man known as "the Oracle of Omaha" announced that some $30 billion of his fortune would be transferred to the Bill and Melinda Gates Foundation, which already has the biggest endowment of any in the country. "I'm lucky enough to have accumulated it," Buffett said, "and I thought it was time to contribute back to society. The only question was how to do it."[48] And the way he did it was with the largest philanthropic gift in history.

BUILDING A LEGACY

While the generosity of both Buffett and Gates is remarkable, it is worth remembering that you don't have to be a billionaire investor or a high-tech pioneer to leave behind your own legacy. Even if you don't belong to the mega-rich elite, you can still embrace charitable giving as a way to give back to society and pass down a spirit of charity to your heirs. What cause matters most to you? Education, health care, the environment, the arts, building community or building understanding between cultures? What will your legacy be?

ENHANCING YOUR PROFILE

You can use your charitable activities to benefit not only your community, but also your reputation or that of your company. This type of giving, known as "strategic philanthropy," can be an excellent public-relations solution for a small business owner with limited resources who wants to make an impact on the community and enhance the business's public profile. This is most effective when your contributions are a logical extension of your business.

REDUCING TAXES AND PRESERVING WEALTH

As mentioned earlier, there are also tax incentives to charitable giving. If you are hoping to receive a tax benefit from your charitable donations, make sure you know what constitutes a deductible donation, what deduction ceilings you need to look out for and what records you need to keep when giving to charities.

You may also want to consider establishing a charitable remainder trust. This kind of trust allows you to give your assets in trust to benefit a tax-qualified charity (thus giving you an income-tax deduction), while also letting you receive income based on the value of the assets you've given away, for as long as you're alive. Keep in mind, however, that at death the entire principal of the trust will be paid to the charity (and not to your children, for example). A good trusts and estates attorney can help you crunch the numbers and weigh your options.

Consulting a financial advisor

Financially successful individuals almost always use professional financial advisors. Like a good fitness instructor, a top-notch advisor can guide you on the journey to financial wellness, give you solid advice and whip you into fiscal shape. You cannot be an expert in all areas of wealth management, but if you hire skilled and experienced advisors who have the knowledge you need, you'll be able to grow and protect your wealth.

To get a proper, thorough assessment of your current financial wellness, you must enlist the help of a financial advisor. He or she will give you a baseline assessment and be able to recommend further consultation, as necessary, with other experts who may already be part of your team, such as a certified retirement services professional, an attorney, a certified public accountant (CPA) or an insurance professional. Choose your team carefully.

HOW TO FIND A FINANCIAL ADVISOR

PERSONAL REFERRALS

One of the best ways to find a financial advisor is through your friends, family and colleagues. You can start by seeking out at least three solid referrals from personal contacts whose financial wellness you admire. Your golfing buddy who manages to save for retirement and emergencies and still has money to spare for exotic vacations? Buy him lunch and ask him for the name of his financial advisor. Your older sister with the foolproof estate plan? Call her up and ask who helped her with her will and living trust.

PROFESSIONAL ORGANIZATIONS

If your contacts don't yield enough good leads, you can do some online research with professional groups such as the Financial Planning Association[49] and the National Association of Personal Financial Advisors.[50] The U.S. Securities and Exchange Commission website[51] is an excellent resource for those who want to check out an investment advisor and make sure he or she has a clean record and solid credentials. Choosing your financial advisor is one of the most important financial decisions you'll make, at least at the start of your financial planning.

SCHEDULE A MEETING

Once you've done your sleuthing, checking out the credentials and investment performance of your prospective financial advisors, schedule a face-to-face interview with at least two or three of them before you decide which one is the best match for you.

Treat these preliminary meetings as job interviews: you are interviewing these financial planners to find out what they can do for *you*, not the other way around. If they want to manage your money, they will have to work for it. If you go into your meeting as a knowledgeable client, your prospective advisor is less likely to control the agenda. Remember: your money and your financial wellness are at stake, so you need to be in the driver's seat.

QUESTIONS YOU SHOULD ASK

A number of nonprofit educational and consumer organizations offer free tools to help you choose the right financial professional for your needs. For example, the Association for the Advancement of Retired Persons offers a financial advisor questionnaire in PDF,[52] and the Certified Financial Planner Board of Standards has a list of 10 questions[53] to ask when choosing a financial planner.

Here are some questions you'll want to ask when interviewing prospective advisors:

- What are your credentials?

- How much experience do you have?

- What services do you provide?

- What are your expectations of me (for example, keeping you informed of significant life changes that may affect my finances)?

- How often do you see your clients?

- Can I get references from other clients?

- Do you have any questions for me?

As you speak with these financial planners, you will want to explore their philosophy of money management. Any financial advisor worth his or her salt should be able to clearly articulate his or her philosophy. Does his or her approach appeal to you? Are you compatible? Remember that your financial advisor will, ideally, be a part of your financial wellness team for decades to come. You need to be able to envision yourself having a productive, long-term relationship with him or her. Tap into your emotional intelligence and ask yourself, "Will this person have my best interests at heart?" Call on your reason, then go with your gut.

PREPARING FOR YOUR MEETING WITH A FINANCIAL PLANNER

When you have your first session with your chosen financial advisor, you need to be ready to get down to business. Come prepared to discuss your financial history, the current state of your finances and your financial objectives for the future. Bring all the documents that represent your current financial position—assets and liabilities, insurance policies and so on. The advisor may let you know beforehand what documents he or she would like to see at your first meeting. Make sure you know where they are.

WHAT TO EXPECT

QUESTIONS THE FINANCIAL ADVISOR SHOULD ASK YOU

A good financial advisor will let you do most of the talking in your first few meetings to get a handle on your needs and goals. When it comes time for him or her to take the reins, he or she should ask specific questions about your goals, your job security and health, whether you have a will, if you currently own a home or plan to buy one in the future, and what kind of non-mortgage debt you have. If you have children, the advisor should ask what your plans are for their college education and talk to you about estate planning. A smart advisor will ask if you expect to receive an inheritance and if you anticipate needing to provide financial support for your parents. Talk of investing should come later in the conversation, but when you do discuss it, the advisor should ask about your timelines—for example, do you need to access money for your child's college education in five years or in 15?—and your investment personality.

SETTLING THE TERMS OF YOUR PROFESSIONAL RELATIONSHIP
When you enter into a new relationship with a financial advisor, there are certain administrative questions you will want to have answered up front:

- *What will the services cost?*

- *How will I pay for your services?* – Planners can be paid in several ways (salary, fees, commissions or a combination of fees and commissions). Find out how you will be charged.

- *What services will be provided?* – Ask the planner to provide you with a written agreement that details the services that will be provided. Keep this document in your files for future reference, and be sure to ask for clarification on any points that are confusing to you.

UNDERSTANDING AND EVALUATING THE RESULTS

Once you have completed your financial self-assessment and followed it up with a meeting with your financial advisor, you should have a clear road map of the path you need to follow to achieve financial wellness. You are likely to find areas in which you're doing exceedingly well—perhaps you're the very model of conservative spending and diligent saving—and other areas in which you could be doing better. Evaluate the results and identify which areas require urgent attention and which should be addressed in the near future.

In the next chapter, you will find tips on how to prioritize your goals and identify motivators to make changes in the areas you have isolated. You will use your *knowledge* to check and refine your *attitude*, *prepare* for change through goal setting, take precise and deliberate *action* steps toward wholeness, and mark and *evaluate* your progress.

Frank taunted Katie in a playground chant, "Katie's belly's gettin' bigger, Frankie's belly's gettin' smaller…." Frank was still losing weight steadily and feeling good about it.

"You're so juvenile, Frank. Who's gonna be the child in this family? Remind me." Frank was rubbing her still-flat stomach and she gently pushed him away. "I thought you wanted to go over these numbers with me." They had been reviewing their finances and looking at how their income and expenses would change over the next year or two. Katie knew she wanted to reduce the time she was working every week, but they had to consider what it would cost to buy a new home, too. They weren't in any kind of financial trouble, but there would be some changes, for sure.

"Frank Junior," Frank interjected.

"What?" Katie glared at him.

"The child in this family will be Frank Junior."

Katie wagged her finger at Frank. "No... no, no, no, no. If this baby is a boy, he will certainly not *be another Frank. It's bad enough having one. What would I do with* two *of you running around here?"*

"Well, first off, we won't be around here. We'll probably be in some suburb somewhere, remember? Me fixing the engine in the pickup truck and you in a flowery frock dandling Frank Junior on the front porch...." He started kissing her neck.

"I'd die if you even bought *a truck—and there will be* no *frock and* no *dandling. The porch I could maybe see. And speaking of which, when are we supposed to meet the real estate agent?" She was half-heartedly pushing him away.*

Frank persisted. "Not for another half hour. Plenty of time to..."

"Hold up, big boy. We've had plenty of 'relational wellness' this week." She got up and dragged him to his feet by the arm. "Come on, Frank Senior. Let's go look for our house. Maybe we'll find you something with a garage you can tinker in. If you're lucky, maybe I'll meet you on the driveway sometime in a flowered frock." She kissed his cheek.

They made their way to the door. "OK," Frank said, sighing. For a moment, he imagined them in their home—maybe enjoying a pool in the backyard—as a family. He could see a wet creature like a tadpole, diving and bobbing, squealing playfully. The little creature in his scene surfaced, wiped water away with little pink hands and clambered over the edge of the pool. Two innocent bright green eyes looked at Frank through long dark locks, plastered flat against small, round pink ears.

"Daddy!" the creature called, embracing Frank's waist with her pudgy arms. She was adorable. Frank stirred from his reverie. Katie was already in the hall.

"What about 'Francesca'?" he called after her. He turned out the light and closed the door behind him, leaving the room dark.

8 *Your financial wellness:*
Realizing your true capital

"Money frees you from doing things you dislike. Since I dislike doing nearly everything, money is handy."

Groucho Marx, actor and comedian

There on the screen was their baby, with what the ultrasound technician assured them were 10 fingers and 10 toes, along with all the other requisite body parts. Suddenly, the reality of this life growing inside her hit Katie in a new way. This little person was going to change her life. Those little feet would learn to walk and then run. Those fingers would wrap themselves around hers; those arms would embrace her. From what she had heard from her friends who had children, those fingers would also smear stewed prunes and peas on the wall and find ways to get into all sorts of trouble. No matter, Katie thought.

Frank was fixed on the screen, looking for telltale signs of the baby's sex. "There, there!" Frank pointed. "It's a boy! What'd I tell you, Katie?"

"Actually, Mr. Johnson," the ultrasound technician said gently, "that's the baby's kidney. Your baby isn't in a position where we can determine the sex at this time."

Frank had mixed feelings. He and Katie had determined that they wanted to know the sex of their baby before he or she was born, mostly to help them plan for the child's arrival. They would know what clothes to buy and how to decorate a nursery. Katie was adamant that their baby, boy or girl, not be constrained by strict blues or pinks, but she did want her child to be dressed to the nines and have a room of his or her own, customized with an individual in mind. It didn't look like they'd be able to get that information today. Everything looked good, though, which was a relief.

Frank didn't want to have to think about it, but he had an important meeting to chair in an hour. He was supposed to hear from his design team on their pitch to a potential new client. It would be a big contract if they landed it. Frank felt torn. It was so easy to become focused on the baby, on the new house they were set to buy (theirs if the sale closed in the next 48 hours) and on how Katie was feeling. Still, he knew he needed to harness that interest in his family life and let it drive his commitment to things at work as well. He and Katie wanted to make sure they provided their child with a stable home. That meant a sure financial foundation to build on.

Katie had been slowly delegating more and more work to Jude, pulling back on her hours. Frank was ambivalent about this: he was proud of Katie for being able to let go of some of the responsibility, and also of the way she could become so consumed with work because of it, but he also felt pressure to pick up the financial slack. They'd gotten a good price on their condo, but the new house was definitely a step up. The mortgage payments were larger, transportation would be trickier, and they didn't know anyone in their new neighborhood. Frank felt a lot of weight on his shoulders.

He knew Katie had mixed feelings, too. She loved having her hands in the business, literally. It was a good day when she came home covered in flour or smattered with hollandaise. She didn't like feeling torn, stuck in the no-man's-land between two different potential realities: full-fledged career woman and full-time caregiver to her child. Frank couldn't scale back his position. Could any mother have it all? What was "it all" exactly anyway? She wasn't even sure she knew what she wanted.

Still, both Frank and Katie were already embracing this new life they would bring into the world. They were also trying to embrace the idea of the new life they would live—and its challenges—as best they could. Their baby's image on the monitor squirmed as the probe gently disturbed the usual calm of the womb. The heart pulsed visibly, strong. Ba-bum... ba-bum... ba-bum.... Frank and Katie felt their own hearts beat faster.

Jack Welch, General Electric's no-nonsense former CEO, once said, "An organization's ability to learn, and translate that learning into action rapidly, is the ultimate competitive advantage."[1] Throughout your career, you've probably seen that the same applies to individuals: those who take their knowledge and put it to work for them are guaranteed to see better results than those who hesitate to apply what they've learned.

In their meetings with The Healthy CEO, Frank and Katie were learning that true financial wellness comes not from a hefty paycheck, but from smart money management—things like creating a spending plan, saving for their child's needs, planning for retirement and protecting themselves with good insurance. They were eager to put theory into practice and to start making some positive changes.

The sooner you put your financial knowledge into action, the sooner you can overcome any obstacles presently blocking your path to financial wellness. In this context, time truly *is* money. Those who carry large amounts of debt know all too well the real cost of delaying action: the longer you wait to pay off your debt, the more you owe, thanks to late-payment penalties and accumulating interest on your balance. While it is true that it's never too late to build a significant cache for retirement, the consensus among financial advisors is that the more you can put away sooner, the more dramatic that fund's growth will be.

The sooner you start saving and investing your money, the greater the returns you will see in the long run, thanks to the power of compound interest. Albert Einstein is said to have called compound interest "the greatest mathematical discovery of all time."[2] The concept of compounding is simple: When you invest your money, you earn interest on your capital. The following year, you earn interest on both your original capital and the interest from the first year. In the third year, you earn interest on the original amount and the first two years' worth of interest. And on it goes. Compound interest, or earning interest on interest, is yet another reason why time is money. The earlier you start investing, the more time you leave for your money to work for you and *earn* for you—all by itself.

Your business experience can give you an advantage over the millions of people who carry debt and struggle to live within their means every day. You already understand the importance of balance sheets, budgets and spending plans, and you have seen firsthand what it takes to make a company prosper. Now you can apply that knowledge, along with the information you gathered in your financial self-assessment, to your personal finances. If you were asked to provide up-to-the-minute financial statements to your board, or if you were forced to cut costs in your own business, you would closely examine your financial standing and produce results quickly enough. Assessing and improving your personal finances should be approached with the same discipline. Yes, tracking your expenses, facing any debt you may have and researching insurance plans will often feel like pure drudgery, but the time and effort you invest in your finances today will yield huge dividends in the future.

The previous chapter summarized the key elements of financial wellness. Acquiring *knowledge* is only the first step in making real and lasting change. Whether you are working on your physical, relational or financial wellness, building and maintaining the life you want requires a genuine desire for change, a sense of purpose, a commitment to action and the discipline to see things through. In other words, it requires the right *attitude, preparation, action* and *evaluation*.

Your attitude toward financial wellness

Your financial wellness—everything from how much you earn and save to how much you owe and how much you leave to your heirs—is entirely within your control. If your assets are dwindling and your liabilities keep piling up, you may feel the all-too-human urge to blame others for your problems: You wouldn't be in debt if your board would give you another raise. You could save more for retirement if your kids would stop pressuring you to buy more things. You could take your business to the next level if your spouse would give you the support you need. Passing the buck is usually easier than admitting the crucial role you play in your own success or failure. But a decision to assume personal responsibility for your finances can be one of self-respect, as much as it is about who's in charge.

Self-respect, which most of us would identify as a matter of relational wellness, is also key to our financial wellness. For many of us, our debt is about more than money: it is often about trying to compensate for an *emotional* debt. Dr. Robin Smith, a psychologist and regular contributor to *The Oprah Winfrey Show*, says that those who struggle with financial debt are typically "trying to fill a spiritual wound with a cheap surrogate... the deeper the wound, the more I go spend."[3] The wound may stem from a feeling of being neglected or hurt in childhood, of being rejected by one's peers or of being disrespected by one's spouse. The details will differ for each person, but the "cure" or the antidote is the same for everyone: to cultivate a sense of self-respect, a sense that we are good enough and that our worth as individuals does not depend on flashy cars, lavish houses or expensive suits.

Being able to cultivate a clear sense of who we are and what gives us worth—apart from our net worth—allows us to use money as a helpful tool. Our finances, our material means, can become the means by which we can live out our life purpose, align our circumstances with our values and achieve true financial wellness. But we have to assume 100 percent responsibility for our finances and our financial wellness first.

ASSUMING RESPONSIBILITY

When Melinda French was about to marry Bill Gates, Gates's mother, Mary, wrote the bride a letter about marriage that concluded, "From those to whom much is given, much is expected."[4] Thirteen years after their 1994 wedding, the Bill and Melinda Gates Foundation has the largest endowment of any foundation in the United States—a staggering $29.2 billion—and the organization is doing significant work to reduce inequities and improve lives around the world.[5]

If you're earning a comfortable income and have a healthy net worth, you're probably familiar with the responsibilities that come with financial success. Building wealth takes hard work, but preserving that wealth and using it properly comes with its own challenges and potential pitfalls. You control your funds: how you invest, how you spend or save, how broad your insurance coverage is, whether or not you give to others and so on. If you are a parent, there's the added responsibility to pass on good money-management skills (as well as good physical and relational wellness principles) to your children. Frank and Katie wanted to give their child the best possible tools to grow up and become a competent, successful adult, with the best possible chance of sustained wellness. They knew, however, that they had to learn to take responsibility for their own wellness, specifically their finances, first.

What about you? Are you charting your own course, or are you letting financial currents around you steer you? Whether you hire a financial advisor to help you on your journey to financial wellness or not, it is up to you to take the reins. You are the only person who can ensure your success.

FINDING MOTIVATION

As much as we may hunger for positive change in our personal and professional lives, we fear it too. The status quo may feel stifling and boring, but its familiarity is also safe and comforting. Change is unpredictable, so we fear what might happen if we pursue it. Will we fail and end up worse off than we were before? Or will we succeed and feel overwhelmed by newfound responsibilities and opportunities?

Change often takes a leap of courage and a break with old ways of thinking, and the payoff is not guaranteed. But if you want to take the lead in your financial wellness, you need to take risks and take action. Business speaker and best-selling author Brian Tracy says, "The key to success is to get started and then to move forward one step at a time, learning and growing as you go."[6]

SETTLING THE "WHYS" OF CHANGE

Personal goals and values are powerful motivators. In his book *Smart Couples Finish Rich*, David Bach writes: "When you understand your values, you tend to live the life you really want almost automatically. Instead of having to 'motivate yourself' to do the right things, you find yourself being pulled in the right direction by the power of your values."[7] Do you and your partner dream of checking out of the corporate rat race and retiring abroad? This goal and its attendant values—freedom and security—can motivate you to contribute a healthy percentage of your income, on a consistent basis, to a pre-tax retirement plan. Do you intend to put your child through college in the next 10 years? Then you and your partner will probably be motivated to cut down on your household's incidental spending and focus on investing your money. Once you define and pursue your primary goals and values, you can truly put your money to work for you and reap the rewards of financial wellness.

For some people, a positive motivator—the promise of something better just over the horizon—is guaranteed to incite action. For example, the prospect of enjoying a newly renovated kitchen in your home and using it to entertain friends and family could inspire you to save money in a "fun fund." Other people will find that negative motivators—such as depression and marital difficulties stemming from a compulsive shopping habit, or stress and anxiety caused by unpaid bills—will push them to take decisive action. We can also be motivated to change by an outright crisis—for example, looming bankruptcy, marital breakdown or health problems caused by financial stress. Ideally, we won't wait for a financial crisis before we take action and implement good money-management habits. Identify what motivates *you* and tap into that energy.

Preparing to improve financial wellness

Since their emergence on U.S. network television in 2000, reality TV programs have become something of a national obsession. Shows as diverse as *Survivor*, *The Apprentice*, *Joe Millionaire* and *The Amazing Race* attract millions of viewers with the promise that even an average Joe or Jane can attain fame and fortune. In the first season of *Survivor*, a staggering 51 million people—41 percent of the American viewing public—tuned in for the show's dramatic finale, in which corporate trainer Richard Hatch won the coveted $1-million prize.[8] Sadly for Hatch, becoming an instant millionaire did not lead to financial wellness. In January 2006, a federal jury found him guilty of tax evasion for failing to pay taxes on his *Survivor* winnings, and he was subsequently sentenced to 51 months in prison. So much for easy money.

SETTING GOALS: THINKING IN THE LONG AND SHORT TERM

Real wealth—the kind that can't be won on a reality TV game show—takes time and discipline to build. There is no quick fix, so it is best to think of improving your financial health as a long-term goal. Popular business coach Jim Rohn advocates setting goals "enough out of reach to cause you to grow and to stretch... high enough to excite your imagination and motivate you to action." However, Rohn also cautions, "Don't set them so far beyond you that you lose heart before you begin."[9] As you embark on a plan of action to achieve financial wellness, your goals should be far-reaching, but they should also be immediate enough that you can reach them and feel encouraged to go further.

If you were trying to get physically fit and your doctor advised you to lose 25 pounds, you wouldn't expect it to happen all at once. You would assume that shedding the extra weight would require you to do several things: change the food you eat, practice portion control, become more active and so on. Likewise, if your goal is to shed the weight of a financial burden—an out-of-date or unfinished estate plan, for example—you can break this larger goal down into smaller, manageable action steps that can be completed today, this week or this month.

Chapters 3 and 5 outlined the go-**FAR** principle in the context of setting physical and relational wellness goals. We can apply the same approach to financial wellness.

Focusing Your Financial Wellness Goals

Make them specific

Reducing your debt—or eliminating it, if that's a possibility for you—is a longer-term goal that makes sense. If you want to begin by tackling your credit card debt, you may lay out the following action steps:

- This evening I will gather all of my credit card bills and calculate exactly how much I owe on each card and at what interest rate.

- Tonight I will also check out a reliable website such as Bankrate.com and compare the interest rates on my cards to current rates offered by other credit card companies.

- Tomorrow I will call my credit card companies and ask for a reduction in my interest rates.

- By the end of the month, I will consolidate my debt—either by transferring my credit card balances to one card with a lower interest rate or by taking out a line of credit to pay all the credit card debt at once.

- Every month I will make more than the minimum payment on each card and make the largest payment on the card with the highest interest rate.

- When paying for incidental expenses such as clothes, restaurant meals, entertainment and housewares, I will use cash or debit instead of credit.

- Once I've paid off my credit cards, I will keep one in my wallet for exceptional expenses and cut the rest up.

Every one of these action steps, taken on its own, may seem too small to have any significant impact on your debt load; however, taken together, these actions can make a huge difference. As Bach puts it, "sometimes all it takes to change your life massively for the better is a small action and a small success."[10]

You will notice that each action step listed above also has a timeline attached to it. Some activities will be done "this evening," "tomorrow" or "by the end of the month," while others will be ongoing. When you give yourself a specific date by which to complete an action or achieve a goal, you make your goals less abstract and you increase your sense of commitment to getting the job done. You make yourself accountable to the one person you cannot fool—yourself.

Take care of the most immediate action items first and savor the satisfaction of crossing them off your to-do list. For example, if you and your partner want to create a household budget or spending plan with the help of personal-finance software, your first action step is an easy one: download the software or go out and purchase a program such as Microsoft Money or Quicken. Even this simple task will create momentum that will encourage you to tackle other action items.

In previous chapters, especially in context of improving your physical wellness, you have seen the importance of setting benchmarks to make your goals as specific and measurable as possible. Just as you can quantifiably track weight loss (by pounds or inches) and follow improvements to your diet (through increasing servings of vegetables, for example), many of your financial goals can be followed empirically—in percentages, dollar amounts or points. For example, if you're tired of seeing your savings languish in a standard bank account that pays one percent interest, a benchmark for you might be, "By the end of this week, I want to find and switch to a high-interest savings account that will earn me three percent interest or higher." If you've checked out your current FICO (Fair Isaac Company) score and you would like it to be higher so you can obtain the best rates on loans, your benchmark might be, "I want to boost my FICO score by 20 points within the year." This would be an ambitious—but still attainable—goal, given that the Fair Isaac Company says it is possible to raise your score by up to 25 points in one year.[11]

Remember, virtually any large task can become more manageable and less intimidating if reduced to a series of smaller, specific tasks.

CREATE A MENTAL PICTURE

If you participate in challenging physical activities—for example, mountain climbing expeditions with friends, marathons or even triathlons—you are probably familiar with visualization. Popular fitness magazines, such as *Men's Health*, advise readers training for a competitive event to "spend a few moments visualizing in full-color detail every part of your event—from when you arrive to when you cross the line. Picture yourself racing and finishing confidently."[12] Top athletes such as Serena Williams, Michael Jordan and Tiger Woods have pointed to this psychological skill as a key part of their success. Not surprisingly, the practice has become more and more popular as a motivational and cognitive tool in the corporate world. You may have used visualization to steady your nerves before an important business meeting, for example, or to help anticipate a client's response to a new initiative. When you're able to rehearse and prepare for any outcome, it's easier to move forward with confidence. By envisioning a desired outcome in vivid detail, you can train your mind and body to put into action what you've imagined.

Visualization can be a useful tool when it comes to improving your financial wellness. You've set specific and measurable goals for yourself; now it's time to visualize the results. If one of your goals is to rid yourself of debt, paint a positive, detailed picture of the outcome in your mind. Visualize yourself scanning your credit card statement and seeing a balance of $0.00. Imagine a wave of relief washing over you as you realize that you are free of credit card debt. Feel the stress and anxiety of mounting debt leave your body, and feel your confidence and optimism soar. If debt isn't a concern for you, but your goal is to become more philanthropic, then picture yourself listening to the stories of people you've had an impact on. Imagine how you would feel if you contributed to cancer research, for example, and then read a front-page story on innovations in cancer therapies, or even an anti-cancer vaccine. Does that mental picture make your efforts seem more worthwhile?

Now picture what might happen if you don't update or refine your estate plan. After you've passed on, how will your loved ones deal with the distribution of your assets? Picture how those concerns might add to the stress that they are already enduring in their grief. If you have a business, what is happening to it? Is it being dismantled? What financial legacy are you leaving behind? Are you pleased with these images or are they hard to take? While it may be unpleasant to create these mental pictures, the reality check they provide can be the catalyst for making prudent financial decisions. Once you address your financial loose ends, you can replace those less-than-comforting images with ones that leave you at ease. In his book *Getting Rich Your Own Way*, Brian Tracy writes, "The greater clarity you can create in your mind of the goal that you desire, the more you will come up with ideas to help make your goal a reality."[13]

ADD VALUE TO YOUR FINANCIAL WELLNESS GOALS

DO A COST-BENEFIT ANALYSIS

Contrary to popular belief, most people who file for bankruptcy are not reckless spenders who abuse their credit cards. They do not run up enormous bills with no intention of ever paying them. According to the attorneys and financial counselors who frequently work with people in financial crisis, the vast majority (approximately 90 percent[14]) of people who declare bankruptcy do so as a result of one of three calamities—serious illness or injury affecting them or a person who contributes income to the household, job loss or divorce.[15]

Currently, the cost of filing for "Chapter 7 personal bankruptcy"— the kind that allows individuals to entirely eliminate most of their debts—is approximately $400. But that is likely to go up. Between 2005— when stricter bankruptcy laws went into effect—and mid-2006, the cost of filing for bankruptcy jumped 90 percent.[16] "Chapter 7" is a way for individuals to erase most personal debts, but getting this "clean slate" is neither easy nor cheap: a court-appointed trustee assembles all of the person's assets (some exceptions apply, depending on state-specific laws), sells them for cash and then allocates and distributes the money to the person's creditors.[17] In addition to giving up much of their personal property, people filing for Chapter 7 can also expect to pay a tidy sum for the services of an attorney during bankruptcy proceedings. And then there are the long-term emotional and financial consequences of filing for bankruptcy. In most of the United States, Chapter 7 bankruptcy will stay on a person's credit report for 10 years. No wonder many people call it "the 10-year mistake."

How can you protect yourself from the financial blow of exorbitant medical bills or sudden and prolonged unemployment, or both at the same time? How can you safeguard your family from bankruptcy and its consequences? By being prepared. Even short of financial disaster, it makes sense to hang on to all the money you can instead of paying exorbitant interest charges or unnecessary tax offerings, for example.

The "pros" of sound money management are better grasped in the context of very real, measurable "cons." Insurance is a perfect example. With sufficient health insurance, you don't have to fear that a serious illness or accident will wipe you out financially. Without it, a hospital stay could put you and your family in debt for years. With a top-notch long-term-care policy, any type of medical, social or support service that you may need over an extended period of time because of chronic illness or old age will be taken care of. Orman says that without it, you can expect to pay around $150,000 *a year* to stay in a nursing home approximately 25 years from now (assuming an annual rate of inflation of 5 percent and assuming you live in middle America).[18] In fact, a nursing home stay in metropolitan New York *already* costs over $125,000 a year.[19]

With disability insurance, you have peace of mind knowing that if you become critically ill or injured and can no longer work, your insurance will replace a portion of the salary you were earning before you became disabled. Without it, your family may face serious financial trouble if you are the sole income provider in your household and you become unable to work. Even if your partner also works, you will have to consider whether the household can function smoothly on just one salary.

Media personality and personal finance expert Suze Orman says: "No matter what your age or state of health, protecting yourself with adequate medical insurance is an act of self-respect."[20] Again, the cost of various types of insurance may seem high, but the cost of not having the right insurance at a time of crisis could turn out to be much, much higher. Are you willing to risk the security and well-being of yourself and your family to save some money and avoid some paperwork?

Even if we compare less drastic potential financial outcomes—say, by looking at the different results that come from using or not using strategic money management—we can see how our behavior is either putting money in our pocket or preventing us from realizing our true financial potential. When it comes to your finances, the cost-benefit analysis should be quite straightforward. You know what you stand to gain by pursuing your financial wellness goals, and you know what you stand to lose if you don't.

IDENTIFY POTENTIAL BARRIERS

On your journey to financial wellness, you will probably encounter bumps in the road, roadblocks and seemingly insurmountable barriers. Life experience teaches us that the path to success is rarely smooth, but we also learn that almost anything can be overcome through preparation, perseverance and discipline. You will endure personal financial setbacks, large or small, in the same way that your business turns profit at a variable rate. By definition, mutual funds are funds designed by investors to anticipate market fluctuations. You can have a plan for your own tendency to be financially variable, too. Remember that your trends are more important than your point-by-point financial performance.

The key to tackling obstacles is to anticipate and have a plan for dealing with them. Many stumbling blocks will be predictable, and therefore easier to avoid. For example, if you and your spouse have worked diligently to pay off your credit card debt, but you realize that you still have a shopping problem, there are measures you can take to avoid a setback. First, if you can't walk by a sale sign without going into the store and charging things you don't need, then leave your credit cards at home and stick strictly to cash when shopping. This should prevent you from making purchases you will later regret. Maybe you and your partner have developed a household spending plan and followed it for a few months, only to discover that both of you are regularly spending hundreds or thousands a month on items designated as "miscellaneous." How will you break the habit? If you go out for lunch with a friend every workday, then consider brown-bagging it four times a week and eating lunch with your friend in a park. Not only will you save money, you'll probably lose weight and enjoy some sun and fresh air at the same time. On the last day of the workweek, you can treat yourself to a restaurant meal with your friend and not feel guilty about it. You and your partner may also want to go back to tracking every one of your variable expenses in a notepad for a week or a month, just to see how much you are spending and on what. The frills you spend money on today may be sabotaging your plans for the future. When the numbers are staring you in the face, you will probably be encouraged to change your behaviors and spend more conscientiously.

Relish your financial wellness goals

Tailor your goals to fit you

Companies set goals that suit their brand, business objectives, organizational philosophy and products or services; their goals are tailored to their corporate identity. For example, Payless ShoeSource, home of the "buy one, get one half off" sale, won't have many of the same goals as De Beers Diamonds, a company steeped in tradition that offers its customers a sense of luxury and exclusivity. Likewise, if your time horizon and risk tolerance make you well-suited to a growth portfolio or even alternative investments, you won't feel terribly motivated to build a conservative investment portfolio focused on safe fixed-income assets. Nor would it make much sense for you to track every one of your variable expenses for a month if your penny-pinching ways have already earned you the nickname Ebenezer Scrooge.

When you set goals that are tailored to your needs and personality, it is much easier for procrastination to stop and progress to begin. Your goals should feel exciting, challenging and worth pursuing. If you don't feel motivated to achieve them, it may be because they don't suit you. Your financial self-assessment, combined with your consultation with a financial advisor, should help you identify the right goals for your age, net worth, expenses, family situation and personality. When your goals are customized to your specifications, you'll feel encouraged to pursue them. Goals will become actions, and actions lead to results.

As you set goals in the three wellness categories—physical, relational and financial—put your problem-solving skills to work and find ways to achieve multiple goals through the same action. If one of your physical wellness goals is to eat healthier meals, you might decide to cook at home more often. By doing so, you could also target one of your relational wellness goals: to spend more quality time with your family. Cooking and eating meals at home with your spouse and your children will not only satisfy your physical and relational goals, but it can also suit one of your financial goals: to cut down on variable expenses by dining out less often. One action—forsaking restaurants for home cooking more often—can help you achieve three goals tailored to your needs: losing weight, increasing communication with your family and saving money.

Whatever your personal goals, keep this in mind: if you're in a committed relationship, you should also take your partner's needs into consideration. The goal-setting process will probably require negotiation and compromise by both parties. After all, you are individuals coming together in a partnership, and you may value money differently, spend it differently and have acquired different money-management habits from your parents. Most couples don't worry about financial compatibility when they fall in love, but by working together, you can make financial decisions that satisfy both of you, even if you've come to the marriage with conflicting values about money. In successful relationships, couples learn to adapt and change together, accepting that change is an inevitable part of human life. They also learn to navigate and bridge the differences that might drive other couples apart. Many people fear that discussing their finances with their partner can only lead to conflict, but Bach says that's not the case: "Working on your money together significantly improves the chances not only of your succeeding financially but of your staying together happily as a couple."[21]

MAKE THEM REALISTIC
Making your goals realistic doesn't mean you can't make them challenging. Indeed, your goals *need* to challenge you if you want to create true, productive change in your life. But if you set your goals too high, they can backfire on you.

If you have a child who plans to attend college five years from now, and you have saved $8,500 for her tuition in your college savings fund, aiming to save enough to pay for 100 percent of projected college costs by the time she begins college may be an unrealistic goal. Consider the math:

- It's feasible that your child will attend a college that currently costs $25,000 annually (tuition and fees), and you expect college costs to increase by six percent per year (a reasonable estimate given current trends identified by the College Board's *Annual Survey of Colleges*).[22]

- If your child plans to enter college five years from now and do a four-year degree on a full-time basis, 100 percent of her total college costs will be approximately $146,356. That's your savings goal.

- You currently have $8,500 saved for your child's college expenses and you want to meet your savings goal by the time she *starts* college. Let's say you expect to earn five percent after tax each year in your college savings fund, and you plan to make monthly contributions to this fund. You will need to make monthly contributions of $1,984 for the next five years to meet 100 percent of your child's college costs by your target deadline.[23]

If you have more than one child nearing college age, your savings goal becomes even more daunting. Instead of making you feel motivated, these goals can make you feel defeated. So how do you avoid setting yourself up for failure? By tailoring your goals to what is desirable and realistic for you, given your financial situation.

In the case of the example above, there are some ready solutions. First, by changing the *timeline* of your goal from "when my child begins college five years from now" to "when my child completes college *nine* years from now," you can decrease your monthly contributions to your savings fund by hundreds of dollars. By increasing your time horizon for this savings goal by four years, your monthly contributions drop from $1,984 to $1,331. Second, if you and your spouse talk it over with your child and decide that she will start saving for college now by working part-time during the school year and full-time during the summer, then you might commit to covering 75 percent of her total college costs ($109,767). Combine that change with your revised timeline, and your monthly contributions drop to $998. The college expenses that cannot be covered between you, your spouse and your child can be paid for with a combination of student loans, scholarships, grants and money earned by your child during her college years. Depending on family circumstances, grandparents may also want to contribute.

BUILD IN FUN

Your neighbors just bought another new car and your friend and his wife are off on their third ecotourist vacation this year—to Tierra del Fuego, Nepal or some other far-flung locale. Why does it seem that everyone is spending their money and having fun with it *now*, while you sit at home making pie charts of your household expenses?

The fact is, you don't know how your friends or neighbors are financing their lavish lifestyles. They may owe thousands in credit card debt and car loans, they may not be saving for retirement or for their children's college education, they may be enjoying a windfall such as a bonus or an inheritance and so on. Because discussing our finances with others is one of our society's last remaining taboos, you will likely never know how or if your friends and neighbors can afford their lifestyles. Jeff Opdyke, an author and *Wall Street Journal* personal finance reporter, writes, "It's difficult, bordering on impossible at times, for people to fathom the financial actions of another, because they can't even begin to understand the divergent definitions of *money* that separate all of us."[24] Fortunately, everyone else's finances are not our responsibility, nor need they concern us. If you can feel secure and confident about your own money management (and that of your partner), you're on your way to true and lasting financial wellness.

So where's the "fun factor"? Remember that your financial wellness goals include building a "fun fund": putting aside money for the sole purpose of pursuing your dreams and interests. When most people think of having fun with money, they think of spending it now, not investing in mutual funds and retirement accounts and planning for the future. But saving and investing will give you the money to do all kinds of enjoyable things throughout your life, and you will be able to do them without mortgaging your future. Imagine the sense of accomplishment and gratification you'll feel as you fulfill your dreams *and* see your net worth grow.

Groucho Marx was onto something when he said that money frees you from doing many things you dislike. More importantly, it frees you to pursue the things you *do* like, whether these are material possessions or intangibles such as quality time with family and friends. How do you do this without living beyond your means? You do it by managing your money with foresight and intent, by putting your money to work for the things that matter most to you and—as Orman says—by not "sacrific[ing] tomorrow's needs to today's desires."[25]

In the short term, you *can* make tasks such as paying bills less of a chore by sitting down with your partner and doing it together every month, with a glass of wine by your side and some relaxing music in the background. You can also promise each other rewards—say, cooking a great dinner at home or giving each other relaxing massages—as an incentive to get the job done.

Financial wellness in action

GET MOVING

You already understand the power and the benefits of investing your money for a long time so you can earn interest on your interest. When it comes to money, procrastination can be very costly. But did you know that someone has come up with a mathematical formula to show that time actually *is* money? In 2002, CNN reported that Ian Walker, a British professor of economics, had developed an equation that takes into account a person's hourly wage, tax rate and the local cost of living to determine the cost of time. Walker found that the average minute (in 2002) was worth 15 cents U.S.—making the average hour worth $9.00.[26] Do you really want to spend your precious time setting goals that you then fail to pursue?

In *Go for the Goal: A Champion's Guide to Winning in Soccer and Life*, soccer star Mia Hamm writes: "Most people have a vague idea in their mind about the future, and that uncertainty impedes their ability to achieve greatness.... Dreams without follow-through are just that—dreams."[27] Putting pen to paper and writing down your financial goals is the easy part. Following through and turning those goals into results is the real challenge.

Do you need to write a will and develop an estate plan? Have you been putting it off for months or even years? Pick up the phone and call your financial advisor. Ask him or her to refer you to a certified estate-planning attorney who can guide you through the estate-planning process; it's not something you want to do without a professional. Once you get the referral, call that attorney right away and make an appointment. If you put this phone call off until tomorrow or next week, you may end up procrastinating for another year. If you get started on your estate planning now, you can make thoughtful choices that will allow you to preserve your wealth and pass it on to your beneficiaries as you will. You can also spare your loved ones avoidable legal and financial difficulties when you pass away. On the other hand, if you die intestate (without a legal will), the distribution of your assets will become the responsibility of a probate court, and the state will determine how your property is passed to your heirs.

When you tackle a difficult financial wellness goal, like working on the minutiae of your estate plan with an attorney or taking on a huge philanthropic commitment, you may feel more stress than you did when you had no financial wellness plan. Remember to pace yourself. Money management can be frustrating, exhausting and stressful work—and the stress may be felt not just by you, but also by your spouse, your children, your business partners and so on. Be disciplined, but don't be too hard on yourself. Ultimately, the journey to financial wellness should be positive, not punishing.

ENLIST SUPPORT

In early 2006, *The Oprah Winfrey Show* first aired its now wildly successful "Debt Diet" series, which challenged Americans to free themselves from debt and tackle their overspending as they would compulsive overeating. The series featured three families feeling overwhelmed by debt and paired them with three of the country's top financial experts: David Bach, Glinda Bridgforth and Jean Chatzky. Each family profiled on the show was facing debt well in excess of its annual income. The experts guided the families through a step-by-step action plan that would help them lose the debt and find financial freedom. The families on the show were in an exceptional situation: not only were they accountable to themselves, but they were also accountable to the nation's foremost financial advisors, to Oprah Winfrey and her show's producers, and to the millions of viewers watching at home. And yet, most of the families "cheated" on their spending plan at least once before they were able to stick to it.

ACCOUNTABILITY PARTNERS

In much the same way that we tend to equate diets with deprivation, we see budgeting as an act of self-denial. And what happens when we feel deprived and constrained? Well, we tend to act out and "cheat." Unfortunately, when you cheat on your saving and investing plan, you really are cheating yourself and your family.

You need accountability partners to keep you honest and on track. Because discussing our personal finances with others can be uncomfortable and embarrassing, you should rely on people close to you whom you trust: a close friend, a sibling or a business partner, for example. And don't forget your financial advisor. Schedule regular appointments—say, at the end of every financial quarter—with him or her to stay on top of your goals, reassess as needed, monitor your progress and receive the encouragement you may need to carry on.

You may have one accountability partner or many; the choice is yours. But whoever you choose, understand that this person's role should be not only to cheer you on, but also to administer tough love if needed. You may not always like it, but having to account to someone else for your actions on a regular basis can be just what you need to ensure your success.

CO-PARTICIPANTS

If you're in a committed relationship, your partner is an obvious choice to fill the role of co-participant, given that you will be working on matters that affect both of you, such as household budgeting, planning for retirement or saving for your children's education. While it's true that financial issues can be a major source of conflict between partners, working on your finances as a *team*—rather than as isolated individuals or adversaries—can actually enhance your relational wellness.

When couples experience conflict over finances, money is often not the true cause of conflict. At the very least, it's about more than just money. More often than not, when you argue about money with your partner, it's symptomatic of other relational problems: If your credit card bill testifies to your tendency to buy things on impulse, this could be a manifestation of a lack of self-control or self-awareness. If your partner is frustrated that you're not helping him or her rein in the household spending, the problem may be that you're not empathizing with your partner and tuning in to his or her concerns. And if you and your partner frequently find yourselves fighting over finances and getting nowhere, it's probably a sign that you both need to develop more effective communication skills.

If you and your partner have argued over money matters in the past, you will probably find that your disagreements become less frequent and less intense if you talk openly and work together as co-participants, sharing equal responsibility for your success.

Children—especially teenagers or young adults—are other possible co-participants. Make the time to teach them good money-management habits at home, because they probably won't learn how to pay for a mortgage or invest in stocks and bonds in grade school.

COMPETITORS

If you can keep things lighthearted and not contentious, you can turn saving money into a fun family competition. Have a money jar at home and see who in the household can put the most dollars and cents in the jar in a month. At the end of the month, put a portion into savings and spend the rest on a family fun night, or put it toward a family vacation. Or challenge your children with a friendly "kids only" competition designed to teach them to be budget conscious: ask them to comparison-shop and find the best deal on something they want, such as an MP3 player, a new gaming system or a pair of runners. They'll become conscientious consumers without even knowing it.

STAKEHOLDERS

If you run your own business and plan to restructure your finances to expand the business, you may want to tell your employees about your goals. Because they stand a good chance of being affected by changes to the business, they will appreciate your openness. And there's another benefit: your coworkers will probably be inspired when they see that you are motivated, goal oriented and committed to positive change and growth. This will give them even greater confidence in the business and in you as a leader.

REFRAME SETBACKS AND REENGAGE

When you adopt new habits that are in sync with your larger life goals, the process should feel quite natural. If your financial wellness goals have been tailored to your needs and desires, you shouldn't feel as though you are continually straining to reach targets and deadlines. However, that doesn't mean you won't experience setbacks. When things do go wrong, maintain a positive attitude. Don't deny that a setback has happened, but don't dwell on it either. Make the choice to look for the valuable lesson in every roadblock or setback along the way, and then push on. As Tracy writes: "Think in terms of 'I can' rather than 'I can't.' Think continually about all the different ways that your goals can be achieved, rather than thinking about the obstacles and problems that may be holding you back right now."[28]

Evaluating your progress

As you start to take action and see results, you will want to evaluate your progress. Failing to do this would be like embarking on a weight-loss program without ever weighing yourself or without checking your measurements along the way. You need some feedback.

Throughout your career, you've probably been involved in a fair share of evaluations. Your performance at work has been evaluated by your board or your peers, and you've had to conduct employee evaluations and job interviews. When you evaluate yourself, be sure to hold yourself to the same standards you would apply at work. Have you set realistic and specific goals? Have you followed through on them? Are you meeting the deadlines you gave yourself to get your action steps done? Are you and your partner talking openly about money and managing your finances together? Are you having regular meetings with a financial advisor? Have you been procrastinating on important paperwork? Are you meeting your benchmarks? And, perhaps most importantly, do you feel good about the changes you've made?

TAKE STOCK REGULARLY

Specific and measurable goals give you something tangible to assess. So if your goal was to improve your FICO score by 20 points within the year, you can monitor your progress in six months by checking your score again and comparing it to the number you started with. If your goal was to pay off your credit card balance, you can monitor your progress every month when you get your credit card statement. If you wanted to cut down on restaurant meals as a way to rein in your variable expenses, use a calendar to keep track of every time you went out to eat or ordered in.

REASSESS AS NECESSARY

Adopting new habits involves some trial and error. Don't be frustrated if you're not seeing results as quickly as you'd like. It may mean that you need to go back to your goals and adjust them. What works for some people may not work for you. If you decided to save money on non-essential expenses like getting your lawn mowed and getting your car washed by doing it yourself, and now you're resenting the time and effort these activities take, then give yourself a break. Your time may be worth more than what it costs to get someone else to do these tasks for you. Look at your household's variable expenses and find other areas where you can cut costs instead.

Maybe you were overly ambitious in your initial goal setting, and now you see that it's unrealistic to pay off your credit card debt in eight months. Sit down at the computer and reassess how much money you're making versus how much you owe. What is a reasonable amount for you to pay the credit card companies, while still paying more than the monthly minimum? Write down that amount and commit to paying it every month. Then if your income increases, or if you land a great new client, you can ramp up your payments again and pay off your debt faster. Remember that adjusting your goals doesn't always have to mean scaling them back. If your new personal-finance software makes budgeting a breeze and you discover that you can pay your debt off *sooner* than you initially expected, seize the opportunity.

Keep in mind that as your circumstances change, your financial priorities will shift. Marriage, children, promotions, career changes, inheritances—these are just some of the life events that may require you to reassess your goals.

BUILD IN REWARDS

When Frank and Katie looked back at the progress they had made since they first met The Healthy CEO, they could scarcely believe the results. Their net worth was growing as their debt dwindled, and they were well positioned to buy a comfortable home in the suburbs—with a pool—for their expanding family. Because Frank and Katie knew that having a child meant they needed to expect the unexpected, they were each putting 10 percent of their after-tax income into a high-interest savings account that served as their "peace-of-mind fund." And Frank's health scare on the golf course, while terrifying to both of them, had been just the motivation Frank and Katie needed to sit down with an attorney and prepare an estate plan. Now that they were about to have a child, Frank and Katie felt more secure than ever about the strength of their relationship and their finances.

In one of his sessions with Frank and Katie, The Healthy CEO talked about the importance of rewarding yourself for a job well done. "When you experience success—and I have no doubt that you will because you're both committed to change—make sure you take the time to celebrate it," he told them. "Feeling good about what you've accomplished will motivate you to keep at it, and with every new success, you can raise the bar a little higher." Frank and Katie liked the sound of that. So when they sold their condo for well above their asking price, they decided it was time to dip into their "fun fund" for the first time and celebrate their success. Frank was determined to fulfill one of Katie's dreams before the baby's arrival: to rent a villa in Tuscany for a week and spend the time soaking up Italy's culinary culture, buying fresh local ingredients in the markets and cooking like the locals do. It was every foodie's dream, and they both deserved the vacation.

How will you reward yourself? Use your imagination. The reward can be something that costs money, like Frank and Katie's trip to Italy, or it can be free, like a relaxing walk through a park or an evening alone with your spouse while the grandparents babysit the kids. Rewarding ourselves for saving and investing money can be tricky, since we typically equate celebrating with spending money. In fact, we can find ways to still have fun without spending a dime, if we make the effort. Best-selling author Thomas J. Stanley surveyed over 1,000 millionaires in preparation for his book *The Millionaire Mind*. What he found was that many millionaires are what he calls "cheap dates." According to Stanley, these people recognize that "the best things in life are free, or at least reasonably priced. It doesn't cost much to attend your son or daughter's sporting event, visit a museum, or play bridge with good friends."[29]

With every new success, you'll feel encouraged to take on other challenges to further improve your personal finances. Like an athlete who trains continually to beat his or her personal best, you will find that accomplishing the first of your financial goals will propel you forward. You'll want to push the limits of what you thought you could achieve. For example, if you started off with major debt and you paid it off, the money that used to go to debt repayment can now go toward another goal: a second home, a trip around the world, a gift to your alma mater or a trust for your children. The question is not where you will find the money to achieve your goals; the question is what you will do with the money you uncover when you tap into the success cycle and achieve your true financial potential.

"I refuse!" Katie shouted. "Your parents our child's legal guardians?! Over my dead body!"

"You will be dead, Katie. We're talking about our will here." Frank knew right away that his attempt at humor was lost on her.

"Then I'll make sure you're dead first." She turned away and put her hand to her forehead. Then she faced him again. "You know precisely what I mean, Frank. Don't patronize me. I will not have that woman raise my child. I'd be turning over in my grave. Can you imagine? Our precious baby would grow up in a stranglehold. Don't get me wrong, Frank—I love your mother. But I love our child too much to let her do that."

Frank sighed and put his hands on his hips. "Who would you suggest we name instead? Your mother isn't a vast improvement."

Katie didn't hide her near horror at the thought. She shuddered and said, "Might as well have the child raised by orangutans...." She sank into the nearby couch and took in some long, deliberate breaths.

"You OK?" Frank asked.

"Yes," she replied unconvincingly. "I'm a little nauseated, but I'll be OK. I'm trying to find my 'happy place,'" she said sarcastically. "My 'happy and not-about-to-throw-up' place."

"What can I get you?" Frank asked, moving toward the kitchen.

"How about someone like Mother Theresa interested in raising our child, in case we get picked off in suburbia." She started to cry, but warned Frank through tears, "If you accuse me of being hormonal, I'll break your kneecaps."

Frank got her some tissue and sat down beside her. He didn't pretend to know why Katie was crying. She did seem more emotional now that she was pregnant, but he didn't know if he should attribute that to hormones or her willingness to show her soft side more often.

He took her hand and eased in gently, "We can figure this out, Katie. We'll make a list and really think this through together. We know people—a lot of good people—and we'll make the right decision."

"OK," Katie relented. "It's just that I have never cared more about anything in my life than this baby. I never thought I would even want to be a mother, you know—and now it's all I can think about. I don't want to screw this up. I don't want to mess this kid up in any way, Frank. Do you know what I mean?" She looked at him plaintively, her eyes filling with tears.

"Yes," he answered. "I think I do. It's amazing how a small helpless creature can exert so much control over two grown adults." He clasped her hand in both of his. "We are going to do this, Katie. We are going to do it well. We both care about it so much that we have to. I mean, look at us! We're getting healthier, we're connecting more. For God's sake, even our arguing is connecting, isn't it? We're putting all of these financial pieces into place. We're doing all we can, and I think we're doing just fine. We'll be great parents—not perfect parents, but good ones nonetheless."

Katie withdrew her hand and blew her nose. "Well, I'll be a great parent. And I'll show you the ropes enough that you'll be passable."

Frank smiled. He was glad she was acting like her old self again.

The first step to getting the things you want out of life is this: Decide what you want.

Ben Stein, actor, comedian and former White House speechwriter

Frank flipped his cell phone shut. He walked back into their new living room, where Katie was sitting on a cardboard box. She was surrounded by a dozen cardboard boxes. The one she perched on defiantly displayed its "This side up" arrow pointing straight down. Katie was looking at Frank pensively, her hands clenched, her body leaning forward as far as her now-protruding belly would allow her. She was biting at her lower lip, waiting to hear what had happened on the phone.

"She's not coming," Frank said simply.

Katie emptied her lungs in relief, let her head drop and dragged her hand over the back of her neck. Frank watched her shoulders relax. He had just finished asking his mother not to come help them unpack their things tomorrow. Katie, imagining her mother-in-law bustling around their new home, taking charge like the alpha female and patronizing her daughter-in-law in her pregnant state, had felt ready to lose her sanity. She had told Frank earlier that if he didn't hold his mother off somehow, he might as well make himself at home in a tent in their new backyard. "You've always wanted a backyard...," she'd said sarcastically. Now, for a fleeting but delicious moment, Katie imagined marking big, cheery, bright red Xs on the calendar, one for each day Frank's mother would not yet cross their new threshold. He probably wouldn't go for the idea though, Katie mused.

Frank walked around the boxes with slow, deliberate strides. Then, after an about-face to the living room bay window, he let out a barbaric, resounding bellow that echoed through the still-naked house. Katie cried out, startled. "Wha! What the...? Are you out of your mind? What are you doing?" She was taken aback, and then laughed gently when she saw the childlike mirth on her husband's face. He looked at her, delighted.

"What?" she asked, smiling.

"There are no rules about that here, you know," he beamed.

Katie pretended to be indifferent. "About what? Losing your marbles?"

"No...," he said, pulling up a box near her. "This is our place. No one lives under us or above us. There's just dirt and sky."

"And two sets of next-door neighbors, who won't be bringing us fresh-baked welcome-to-the-neighborhood cookies after that crazy racket," she chided gently.

Frank thought for a moment about the past few months: his first visit to The Healthy CEO, the new buddies he'd made at the gym, the date nights he and Katie had started planning, the baby they were going to have and now their new home. It was almost overwhelming, but it was all real. He'd helped to make all those things happen. He knew Katie had worked hard to change things, too. He looked at her. He could tell she was tired, but happy.

"We're home, K. We did it," he said. He leaned in and kissed her forehead. She leaned into him and was silent. They sat there, soaking in the moment for what seemed like a long time. Finally, Katie broke the silence.

"I have to pee," she said, matter of fact. "Your child is sitting on my bladder."

Frank chuckled softly, kissed her again and helped her to her feet. "I'll go make up the bed," he told her.

"Thanks, love," she said, moving toward the bathroom. "And try to keep it down in here, wouldja?"

"I promise," he replied, hand over his heart. Yep. This felt like home, all right.

Frank and Katie Johnson had been working hard to achieve balance in their lives. They'd made sacrifices, changed the way they spent their time, adjusted their eating and exercise habits, started practicing better communication with each other and—with the added motivation of a baby on the way—started looking at their finances more deliberately. It was a lot of change in a relatively short time, but they were glad they had made the effort. There were no illusions that life was perfect: Katie still got tension headaches and Frank still succumbed to rocky-road ice cream every now and again. They fought sometimes, and they fought hard sometimes, but they were now more often saying things that were real and that they meant—even if they were saying them loudly on occasion. The new house and reduced monthly income, since Katie had reduced her hours, were proving a challenge to get used to, but the two of them were finding ways to spend less money without feeling any less alive. They had given up a few things, but gained far more. Now, they couldn't imagine living the way they had just a few short months earlier. Their lives felt more in balance; they were feeling more and more *well*.

The Johnsons were learning that balance could be achieved in their lives as they let their physical, relational and financial wellness grow and operate in concert. As Stephen Covey, author of *The 7 Habits of Highly Effective People* and *First Things First,* writes: "Balance in our lives isn't a running between compartments; it's a dynamic equilibrium. It's all parts working synergistically in a highly interrelated whole. Balance isn't 'either/or,' it's 'and.'"[1] Results of a 1986 survey conducted by leading cardiologist James M. Rippe demonstrated that professional success and satisfaction was directly linked to how physically active top executives were. Furthermore, the picture painted by the responses of some 1,139 chief executives was that "the highest source of satisfaction, by a wide margin, [was] family, spouse and children," even over salary or work. One respondent, Ronald Thomas, chairman of the board of Ciprico Inc., said: "You have to make a conscious decision to put this much effort into family, this much into health and this much into business. It's something you should give a lot of thought to, trying to balance everything out."[2]

A generation or so later Robert Putnam, professor of public policy at Harvard, wrote a groundbreaking national best-seller, *Bowling Alone,* in which he echoes the findings of Rippe's survey for the population at large. Putnam's book is an in-depth, data-rich discussion of the ways American society has lost much of its sense of community—its "social capital," or "the ways in which our lives are made more productive by social ties"—across all sectors, including economic.[3] This social connectivity—which an individual achieves by belonging to clubs, religious groups, sports leagues and, specifically, to a marriage relationship—fosters a greater sense of well-being and satisfaction with life and contributes to physical health. Putnam writes:

More than a dozen large studies... in the United States, Scandinavia, and Japan have shown that people who are socially disconnected are between two and five times more likely to die from all causes, compared with matched individuals who have close ties with family, friends, and the community.[4]

Moreover, Putnam acknowledges that money can indeed buy happiness, to a degree—that financial wellness leads to greater fulfillment—but that money can't come close to having the same personal benefit of a good marriage. He says, "Getting married is the 'happiness equivalent' of quadrupling your annual income."[5] While material well-being seems to correlate with personal fulfillment, Putnam says social ties seem to contribute even more directly to personal fulfillment:

In study after study people themselves report that good relationships with family members, friends, or romantic partners—far more than money or fame—are prerequisites for their happiness. The single most common finding from half a century's research on the correlates of life satisfaction, not only in the United States but around the world, is that happiness is best predicted by the breadth and depth of one's social connections.[6]

The lesson to be learned from all of this? Pursue your career goals and financial freedom. You spend a significant amount of your life working, so you might as well be doing what you enjoy. In terms of money, getting your finances in order—creating financial wellness—helps you lower your stress level and builds confidence. However, don't stop there. Your physical wellness contributes to better overall achievement at work, a better mood and more energy for the things and people most important to you. Research proves that your relational wellness—building significant social capital—can contribute to keeping you healthy, wealthy and wise. A fulfilling life is about achieving overall wellness or, in a word, balance.

Some other CEOs and business owners have learned how to find at least a measure of balance in life. Carson, who runs an industrial signage company, says, "My life is balanced. Once in a blue moon I wander. But wandering is good every once in a while. It's an adventure." Striving for balance can also help stir up courage, as one CEO can attest to:

> **"I've been working on balance for years. I'm unafraid and ready to do whatever it takes to enjoy life to the max. I strive to live each day with a positive spin on everything I encounter. My motto is 'Never give up and luck will come your way.' There's always another pot of gold waiting around the corner...."**

Sunia, CEO of a fitness firm

Here's what some other business leaders had to say about balance:

"Opportunities arise at work and I'm not always sure whether I should pursue them or let them pass. I love the challenge, but I know I need balance in my life, too. Now, I deal with these situations by forming a committee to review the opportunity and to determine exactly what's involved and who would implement it before I commit to anything."

Ben, CEO of a transportation company

"I turned 50 this past summer. I would have said before that life was running me. Now, I feel that I have taken better control of my life... and I am working smarter and happier."

Oliver, real estate developer

"My free time is spent with family and friends. I've learned that's what's important."

Gordon, president and CEO of a wealth management firm

"This year, I'm living by the phrase, 'Life is too short.' My objective is to focus on what's important and to not get stuck in the noise."

John, CEO of a computer technologies company

"I feel like I run my own life. I have a successful firm, a solid marriage and great kids. I also take time off when I need it."

Kevin, founding partner of a management consulting firm

In *The Healthy CEO*, you've looked at the ways your life can become more satisfying by improving your physical, relational and financial wellness. You can harness your sense of life purpose as motivation to help you reach your goals in each of these wellness areas. We've identified a myriad of ways each wellness area can contribute to the others and to the overall balance possible in your life. You're used to being the boss. Now, take the lead not only at work, but also in your overall wellness. Your own self-assessment and what you choose to do with it will be key to your success. Your drive to achieve in business can be the same drive that helps you create a more fulfilling, healthier, more balanced life. When you come to the end of it, you will no longer be working, but you will still have your body, your finances and your relationships to enjoy. Create your own destiny and choose to take the lead in your physical, relational and financial wellness—*today!*

Here are some of the life lessons that a number of CEOs or business owners have learned:

"You need to let your yes be yes and your no be no!"

Len, owner of an industrial distribution company

"You will never regret spending more time with your family than you spend at work."

John, senior executive of a manufacturing company

"Have children early."

David, architect

"You cannot control 90 percent of what happens to you, but you have 100 percent control over how you react."

Gordon, president and CEO of a wealth management firm

"The legacy of relationships with those who matter most to us is substantially more enduring and more powerful than worldly success."

Blake, physician and administrative leader

"I've learned that I'm actually quite dispensible."

Brad, registrar of a medical regulating body

"Don't be afraid to ask questions."

Andrew, senior partner of an investment firm

"Be comfortable in your own skin."

Mark, director of an international IT firm

"In a business context, you are only as good as your last shift. On a personal level, if you're there for others when they need you, they'll be there for you when you need them."

Byron, executive search consultant

"What you say and do defines you... and you are forever."

Don, president of a private and business aviation company

You are forever. You are your own corporation. What does your personal balance sheet look like? Is there net growth in you, the "company"? Is your personal stock a sound investment? What are you selling and what are you buying? Personally, are you a fledgling enterprise or a Fortune 500 entity? Most importantly, are you truly the CEO of your own life? Take the lead in your physical, relational and financial wellness. Lead your life and live *well*.

Epilogue

A little more than a year after Frank's collapse on the green and his trip to the hospital, here they were at the hospital again. But this time, it was Katie who was in the bed and Frank who was anxious. She was about to have their baby. Katie had begged (more like screamed) for drugs a few hours earlier, abandoning what she now felt had been an ill-advised and premature commitment to have a natural labor. Now, she was sipping gingerly at a glass of ice water, comfortably numb from the waist down thanks to a timely epidural. After watching her struggle in pain for hours, Frank was just as glad for this advance in modern medicine. Earlier, Katie had snapped at him for squeezing her hand too hard—a gesture ostensibly meant to help her, but also to help him cope with his feelings of anxiety and helplessness.

Whenever a contraction came, Katie directed Frank to the monitor at her bedside, remarking on the thickening and more heightened lines building and then receding on the screen that marked her contractions. It was like a play by play. She's even in charge in the delivery room, Frank thought, somewhat in awe. The bunches of lines were coming in more rapid succession now. The doctor "checked" and gave word that it was time for Katie to push. She bolstered herself and followed the doctor's instructions, mustering her physical and emotional strength. She was excited, but afraid; even here, however, she was driven. During one push, her head started to spin and she laid her head back on the pillow just as the room seemed to fade away. She lost consciousness for a few seconds.

"Katie! Katie!" Frank called out, concerned.

A nurse moved past him and to the head of the bed, putting her hand to Katie's brow. "She's OK. She just pushed too hard." The nurse gently patted Katie's cheek. "Come on, dear. Come back to us...."

The nurse watching the monitor made a comment about the baby's oxygen level starting to dip. Katie was half roused when she heard someone say they might need the forceps. That was enough to snap her back to reality. She took a deep breath, propped herself back up on her elbows and was back in the game. A nurse reported that the baby's oxygen level was fine.

Three minutes later, Frank was cutting the umbilical cord. "Welcome to the world," he said to his new baby girl. After their daughter was examined and cleaned up, a nurse swaddled her and handed her to Katie. Frank was a blubbering mess.

"Look at you, Daddy," Katie teased, but very gently. She reached out and pulled his head down to hers, burying her nose in his hair. Her eyes were wet, too. "I love you, you big lug." Frank kissed her.

They looked at their baby girl. "You know, Katie," Frank said, sniffling a little, "you've always been a high achiever, but I think this may be some of your best work yet."

"Thank you, sir," she replied, smiling. "I did have help, you know."

Their daughter looked at them with tiny grey-blue eyes, studying their faces. She was slightly shriveled but, Katie thought, the most beautiful baby she'd ever seen. One of the nurses asked, "So, do you have a name for her?"

Katie looked at Frank and then at her daughter. "Her name is Zoe. It means 'life.'"

They were sure this little life would make theirs very different. They were going to give her everything they could, but they knew already that she'd give them back that much and more.

	Physical Wellness	Relational Wellness	Financial Wellness
KNOWLEDGE			
Self-assessment factors:	• body composition • level of exercise • quality of nutrition • dental care • sleep patterns • stress level • capacity for leisure • mental state • substance abuse	• self-awareness • self-regulation • motivation • empathy • communication skills • conflict management • consciousness • commitment • connection • cooperation	• net worth • household budget • debt management • saving • investment • tax efficiency • insurance • estate planning • philanthropy
Workbook	Complete self-assessment	Complete self-assessment	Complete self-assessment
Expert assessment:	Primary health practitioner	Relational expert, as desired	Financial advisor
ATTITUDE	Assume responsibility Find motivation	Assume responsibility Find motivation	Assume responsibility Find motivation
PREPARATION			
Set goals	**Focus your goals** **Add value to your goals** **Relish your goals**	**Focus your goals** **Add value to your goals** **Relish your goals**	**Focus your goals** **Add value to your goals** **Relish your goals**
ACTION	Get moving Enlist support Reframe setbacks and reengage	Get moving Enlist support Reframe setbacks and reengage	Get moving Enlist support Reframe setbacks and reengage
EVALUATION	Take stock regularly Reassess as necessary Build in rewards	Take stock regularly Reassess as necessary Build in rewards	Take stock regularly Reassess as necessary Build in rewards

Notes

Introduction

1. Carmona, "Obesity Crisis in America."
2. Centers for Disease Control and Prevention, *National Diabetes Fact Sheet.*
3. Associated Press, "More TV Sets."
4. American Heart Association, *Physical Activity.*
5. Ibid.
6. American Psychological Association, "Stress and Emotions."
7. Duxbury, Higgins and Coghill, *Voices of Canadians*, 27.
8. Bannister, "25 Fascinating Facts."
9. Marano, "Depression Suite."
10. FindBalance, "The Perils of Perfectionism," *Find Balance*, http://www .findbalance.ca/perils_perfectionism.htm (accessed February 25, 2006).
11. Marano, "New Focus."
12. Lewis, "First and Second Things," 22.
13. Covey, *First Things First*, 85.
14. Sharma, *Monk Who Sold*, 74.

Chapter 1

1. Covey, *First Things First*, 45.
2. Canfield and Switzer, *Success Principles*, 19.

Chapter 2

1. Neck et al., *Fit to Lead*, xix.
2. Berger et al., "Healthy Human Capital," 1213–25.
3. Davis et al., "Obesity," 2187.
4. Newman, "Why Are We So Fat?" 47–61.
5. Roizen and Oz, *You: The Owner's Manual*, 125–26.
6. Ibid., 108.
7. Ibid.

8.   Pate et al., "Physical Activity," 402–7.

9.   Neck et al., *Fit to Lead*, 4.

10.   Guallar and Podewils, "Mens Sana," 135–36.

11.   Yoga Journal, "The YJ Story," http://www.yogajournal.com/about_yjstory.cfm (accessed November 14, 2005).

12.   Harvard School of Public Health, "Food Pyramids," http://www.hsph .harvard.edu/nutritionsource/pyramids.html (accessed April 5, 2006).

13.   Institute of Medicine, *Dietary Reference Intakes*, 339.

14.   Pearson et al., "AHA Guidelines," 388.

15.   Willett and Skerrett, *Drink and Be Healthy*, 16.

16.   American Dental Association, "Cleaning Your Teeth and Gums (Oral Hygiene)," http://www.ada.org/public/topics/cleaning.asp (accessed November 10, 2005).

17.   National Sleep Foundation, *Sleep in America Poll.*

18.   Vgontzas, *Understanding Insomnia*, 1.

19.   Szabo, "Development of Stress Concept," 19–27.

20.   Gardner, "Ha-Ha-Heart Healthy."

21.   University of Maryland Medical Center, "Laughter."

22.   Roizen and Oz, *You: The Owner's Manual*, 84.

23.   Burr, "Depression."

24.   Roizen and Oz, *You: The Owner's Manual*, 92.

25.   Centers for Disease Control and Prevention, "Lung Cancer: Risk Factors," http://www.cdc.gov/cancer/lung/basic_info/risk_factors.htm (accessed October 10, 2006).

26.   Miller and Brady, "Addictive Disorders."

27.   Lublin and Machalaba, "CEO Who Drinks."

28.   Calandra, "What You Need."

Chapter 3

1.   Greene, *Get With the Program*, 34.

2.   Phillips and D'Orso, *Body for Life*, 103.

Chapter 4

1.   Britten and Lyle, "What's Love."

2.   Loehr and Schwartz, *Power of Full Engagement*, 75.

3.   Cooper, *Other 90%*, 18.

4.   Barsade et al., "To Your Heart's Content," 826–27.

5.   House, Landis and Umberson, "Social Relationships and Health."

6.   Rosengren et al. "Stressful Life Events," 1102–6.

7.   Gallo, Ghaed and Bracken, "Emotions and Cognitions," 675.

8.   Ibid.

9.   Ibid., 676.

10.   Laino, "Social Ties."

11.   Wallace, "Healthy Love Life."

12.   Stone et al., "Secretory IgA," 3.

13.   Gallo et al., "Marital Status and Quality," 455–61.

14.   Najib et al., "Regional Brain Activity," 2245.

15.   Maslow, *Psychology of Being*, 21.

16.   These concepts are distilled from emotional intelligence attributes in Goleman's *Working with Emotional Intelligence*.

17.   Goleman, *Emotional Intelligence*, 36.

18.   Ibid., 47.

19.   Goleman, Boyatzis and McKee, *Primal Leadership*, 92.

20.   Whitfield, *Boundaries and Relationships*, 1.

21.   Stein and Book, *EQ Edge*, 103.

22.   Goleman, *Emotional Intelligence*, 79.

23.   Loehr and Schwartz, *Power of Full Engagement*, 73.

24.   Ibid.

25.   Cooper, *Other 90%*, 242.

26.   Witte, "Schwinn Bicycle."

27.   Peterson, "Microsoft Learns to Crawl."

28.   Ibid.

29.   *Medical News Today*, "Commitment to Marriage."

30.   Merriam-Webster OnLine, "Optimism," http://www.m-w.com/dictionary/optimism (accessed June 6, 2006).

31. Bender and Tracz, *Secrets of Face-to-face Communication*, 134.

32. Goleman, *Emotional Intelligence*, 88.

33. Appleby, "Many Who Lost Savings."

34. Roots of Empathy, "Research and Effectiveness of the Roots of Empathy Program," http://www.rootsofempathy.org/Research.html (accessed June 7, 2006).

35. Goldberg, "For Good Health."

36. Campbell, *Saying What's Real*, xvii.

37. Mehrabian and Ferris, "Inference of Attitudes," 248–52.

38. Campbell, *Saying What's Real*, xviii.

39. McGraw, *Relationship Rescue*, 132.

40. Goleman, *Emotional Intelligence*, 59.

41. Ibid., 65.

42. Gallo et al., "Emotions and Cognitions," 675.

43. Maslow, *Maslow Business Reader*, 138.

Chapter 5

1. Hendrix, *Getting the Love*, 48–49.

2. Ibid., 57.

3. Campbell, *Saying What's Real*, 64.

4. This list of common myths is adapted from similar lists in McGraw's *Relationship Rescue* and Gottman and Silver's *Seven Principles*.

5. McGraw, *Relationship Rescue*, 51.

6. Schnarch, *Resurrecting Sex*, 149.

7. Gottman and Silver, *Seven Principles*, 130.

8. Hendrix, *Getting the Love*, 248.

9. Haltzman and DiGeronimo, *Happily Married Men*, 206.

10. Hendrix, *Getting the Love*, 90.

11. Ibid., 114.

12. Haltzman and DiGeronimo, *Happily Married Men*, 34.

13. Schoenborn, "Marital Status and Health."

14. McGraw, *Relationship Rescue*, 120.

15. Hendrix, *Getting the Love*, 100.

16. Gottman and Silver, *Seven Principles*, 23.

17. Ibid., 244.

18. McGraw, *Relationship Rescue*, 116.

19. Schnarch, *Resurrecting Sex*, 123.

20. Hendrix, *Getting the Love*, 174–75.

21. Haltzman and DiGeronimo, *Happily Married Men*, 201.

22. Ibid., 192.

23. Gottman and Silver, *Seven Principles*, 48.

24. Chapman, *Five Love Languages*, 15.

25. Haltzman and DiGeronimo, *Happily Married Men*, 194.

26. Kimura, *Sex and Cognition*.

27. Shaw, "Mind of a Man."

28. Ibid.

29. Haltzman and DiGeronimo, *Happily Married Men*, 172.

30. Gray, *Men Are from Mars*.

31. Haltzman and DiGeronimo, *Happily Married Men*, 211.

32. Schnarch, *Resurrecting Sex*, 13–14.

33. Ibid., 14–15.

34. Somers, *Sexy Years*, 29.

35. Rosen, Lane and Menza, "Effects of SSRIs," 67–85.

36. Schnarch, *Resurrecting Sex*, 89–90.

37. Ibid., 92.

38. Gottman and Silver, *Seven Principles*, 203.

39. McGraw, *Relationship Rescue*, 133.

40. Haltzman and DiGeronimo, *Happily Married Men*, 125.

41. Gottman and Silver, *Seven Principles*, 135.

42. Ibid., 158.

43. Ibid., 150.

44. Schnarch, *Resurrecting Sex*, 115.

45. Ibid., 117.

46. John Sneep, interview by FinalEyes Communications Inc., August 29, 2006, Edmonton, AB.

47. Ibid.

48. Haltzman and DiGeronimo, *Happily Married Men*, 109.

Chapter 6

1. Conlin, "CEO Coaches."

2. Ibid.

3. Schnarch, *Resurrecting Sex*, 122.

4. Hendrix, *Getting the Love*, 169.

5. Hymowitz, "More CEOs Seek Therapy."

6. Ibid.

7. Ibid.

8. Goleman, Boyatzis and McKee, *Primal Leadership*, 120.

9. Ibid.

10. Ibid., 111, 115–16.

11. McGraw, *Relationship Rescue*, 2.

12. Goleman, Boyatzis and McKee, *Primal Leadership*, 134.

13. Schnarch, *Resurrecting Sex*, 120–21.

14. Nichols, "Power of Visualization."

15. SmartMoney.com, "The Great Divide," http://www.smartmoney.com/divorce/basics/index.cfm?story=divide (accessed July 17, 2006).

16. Hendrix, *Getting the Love*, 172.

17. Schnarch, *Resurrecting Sex*, 125.

18. McGraw, *Relationship Rescue*, 118.

19. Haltzman and DiGeronimo, *Happily Married Men*, 38–39.

20. Ibid., 39.

21. Gottman and Silver, *Seven Principles*, 177.

22. Haltzman and DiGeronimo, *Happily Married Men*, 75.

23. McGraw, *Relationship Rescue*, 67–68.

24. Haltzman and DiGeronimo, *Happily Married Men*, 262–63.

25. Hendrix, *Getting the Love*, 226.

Chapter 7

1. Rohn, *7 Strategies for Wealth*, 91–92.

2. Bucks, Kennickell and Moore, "U.S. Family Finances," A26.

3. Weston, "Bankruptcy Filings Soaring Again."

4. Curtin, "Suicide Also Rises."

5. Weston, "Balanced Checkbook?"

6. Regnier, "Home Prices."

7. U.S. Census Bureau, "Extended Measures."

8. Chatzky, *Pay It Down!*, 29.

9. Ibid., 44.

10. U.S. Census Bureau, "Money Income in 2004."

11. Stanley, *Millionaire Mind*, 4.

12. U.S. Census Bureau, "Money Income in 2004."

13. Orman, *Road to Wealth*, 99.

14. Ibid.

15. Ibid., 100.

16. O'Brien, "What's He Really Worth?"

17. Orman, *Road to Wealth*, 3.

18. Chatzky, *Pay It Down!*, 11–12.

19. Jenkins, "Simpler Way to Save."

20. Chatzky, *Pay It Down!*, 11.

21. Bankrate.com, "You Might Be."

22. Lianne Elias, "Survey Says CEOs Prefer Poker to Golf," *PokerListings.com*, February 23, 2006, http://www.pokerlistings.com/survey-says-ceos-prefer-poker-to-golf-6027 (accessed July 21, 2006).

23. National Council on Problem Gambling, *Problem Gambling Resource.*

24. Canada Safety Council, "Gambling Addiction and Suicide," http://www.safety-council.org/info/community/gambling.html (accessed July 21, 2006).

25. Orman, *Road to Wealth*, 3.

26. Reuters, "Personal Income, Spending."

27. Bucks, Kennickell and Moore, "U.S. Family Finances," A8.

28. Rohn, *7 Strategies for Wealth*, 95.

29. Regnier, "How Retirement Will Change."

30. Tyson, "Social Security Crisis?"

31. Pareto, "Determining Your Post-Work Income."

32. ING Direct website: http://home.ingdirect.com/.

33. Emigrant Direct website: https://www.emigrantdirect.com/EmigrantDirectWeb/index.jsp.

34. McWhinney, "Kids or Cash."

35. Savingforcollege.com, "The Real Cost of Higher Education," http://www
   .savingforcollege.com/tutorial101/the_real_cost_of_higher_education.php
   (accessed August 4, 2006).

36. Langager, "Having a Plan."

37. "John Maynard Keynes Quotes," *The Quotations Page*, http://www
   .quotationspage.com/quotes/John_Maynard_Keynes/(accessed August
   4, 2006).

38. Orman, *Road to Wealth*, 215.

39. U.S. Census Bureau, "Health Insurance Coverage."

40. Ibid.

41. Orman, *Road to Wealth*, 235–36.

42. Ibid., 257.

43. Ibid., 256.

44. Savage, "Critical Illness Insurance."

45. Greenfield, "Greenfield: A Mega-Gift."

46. Kirkland, "Should You Leave It?"

47. Orman, *Road to Wealth*, 538.

48. Greenfield, "Greenfield: A Mega-Gift."

49. Financial Planning Association website: http://www.fpanet.org/.

50. National Association of Personal Financial Advisors website: http://www
   .napfa.org/.

51. U.S. Securities and Exchange Commission website: http://www.sec.gov/.

52. http://assets.aarp.org/www.aarp.org_/articles/bulletin/money/financial
   questionnaire.pdf.

53. http://www.cfp.net/learn/knowledgebase.asp?id=6.

Chapter 8

1. Seijts and Latham, "Learning Goals."

2. *Investopedia*, "Investing 101: The Concept of Compounding," http://www
   .investopedia.com/university/beginner/beginner2.asp (accessed October
   29, 2006).

3. Oprah.com, "The Bradleys' Emotional Debt: Childhood Wounds," http://
   www2.oprah.com/money/debtdiet/family/debtdiet_family_bradley_284
   _302.jhtml (accessed August 26, 2006).

4. Gates, Texas Conference for Women.

5. Bill and Melinda Gates Foundation, "Foundation Fact Sheet," http://www
.gatesfoundation.org/MediaCenter/FactSheet/ (accessed August 26, 2006).

6. Tracy, *Getting Rich*, 117.

7. Bach, *Smart Couples Finish Rich*, 38.

8. Higham, "End of Reality TV?"

9. Rohn, *7 Strategies for Wealth*, 40.

10. Bach, *Smart Couples Finish Rich*, 71.

11. Chatzky, *Pay It Down!*, 36.

12. Men's Health, "Training Timeline," http://www.menshealth.com/cda/article
.do?site=MensHealth&channel=fitness&category=motivation&conitem=
435928fa64605010VgnVCM200000cee793cd____&page=1 (accessed October
20, 2006).

13. Tracy, *Getting Rich*, 202.

14. Larimer, "Bankruptcy."

15. Gardner, "Bankruptcy Reform."

16. Larimer, "Bankruptcy."

17. Orman, *Road to Wealth*, 75.

18. Ibid., 236.

19. Ibid.

20. Ibid., 219.

21. Bach, *Smart Couples Finish Rich*, 8.

22. College Board, *Trends in College Pricing*, 11.

23. The figures in the hypothetical example given were calculated using "World's
Simplest College Cost Calculator," Savingforcollege.com, http://www
.savingforcollege.com/college-savings-calculator/?ref=pro-20060717 (accessed
August 24, 2006).

24. Opdyke, *Love & Money*, xiv.

25. Orman, *Road to Wealth*, 4.

26. CNN, "Time Is Money."

27. Hamm and Heifetz, *Go for the Goal*.

28. Tracy, *Getting Rich*, 200.

29. Stanley, *Millionaire Mind*, 10.

Conclusion

1. Covey, *First Things First*, 122.

2. Rippe, "CEO Fitness: Performance Plus," 53.

3. Putnam, *Bowling Alone*, 19.

4. Ibid., 327.

5. Ibid., 333.

6. Ibid., 332.

Bibliography

American Heart Association. *Physical Activity: Statistical Fact Sheet – Risk Factors*. 2004. http://www.americanheart.org/downloadable/heart/1136820352230PhysActivity06.pdf.

American Psychological Association. "Stress and Emotions Can Negatively Affect Heart Health." News release, January 26, 2006. http://apahelpcenter.mediaroom.com/index.php?s=press _releases&item=22.

Appleby, Julie. "Many Who Lost Savings, Jobs Pleased." *USA Today*, May 26, 2006. http://www .usatoday.com/money/industries/energy/2006-05-25-enron-workers-usat_x.htm.

Associated Press. "More TV Sets Than People in Average U.S. Home." *CTV.ca*, September 21, 2006. http://www.ctv.ca/servlet/ArticleNews/story/CTVNews/20060921/tvsets_us_060921/ 20060921?hub=TopStories.

Bach, David. *Smart Couples Finish Rich: 9 Steps to Creating a Rich Future for You and Your Partner*. Canadian ed. Toronto: Doubleday Canada, 2003.

Bankrate.com. "You Might Be a Shopaholic." *MSN Money*, n.d. http://moneycentral.msn.com/ content/SavingandDebt/P58684.asp.

Bannister, Paul. "25 Fascinating Facts about Personal Debt." *Bankrate.com*, September 20, 2004. http://www.bankrate.com/brm/news/debt/debtguide2004/debt-trivia1.asp.

Barsade, Sigal G., Andre J. Ward, Jean D. F. Turner and Jeffrey A. Sonnenfeld. "To Your Heart's Content: A Mode of Affective Diversity in Top Management Teams." *Administrative Science Quarterly* 45 (2000): 802–36.

Bender, Peter Urs, and Robert A. Tracz. *Secrets of Face-to-face Communication*. Toronto: Stoddart, 2001.

Berger, Marc L., Robert Howell, Sean Nicholson and Claire Sharda. "Investing in Healthy Human Capital." *Journal of Occupational and Environmental Medicine* 45, no. 12 (December 2003): 1213–25.

Britten, Terry, and Graham Lyle. "What's Love Got to Do with It." Recorded by Tina Turner on *Private Dancer*. Hollywood: Capitol, 1984. Compact disc.

Bucks, Brian K., Arthur B. Kennickell and Kevin B. Moore. "Recent Changes in U.S. Family Finances: Evidence from the 2001 and 2004 Survey of Consumer Finances." *Federal Reserve Bulletin 2006*. Washington, DC: Division of Research and Statistics, Board of Governors of the Federal Reserve System, February 2006. http://www.federalreserve.gov/pubs/oss/ oss2/2004/bull0206.pdf.

Burr, Constance. "Depression, Bone Mass, and Osteoporosis." National Institutes of Health, June 2001. http://www.findarticles.com/p/articles/mi_pnih/is_200106/ai_4189768183.

Calandra, Bob. "What You Need, from Pap to Prostate." *WebMD* feature, *MedicineNet.com*, April 2002, http://www.medicinenet.com/script/main/art.asp?articlekey=51509.

Campbell, Susan. *Saying What's Real: 7 Keys to Authentic Communication and Relationship Success.* Novato, CA: HJ Kramer and New World Library, 2005.

Canfield, Jack, and Janet Switzer. *The Success Principles: How to Get from Where You Are to Where You Want to Be.* New York: HarperCollins, 2005.

Carmona, Richard H. "The Obesity Crisis in America." Surgeon General's testimony before the Subcommittee on Education Reform, United States House of Representatives, Washington, DC, July 16, 2003. http://www.surgeongeneral.gov/news/testimony/obesity07162003.htm.

Centers for Disease Control and Prevention. *National Diabetes Fact Sheet: General Information and National Estimates on Diabetes in the United States, 2005.* Atlanta: U.S. Department of Health and Human Services, Centers for Disease Control and Prevention, 2005. http://www.diabetes.org/uedocuments/NationalDiabetesFactSheetRev.pdf.

Chapman, Gary. *The Five Love Languages: How to Express Heartfelt Commitment to Your Mate.* Chicago: Northfield, 2004.

Chatzky, Jean. *Pay It Down!: From Debt to Wealth on $10 a Day.* New York: Portfolio, 2004.

CNN. "Time Is Money, Professor Proves." *CNN.com*, May 29, 2002. http://archives.cnn.com/2002/TECH/science/05/29/time.money/index.html.

College Board. *Trends in College Pricing.* Trends in Higher Education Series. Washington, DC: The College Board, 2005. http://www.collegeboard.com/prod_downloads/press/cost05/trends_college_pricing_05.pdf.

Conlin, Michelle. "CEO Coaches." *BusinessWeek Online*, November 11, 2002. http://www.businessweek.com/magazine/content/02_45/b3807112.htm.

Cooper, Robert K. *The Other 90%: How to Unlock Your Vast Untapped Potential for Leadership and Life.* New York: Three Rivers, 2001.

Covey, Stephen R., A. Roger Merrill and Rebecca R. Merrill. *First Things First.* New York: Free Press, 2003.

Curtin, J. Sean. "Suicide Also Rises in Land of Rising Sun." *Asia Times Online*, July 28, 2004. http://www.atimes.com/atimes/Japan/FG28Dh01.html.

Davis, Ronald M., James M. Lyznicki, Joseph A. Riggs and Donald C. Young. "Obesity: Assessment and Management in Primary Care." *American Family Physician* 63, no. 11 (June 1, 2001): 2185–96. http://www.aafp.org/afp/20010601/2185.pdf.

Duxbury, Linda, Christopher Higgins and Donna Coghill. *Voices of Canadians: Seeking Work-Life Balance.* Hull, QC: Human Resources Development Canada, 2003. http://www.hrsdc.gc.ca/en/lp/spila/wlb/pdf/Voices.pdf.

Gallo, Linda C., Shiva G. Ghaed and Wendy S. Bracken. "Emotions and Cognitions in Coronary Heart Disease: Risk, Resilience, and Social Context." *Cognitive Therapy and Research* 28, no. 5 (October 2004): 669–94.

——, Wendy M. Troxel, Karen A. Matthews and Lewis H. Kuller. "Marital Status and Quality in Middle-Aged Women: Associations with Levels and Trajectories of Cardiovascular Risk Factors." *Health Psychology* 22, no. 5 (2003): 453–63.

Gardner, Amanda. "Laughter is Ha-Ha-Heart Healthy." *HealthDay News*, March 7, 2005. http://www.medicineonline.com/conditions/article.html?articleID=4693&catID=27.

Gardner, Marilyn. "Bankruptcy Reform Hits Women Hard." *The Christian Science Monitor*, April 4, 2005. http://www.csmonitor.com/2005/0404/p13s01-wmgn.html.

Gates, Melinda French. Prepared remarks, Texas Conference for Women 2005, Austin, TX, October 20, 2005. http://www.gatesfoundation.org/MediaCenter/Speeches/Co-ChairSpeeches/MelindaSpeeches/MFGSpeechTexas-051020.htm.

Goldberg, Carey. "For Good Health, It is Better to Give, Science Suggests." *The Boston Globe*, November 28, 2003. http://www.boston.com/news/local/articles/2003/11/28/for_good_health_it_is_better_to_give_science_suggests?mode=PF.

Goleman, Daniel. *Emotional Intelligence: Why It Can Matter More than IQ.* New York: Bantam, 1995.

——. *Working with Emotional Intelligence.* New York: Bantam Books, 2000.

——, Richard Boyatzis and Annie McKee. *Primal Leadership: Learning to Lead with Emotional Intelligence.* Boston: Harvard Business School Press, 2004.

Gottman, John M., and Nan Silver. *The Seven Principles for Making Marriage Work.* New York: Three Rivers, 1999.

Gray, John. *Men Are from Mars, Women Are from Venus.* New York: Quill, 2004.

Greene, Bob. *Get With the Program: Getting Real about Your Weight, Health and Emotional Well-Being.* New York: Simon & Schuster, 2002.

Greenfield, Jeff. "Greenfield: A Mega-Gift from the Super-Rich." *CNN.com*, June 26, 2006. http://www.cnn.com/2006/POLITICS/06/26/greenfield.philanthropy/index.html.

Guallar, Eliseo, and Laura J. Podewils. "Mens Sana in Corpore Sano." *Annals of Internal Medicine* 144, no. 2 (January 17, 2006): 135–36.

Haltzman, Scott, and Theresa Foy DiGeronimo. *The Secrets of Happily Married Men: Eight Ways to Win Your Wife's Heart Forever.* San Francisco: Jossey-Bass, 2006.

Hamm, Mia, and Aaron Heifetz. *Go for the Goal: A Champion's Guide to Winning in Soccer and Life.* New York: HarperCollins, 1999. Quoted in Mia Hamm and Aaron Heifetz, "Success Secrets," 1999, http://www.fitlinxx.com/Article.htm?id=249 (accessed November 6, 2006).

Harvard School of Public Health. "Food Pyramids." http://www.hsph.harvard.edu/nutritionsource/pyramids.html (accessed April 5, 2006).

Hendrix, Harville. *Getting the Love You Want: A Guide for Couples.* New York: Owl Books, 2001.

Higham, Nick. "The End of Reality TV?" *BBC News*, May 22, 2001. http://news.bbc.co.uk/1/hi/entertainment/tv_and_radio/1344160.stm.

House, James, K. R. Landis and D. Umberson. "Social Relationships and Health." *Science* 241, no. 4865 (July 29, 1988): 540–45.

Hymowitz, Carol. "More CEOs Seek Therapy." *The Wall Street Journal Online*, June 22, 2004. http://pqasb.pqarchiver.com/wsj/access/653895791.html?dids=653895791:653895791&FMT =ABS&FMTS=ABS:FT&date=Jun+22%2C+2004&author=Carol+Hymowitz&pub=Wall +Street+Journal&edition=Eastern+edition&startpage=B.1&type=91_1996&desc=More+ CEOs+Seek+Therapy.

Institute of Medicine, National Academies of Sciences. *Dietary Reference Intakes for Energy, Carbohydrates, Fiber, Fat, Protein and Amino Acids (Macronutrients)*. Washington, DC: National Academy Press, 2005.

Jenkins, Richard. "A Simpler Way to Save: The 60% Solution." *MSN Money*, n.d. http:// articles.moneycentral.msn.com/SavingandDebt/LearnToBudget/ASimplerWayToSaveThe60 Solution.aspx.

Kimura, D. *Sex and Cognition*. Cambridge: MIT Press, 1999.

Kirkland, Richard I. Jr. "Should You Leave It All to the Children?" *FORTUNE*, September 29, 1986. http://money.cnn.com/magazines/fortune/fortune_archive/1986/09/29/68098/index.htm.

Laino, Charlene. "Social Ties Guard against Heart Disease." *FoxNews.com*, November 8, 2004. http://foxnews.webmd.com/content/article/96/103874.htm.

Langager, Chad. "Having a Plan: The Basis of Success." *Investopedia*, June 10, 2005. http://www .investopedia.com/articles/pf/05/061005.asp.

Larimer, Rob. "Bankruptcy May Soon Be Unaffordable." *The Colorado Springs Business Journal*, August 4, 2006. http://www.thepbj.com/story.cfm?ID=9558.

Lewis, C. S. "First and Second Things." *In First and Second Things*, 19–24. London, UK: Fount Paperbacks, 1985.

Loehr, Jim, and Tony Schwartz. *The Power of Full Engagement: Managing Energy, Not Time, Is the Key to High Performance and Personal Renewal*. New York: Free Press, 2005.

Lublin, Joann S., and Daniel Machalaba. "How Companies Deal with a CEO Who Drinks." *Wall Street Journal*, November 1, 1994, Eastern edition, B1.

Marano, Hara Estroff. "A New Focus on Family Values: Shifting Attention from Ideology to Research." *Psychology Today*, November–December 1997. http://www.findarticles.com/p/articles/ mi_m1175/is_n6_v30/ai_19979990.

———. "The Depression Suite: For a Shocking Number of CEOs, Getting to the Top Brings only Crippling Emotional Bleakness." *Psychology Today*, May–June 2003. http://www.findarticles .com/p/articles/mi_m1175/is_3_36/ai_n6028128.

Maslow, Abraham H. *The Maslow Business Reader*. New York: Wiley, 2000.

———. *Toward a Psychology of Being*. 3rd ed. New York: Wiley, 1999.

McGraw, Phillip C. *Relationship Rescue: A Seven-Step Strategy for Reconnecting with Your Partner*. New York: Hyperion, 2000.

McWhinney, Jim. "Kids or Cash: The Modern Marriage Dilemma." *Investopedia*, February 23, 2006. http://www.investopedia.com/articles/pf/06/kidsorcash.asp.

Medical News Today. "Study Finds Commitment to Marriage, Emotional Engagement Key to Wives' Happiness." March 4, 2006. http://www.medicalnewstoday.com/medicalnews.php?newsid =38735.

Mehrabian, Albert, and R. Ferris. "Inference of Attitudes from Nonverbal Communication in Two Channels." *Journal of Consulting Psychology* 31, no. 3 (1967): 248–52.

Miller, Norman S., and Kathleen T. Brady. "Addictive Disorders." *Psychiatric Clinics of North America* 27, no. 4 (December 2004). http://www.mdconsult.com.

Najib, Arif, Jeffrey P. Lorberbaum, Samet Kose, Daryl E. Bohning and Mark S. George. "Regional Brain Activity in Women Grieving a Romantic Relationship Breakup." *The American Journal of Psychology* 161, no. 12 (2004): 2245–56.

National Council on Problem Gambling. *Problem Gambling Resource & Fact Sheet*. Washington, DC: National Council on Problem Gambling, 2001. http://www.ncpgambling.org/ media/pdf/eapa_flyer.pdf (accessed July 21, 2006).

National Sleep Foundation. *2005 Sleep in America Poll: Summary of Findings*. Washington, DC: National Sleep Foundation, March 29, 2005. http://www.sleepfoundation.org/_content/ hottopics/2005_summary_of_findings.pdf.

Neck, Christopher P., Tedd L. Mitchell, Charles C. Manz and Emmet C. Thompson II. *Fit to Lead: The Proven 8-Week Solution for Shaping Up Your Body*. New York: St. Martin's, 2004.

Newman, Cathy. "Why Are We So Fat?" *National Geographic*, August 2004.

Nichols, Bill. "Players Use Power of Visualization." *ESPN.com*, March 23, 2005. http:// sports.espn.go.com/golf/news/story?id=2019433.

O'Brien, Timothy L. "What's He Really Worth?" *The New York Times*, October 23, 2005. http://www.nytimes.com/2005/10/23/business/yourmoney/23trump.html?pagewanted =1&ei=5088&en=f6a68ab339142801&ex=1287720000&partner=rssnyt&emc=rss.

Opdyke, Jeff D. *Love & Money: A Life Guide for Financial Success*. Hoboken, NJ: Wiley, 2004.

Orman, Suze. *The Road to Wealth*. New York: Riverhead Books, 2001.

Pareto, Cathy. "Determining Your Post-Work Income." *Investopedia*, May 4, 2005. http://www .investopedia.com/articles/retirement/05/050405.asp.

Pate, R. R., M. Pratt, S. N. Blair, W. L. Haskell, C. A. Macera, C. Bouchard, D. Buchner et al. "Physical Activity and Public Health: A Recommendation from the Centers for Disease Control and Prevention and the ACSM." *Journal of the American Medical Association* 273 (1995): 402–7.

Pearson, Thomas A., Steven N. Blair, Stephen R. Daniels, Robert H. Eckel, Joan M. Fair, Stephen P. Fortmann, Barry A. Franklin et al. "AHA Guidelines for Primary Prevention of Cardiovascular Disease and Stroke: 2002 Update." *Circulation: Journal of the American Heart Foundation* 106, no. 3 (2002): 388–91. http://circ.ahajournals.org/cgi/reprint/106/3/388.

Peterson, Kim. "Microsoft Learns to Crawl." *The Seattle Times*, May 2, 2005. http://archives .seattletimes.nwsource.com/cgi-bin/texis.cgi/web/vortex/display?slug=search02&date= 20050502&query=Microsoft+learns+to+crawl.

Phillips, Bill, and Michael D'Orzo. *Body for Life: 12 Weeks to Mental and Physical Strength.* New York: HarperCollins, 1999.

Putnam, Robert D. *Bowling Alone: The Collapse and Revival of American Community.* New York: Simon & Schuster, 2000.

Regnier, Pat. "Are Home Prices Really So Crazy?" *MONEY*, May 16, 2005. http://money.cnn .com/2005/05/11/real_estate/buying_selling/re2005_pricecrazy_0506/index.htm.

———. "How Retirement Will Change." *MONEY*, October 10, 2005. http://money.cnn.com/2005/ 10/04/retirement/dreamretire_changes_0511/index.htm.

Reuters. "Personal Income, Spending Higher in May." *CNNMoney.com*, June 30, 2006. http://money.cnn.com/2006/06/30/news/economy/income_spending_reut/index.htm.

Rippe, James M. "CEO Fitness: The Performance Plus." *Psychology Today*, May 1989. 50–53.

Rohn, Jim. *7 Strategies for Wealth and Happiness: Power Ideas from America's Foremost Business Philosopher.* Roseville, CA: Prima, 1996.

Roizen, Michael F., and Mehmet C. Oz. *You: The Owner's Manual.* New York: HarperCollins, 2005.

Rosen, R. C., R. M. Lane and M. Menza. "Effects of SSRIs on Sexual Function: A Critical Review." *Journal of Clinical Psychopharmacology* 19 (1999): 67–85.

Rosengren, A., K. Orth-Gomer, H. Wedel and L. Wilhelmsen. "Stressful Life Events, Social Support and Mortality in Men Born in 1933." *British Medical Journal* 307, no. 6912 (1993): 1102–5.

Savage, Terry. "Introduction to Critical Illness Insurance." *Chicago Sun-Times*, April 19, 1998. http://www.suntimes.com/savage/greatest_hits/insure2.html.

Schnarch, David. *Resurrecting Sex: Solving Sexual Problems and Revolutionizing Your Relationship.* New York: Quill, 2003.

Schoenborn, Charlotte A. "Marital Status and Health: United States, 1999–2002." *Advance Data for Vital and Health Statistics*, no. 351. Hyattsville, MD: National Center for Health Statistics, 2004. http://www.cdc.gov/nchs/data/ad/ad351.pdf.

Seijts, Gerard H., and Gary P. Latham. "Learning Goals or Performance Goals: Is It the Journey or the Destination?" *Ivey Business Journal Online*, May/June 2006. http://www.iveybusinessjournal .com/view_article.asp?intArticle_ID=634.

Sharma, Robin S. *The Monk Who Sold His Ferrari.* Toronto: HarperCollins, 1997.

Shaw, Gina. "The Mind of a Man." *WebMD* feature, *MedicineNet.com*, November 17, 2003, http://www.medicinenet.com/script/main/art.asp?articlekey=52315.

Somers, Suzanne. *The Sexy Years: Discover the Hormone Connection—The Secret to Fabulous Sex, Great Health, and Vitality, for Women and Men.* New York: Crown, 2004.

Stanley, Thomas J. *The Millionaire Mind.* Kansas City, MO: Andrews McMeel, 2000.

Stein, Steven, and Howard Book. *The EQ Edge: Emotional Intelligence and Your Success.* Mississauga: Wiley, 2006.

Stone, A. A., D. S. Cox, H. Vadimarsdottir and J. M. Neale. "Secretory IgA as a Measure of Immunocompetence." *Journal of Human Stress* 13, no. 3 (Fall 1987): 136–40.

Szabo, S. "Hans Selye and the Development of Stress Concept." *Annals of the New York Academy of Sciences* 851 (June 30, 1998): 19–27. http://www.ncbi.nlm.nih.gov/entrez/query.fcgi?cmd= Retrieve&db=PubMed&list_uids=9668601&dopt=Abstract.

Tracy, Brian. *Getting Rich Your Own Way.* Hoboken, NJ: Wiley, 2004.

Tyson, Laura D'Andrea. "Social Security Crisis? What Crisis?" *BusinessWeek Online*, January 17, 2005. http://www.businessweek.com/magazine/content/05_03/b3916024_mz007.htm.

University of Maryland Medical Center. "Laughter is Good for Your Heart, According to a New University of Maryland Medical Center Study." News release, November 15, 2000. http://www.umm.edu/news/releases/laughter.html.

U.S. Census Bureau. "Extended Measures of Well-Being in 1998." *Population Profile of the United States: Dynamic Version.* Washington, DC: U.S. Census Bureau, n.d. http://www.census.gov/population/pop-profile/dynamic/WELLBEING.pdf.

———. "Health Insurance Coverage in 2004." *Population Profile of the United States: Dynamic Version.* Washington, DC: U.S. Census Bureau, n.d. http://www.census.gov/population/pop-profile/dynamic/HealthInsurance.pdf.

———. "Money Income in 2004." *Population Profile of the United States: Dynamic Version.* Revised February 2006. Washington, DC: U.S. Census Bureau, n.d. http://www.census.gov/population/pop-profile/dynamic/MoneyIncome.pdf.

Vgontzas, Alexandros N. *Understanding Insomnia in the Primary Care Setting: A New Model.* Sleep Medicine Alert: Insomnia Series, vol. 9, no. 2. Washington, DC: National Sleep Foundation, 2004.

Wallace, Robin. "Healthy Love Life Leads to Well-Being." *FoxNews.com*, February 15, 2005. http://www.foxnews.com/story/0,2933,147453,00.html.

Weston, Liz Pulliam. "Bankruptcy Filings Soaring Again." *MSN Money*, n.d. http://articles.moneycentral.msn.com/Banking/BankruptcyGuide/BankruptcyFilingsSoaringAgain.aspx.

———. "A Balanced Checkbook? Now That's Sexy." *MSN Money*, May 11, 2006. http://articles.moneycentral.msn.com/CollegeAndFamily/LoveAndMoney/ABalancedCheckbookNowthatsSexy.aspx.

Whitfield, Charles L. *Boundaries and Relationships: Knowing, Protecting and Enjoying the Self.* Deerfield Beach, FL: Health Communications, 1993.

Willett, Walter C., and Patrick J. Skerrett." *Eat, Drink, and Be Healthy: The Harvard Medical School Guide to Healthy Eating.* New York: Free Press, 2005.

Witte, Griff. "A Rough Ride for Schwinn Bicycle." *The Washington Post*, December 3, 2004, A01. http://pqasb.pqarchiver.com/washingtonpost/access/751224121.html?dids=751224121 :751224121&FMT=ABS&FMTS=ABS:FT&fmac=&date=Dec+3%2C+2004&author=Griff+ Witte&desc=A+Rough+Ride+for+Schwinn+Bicycle.

Recommended Reading

First things

First Things First, Stephen R. Covey, A. Roger Merrill and Rebecca R. Merrill. New York: Free Press, 2003.

Living at the Summit, Tom Hill and Rebecca McDannold. Columbia, IL: Images International, 1999.

The Monk Who Sold His Ferrari, Robin S. Sharma. Toronto: HarperCollins, 1997.

The 7 Habits of Highly Effective People, Stephen R. Covey. New York: Fireside, 1989.

The Success Principles: How to Get from Where You Are to Where You Want to Be, Jack Canfield and Janet Switzer. New York: HarperCollins, 2005.

Synchronicity: The Inner Path of Leadership, Joseph Jaworski. San Francisco: Berrett-Koehler, 1996.

Physical wellness

Body for Life: 12 Weeks to Mental and Physical Strength, Bill Phillips and Michael D'Orso. New York: HarperCollins, 1999.

Breaking the Rules of Aging, David Lipschitz. Washington, DC: LifeLine, 2002.

Eat, Drink, and Be Healthy: The Harvard Medical School Guide to Healthy Eating, Walter C. Willett and Patrick J. Skerrett. New York: Free Press, 2005.

Get With the Program: Getting Real about Your Weight, Health and Emotional Well-Being, Bob Greene. New York: Simon & Schuster, 2002.

Power Over Stress, Kenford Nedd. Toronto: QP Press, 2004.

Real Age: Are You as Young as You Can Be? Michael F. Roizen. New York: HarperCollins, 2000.

The Relaxation Response, Herbert Benson. New York: HarperCollins, 2000.

The Schwarzbein Principle, Diana Schwarzbein. Deerfield Beach, FL: Health Communications, 2004.

You: The Owner's Manual, Michael F. Roizen and Mehmet C. Oz. New York: HarperCollins, 2005.

You: The Smart Patient, Michael F. Roizen and Mehmet C. Oz. New York: Free Press, 2006.

Relational wellness

EMOTIONAL INTELLIGENCE

Emotional Intelligence: Why It Can Matter More than IQ, Daniel Goleman. New York: Bantam, 1995.

The EQ Edge: Emotional Intelligence and Your Success, Steven Stein and Howard Book. Mississauga: Wiley, 2006.

Working with Emotional Intelligence, Daniel Goleman. New York: Bantam Books, 1998.

OVERALL RELATIONAL CAPACITY

Boundaries and Relationships: Knowing, Protecting and Enjoying the Self, Charles L. Whitfield. Deerfield Beach, FL: Health Communications, 1993.

The Power of Full Engagement: Managing Energy, Not Time, Is the Key to High Performance and Personal Renewal, Jim Loehr and Tony Schwartz. New York: Free Press, 2005.

The Power of Resilience, Robert Brooks and Sam Goldstein. New York: McGraw-Hill, 2004.

Primal Leadership: Learning to Lead with Emotional Intelligence, Daniel Goleman, Richard Boyatzis and Annie McKee. Boston: Harvard Business School Press, 2004.

The Other 90%: How to Unlock Your Vast Untapped Potential for Leadership and Life, Robert K. Cooper. New York: Three Rivers, 2001.

MARRIAGE

The Five Love Languages: How to Express Heartfelt Commitment to Your Mate, Gary Chapman. Chicago: Northfield, 2004.

Getting the Love You Want: A Guide for Couples, Harville Hendrix. New York: Owl Books, 2001.

Relationship Rescue: A Seven-Step Strategy for Reconnecting with Your Partner, Phillip McGraw. New York: Hyperion, 2000.

Resurrecting Sex: Resolving Sexual Problems and Rejuvenating Your Relationship, David Schnarch. New York: HarperCollins, 2002.

The Secrets of Happily Married Men: Eight Ways to Win Your Wife's Heart Forever, Scott Haltzman and Theresa Foy DiGeronimo. San Francisco: Jossey-Bass, 2006.

The Seven Principles for Making Marriage Work, John M. Gottman and Nan Silver. New York: Three Rivers, 1999.

FAMILY

Family First, Phillip McGraw. New York: Free Press, 2004.

COMMUNICATION

Saying What's Real: 7 Keys to Authentic Communication and Relationship Success, Susan Campbell. Novato, CA: HJ Kramer and New World Library, 2005.

Secrets of Face-to-Face Communication, Peter Urs Bender and Robert A. Tracz. Toronto: Stoddart, 2001.

SEX

Resurrecting Sex: Resolving Sexual Problems and Rejuvenating Your Relationship, David Schnarch. New York: HarperCollins, 2002.

The Sexy Years: Discover the Hormone Connection—The Secret to Fabulous Sex, Great Health, and Vitality, for Women and Men, Suzanne Somers. New York: Crown, 2004.

Financial wellness

GENERAL FINANCE

Love & Money: A Life Guide for Financial Success, Jeff D. Opdyke. Hoboken, NJ: Wiley, 2004.

7 Strategies for Wealth and Happiness: Power Ideas from America's Foremost Business Philosopher, Jim Rohn. Roseville, CA: Prima, 1996.

Start Late, Finish Rich: A No-Fail Plan for Achieving Financial Freedom at Any Age, David Bach. New York: Doubleday, 2005.

The Road to Wealth, Suze Orman. New York: Riverhead Books, 2001.

DEBT MANAGEMENT

Pay It Down!: From Debt to Wealth on $10 a Day, Jean Chatzky. New York: Portfolio, 2004.

SAVING

Smart Couples Finish Rich: 9 Steps to Creating a Rich Future for You and Your Partner, David Bach. New York: Broadway, 2001.

Start Late, Finish Rich: A No-Fail Plan for Achieving Financial Freedom at Any Age, David Bach. New York: Doubleday, 2005.

Work Less, Live More: The New Way to Retire Early, Bob Clyatt. Berkeley: Nolo, 2005.

INVESTMENT

The Automatic Millionaire Homeowner: A Powerful Plan to Finish Rich in Real Estate, David Bach. New York: Broadway, 2006.

Jim Cramer's Real Money: Sane Investing in an Insane World, James J. Cramer. New York: Simon & Schuster, 2005.

TAX EFFICIENCY

Loopholes of the Rich: How the Rich Legally Make More Money & Pay Less Tax, Diane Kennedy. Revised ed. Hoboken, NJ: Wiley, 2005.

INSURANCE

The Road to Wealth, Suze Orman. New York: Riverhead Books, 2001.

ESTATE PLANNING

Creating the Good Will: The Most Comprehensive Guide to Both the Financial and Emotional Sides of Passing on Your Legacy, Elizabeth Arnold. New York: Portfolio, 2005.

Family Wealth—Keeping It in the Family: How Family Members and Their Advisers Preserve Human, Intellectual, and Financial Assets for Generations, James E. Hughes Jr. Princeton: Bloomberg, 2004.

PHILANTHROPY

Inspired Philanthropy: Your Step-by-Step Guide to Creating a Giving Plan, Tracy Gary and Melissa Kohner. 2nd ed. San Francisco: Jossey-Bass, 2002.

Strategic Giving: The Art and Science of Philanthropy, Peter Frumkin. Chicago: University of Chicago Press, 2006.